Antibodies and their role in therapeutics

Roohi Bansal, PhD

ISBN - 978-93-5578-160-4

Dedicated to my family and my mentors

About the book

Antibodies are the immunological warriors produced by our bodies to protect us from the harmful pathogens or other agents that our bodies encounter. Since the discovery of hybridoma technology by Kohler and Milstein in 1975, monoclonal antibodies (also referred to mAbs) have revolutionized the field of therapeutics. Today, they are one of the most important classes of therapeutic molecules, saving lives and improving the quality of lives of millions of patients with cancer, autoimmune diseases, infectious diseases, etc. Beginning with the structure, types, functions and gene organization of antibodies, the book aims to shine a detailed light on monoclonal antibodies' properties and therapeutic applications.

The book discusses antibody engineering and explores the various technologies for generating mAbs, including phage display, hybridoma, and recombinant DNA technology. The engineered mAbs chimeric, humanized, and fully human monoclonal antibodies are discussed in detail along with their therapeutic applications and immunogenicity issues.

Furthermore, the book talks about the antibody-drug conjugates (ADC), immunotoxins, ADEPT, antibody-antibiotic conjugate (AAC), which allows the selective drug delivery to the target cancer/diseased cells without harming the normal cells of the body. In addition, bispecific antibodies and their formats: scFv based antibodies (BiTE, DARTs, and TandAbs) and full-length IgG-like antibodies are discussed. The book also focuses on the development and therapeutic applications of catalytic antibodies 'abzymes', Fc fusion proteins, and single-domain antibodies (sdAbs).

The book also covers the modes of administration and side effects of monoclonal antibodies, along with the challenges and issues faced while developing a monoclonal antibody into a therapeutic agent. Modifications introduced by the researchers to decrease the immunogenicity issues and increase the efficacy of therapeutic mAbs are described as well.

Contents

Chapter 1: Introduction to antibodies

Antibodies are one of the crucial warriors produced by our immune system in response to the presence of foreign agents that enter our bodies. These foreign agents are called antigens. A wide range of substances are recognized as antigens by our bodies, such as viruses, bacteria, fungi, and some non-living substances such as toxins, chemicals, allergens, etc. As a result, our immune system generates billions of different antibodies, each capable of recognizing a specific antigen. When an antibody binds to a particular antigen, it sends a signal to the immune system indicating that this antigen is marked for destruction.

1.1. Antibodies are also called Immunoglobulins

In 1890 two immunologists: Emil von Behring and Shibasabura Kitasato, showed that the serum of the animals immunized against diphtheria contains a component that can neutralize diphtheria toxin. Thus, the transfer of serum from immunized animals to the animals infected with diphtheria could cure the infected animals. The serum is the liquid part of the blood that remains after blood cells and clotting factors have been removed. For this discovery, Behring was later awarded the Nobel Prize in 1901. This serum component was later named "antibody" by Paul Ehrlich in 1901.

The first evidence that antibodies are present in the gamma (γ) globulin fraction of serum proteins came from the experiment performed by two scientists: Tiselius and Kabat, in 1939. The scientists immunized rabbits with the antigen protein ovalbumin, i.e., the albumin of egg whites. After immunization, the serum of rabbits was harvested and was divided into two aliquots. Out of two aliquots, when electrophoresis of one aliquot of serum proteins was done, it showed four peaks (represented as solid peaks) corresponding to albumin and alpha, beta, and gamma globulins (*Fig 1-1*).

On the other hand, the second aliquot of serum was reacted with ovalbumin before electrophoresis. The precipitate formed was discarded, and the remaining serum proteins were electrophoresed. When the electrophoresis profiles of the two serum aliquots were compared, the scientists observed that there was a significant drop in the γ globulin peak (represented as dotted peaks) in the aliquot that had reacted with ovalbumin. It suggested that the antibodies are contained in the γ globulin fraction of the serum. Proteins unrelated to antibodies may also migrate with the electrophoretic mobility of γ-globulins. Therefore, antibodies were named "immunoglobulins" (symbol Ig) to distinguish them from any other proteins that might be contained in the γ globulin fraction.

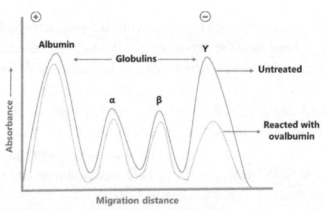

Fig 1-1: Electrophoretic separation of total serum proteins (solid peak) and after reacting with ovalbumin (dotted peak)

1.2. How are antibodies produced?

Antibodies are produced by specialized white blood cells called B cells, specifically plasma cells. When a B cell encounters an antigen, it gets activated and proliferates into a group of identical cells called a clone (*Fig 1-2*). Some of the cells differentiate into antibody-producing plasma cells, and others become long-lived memory B cells. Both the plasma cells and memory B cells are specific to the antigen, which the mature B cell initially encountered. Plasma cells secrete millions of antibodies into the bloodstream and lymphatic system, where they attack and neutralize antigens that are identical to the ones that triggered the immune response.

B cells distinguish antigens through the B-cell receptors found on their surfaces. A B-cell receptor is basically an antibody protein that is not secreted but is anchored to the B-cell membrane. All B-cell receptors located on a particular B cell are identical, but receptors present on other B cells differ.

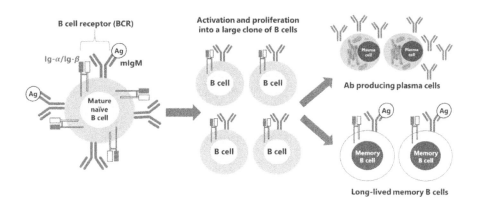

Fig 1-2: Production of antibodies by B cells

1.3. Basic structure of immunoglobulins or antibodies

All antibodies have the same core structure, consisting of 4 polypeptide chains: two identical light (L) chain polypeptides and two identical heavy (H) chain polypeptides, which assemble to form a Y-shaped molecule (*Fig 1-3*). Heavy chains are longer ones, and light chains are shorter ones. The term heavy and light chains refer to their molecular weight. Heavy chains have a molecular weight of 50,000 Da or more, and on the other hand, the light chains have a low molecular weight of about 25000 Da. Since these are polypeptide chains, the N terminal of the polypeptide chain is present at the tip end, and the C terminal at the base of each polypeptide chain.

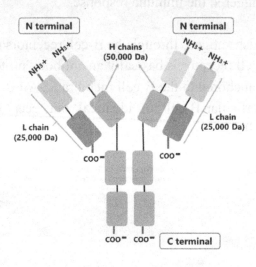

Fig 1-3: Y-shaped structure of an antibody molecule

Each light chain is bound to a heavy chain by a disulfide bond and several non-covalent interactions such as salt bridge, hydrogen bonds, and hydrophobic bonds. Similar non-covalent interactions and disulfide bonds also connect the heavy chains in the mid-region to form the basic four polypeptide chain antibody structure (*Fig 1-4*).

Each light chain and heavy chain contain two distinct regions:
- Variable regions (V) and
- constant regions (C).

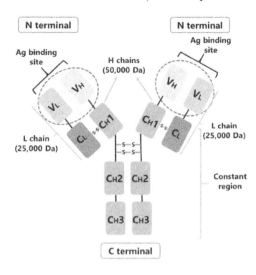

Fig 1-4: V and C regions in an antibody molecule

Variable regions refer to the first 110 amino acids of the amino-terminal region in each heavy and light chain. The variable regions are named because the amino acid sequences in these regions vary significantly among antibodies of different specificities. V regions are called V_L in light chains and V_H in heavy chains. It is the variable region in the light and heavy chain which together forms the antigen-binding site, also called a paratope (*Fig 1-4*).

In an antibody molecule, there are two antigen-binding sites. The variable region is responsible for giving the antibody its specificity to bind to a particular antigen. Or in other words, all the differences in specificity displayed by different antibodies to bind to different antigens can be traced to differences in the V regions' amino acid sequences.

Constant regions: By contrast, within the same antibody molecule, the regions beyond the variable regions of both heavy and light chains

5

are called constant regions. The amino acid sequence in these regions shows less variation among the different antibodies. There is a single constant region present in each light chain, which is designated as C$_L$. On the other hand, multiple constant regions are present in each heavy chain and are represented as C$_H$1, C$_H$2, C$_H$3, etc.

The constant region of the heavy chain of the antibodies forms the basis of the classification of antibodies. In a particular class of antibodies, all antibody molecules have almost the same constant region. But the constant region of the antibodies of one class is different from the constant region of the antibodies of another class. The classification of antibodies will be discussed in Chapter 3.

Another essential thing to know about antibodies is that they are glycoproteins (*Fig 1-5*). Glycoproteins are proteins that have carbohydrates attached to the polypeptide chain. To each heavy chain, short carbohydrate molecules are attached, which serve various functions such as increasing antibody molecules' solubility and facilitating removal of the antigen and death of the pathogen.

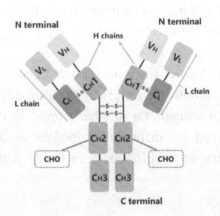

Fig 1-5: Antibodies are glycoproteins

1.4. Functional components of Antibodies

The intact Y-shaped antibody molecule has three components: two fragment antigen-binding domains abbreviated as Fab and the fragment crystallizable written as Fc. The knowledge of functional components of an antibody molecule was derived from various enzymatic and chemical methods conducted by Gerald M. Edelman and Rodney R. Porter, for which they were awarded the Nobel Prize in 1972. In the enzymatic method, the antibody molecule is digested with enzymes papain and pepsin. And in the chemical method, the antibody molecule is treated with mercaptoethanol.

1. When the antibody molecule is digested with the enzyme papain, it cleaves the antibody molecule just above the interchain disulfide bonds linking heavy chains (*Fig 1-6*). As a result, three fragments are produced, two of which have identical structures consisting of variable and constant regions of light chains (V_L and C_L) and heavy chains (V_H and C_H1) linked by disulfide bonds.

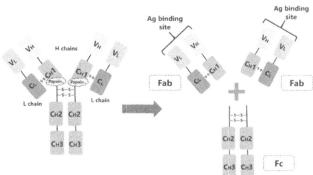

Fig 1-6: Digestion of antibody molecule with the enzyme papain

Since these fragments contain V regions and have antigen-binding sites, they are called fragments of antigen binding, abbreviated as Fab. There are 2 Fab fragments in an antibody molecule, and each of the

Fab fragments can bind only one antigen. The third fragment has no antigen-binding activity. It consists of constant regions of heavy chains held together by disulfide bonds.

It was found that this fragment crystallized during cold storage, so it was called fragment crystallizable abbreviated as Fc fragment. The Fc fragment plays a role in opsonization and complement activation. The functions of antibodies are discussed in detail in Chapters 4 and 5.

2. When the enzyme pepsin digests the antibody molecule, it cleaves the antibody just below the disulfide bonds linking the heavy chains (*Fig 1-7*). The resulting fragment consists of two antigen-binding arms (Fabs) of the antibody linked together by disulfide bonds. This fragment is represented as **F(ab')2**.

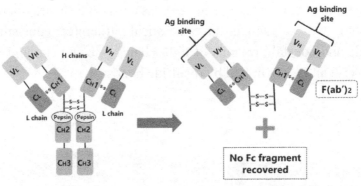

Fig 1-7: Digestion of antibody molecule with the enzyme pepsin

Here F stands for the fragment, and ab stands for antigen binding. The prime symbol represents variation in this fragment's structure as it contains few more amino acids than the Fab fragment. The number 2 represents the two Fabs that are linked together. The Fc fragment was not recovered because it gets digested into multiple peptide fragments by the pepsin enzyme.

3. When the antibody molecule is subjected to mercaptoethanol reduction and alkylation, it cleaves disulfide bonds (*Fig 1-8*). The cleavage of all disulfide bonds leads to splitting the antibody molecule into two identical heavy chains with a molecular weight of 50,000 Daltons each and two other identical light chains with 25,000 Daltons MW each.

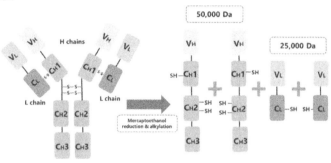

Fig 1-8: Mercaptoethanol reduction and alkylation of the antibody molecule

Thus the enzymatic and chemical methods can determine that each antibody molecule comprises two identical heavy chains of 50,000 MW and two identical light chains of 25,000 MW linked by disulfide bonds. Also, there are two antigen-binding fragments called Fabs in an antibody molecule consisting of variable and constant regions of light (V_L and C_L) and heavy chains (V_H and C_H1) linked by disulfide bonds.

1.5. Antibody sequencing

It was essential for researchers to know the amino acid sequence of heavy and light chain polypeptides to understand their different types. Unfortunately, the unavailability of sufficient numbers of homogeneous antibodies hindered the researchers' initial attempts to determine their amino acid sequences. Although the basic structure and chemical properties of different antibodies are similar, the amino acid sequences of their heavy and light chain polypeptides are quite different.

For amino acid sequencing of heavy and light chain polypeptides, researchers wanted enough homogeneous antibodies with similar antigen specificity because of the similar amino acid sequences of light and heavy chains, making it easier to determine their amino acid sequence. The population of antibodies in serum gamma globulin fraction does not serve the purpose of amino acid sequencing because of the heterogeneous spectrum of antibodies with different antigen-binding specificities. Even if immunization is done with one antigen, the antibodies formed just to one antigen are heterogeneous because they recognize different epitopes of the antigen (*Fig 1-9*). An epitope is the specific part of an antigen to which the antibody binds. This heterogneity of antibodies made them unsuitable for amino acid sequencing studies.

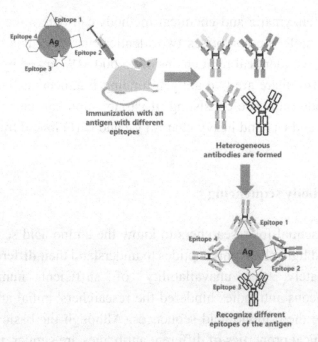

Fig 1-9: Heterogeneous antibodies recognize different epitopes of the Ag

Antibody sequencing eventually became feasible with the discovery of multiple myeloma, a cancer of antibody-producing plasma cells. In a normal individual, plasma cells, in response to an antigen, secrete antibodies for a limited period and then die. But in multiple myeloma, plasma cells escape normal controls of cell proliferation and even do not require any activation by antigen to induce proliferation (*Fig 1-10*). Thus, the cancerous plasma cell continues to secrete a large number of homogeneous antibodies.

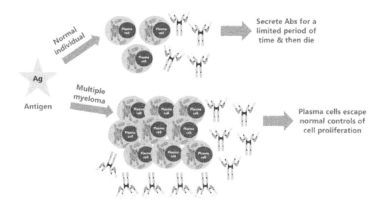

Fig 1-10: Multiple myeloma and plasma cells

Most patients afflicted with multiple myeloma excrete excessive amounts of light chains in their urine, named Bence-Jones proteins on their discoverer's name.

1.6. Types of light chains

To know the different types of light chains, Bence-Jones proteins, or light chains, were isolated from the patients' urine, and then their amino acid sequences were determined (*Fig 1-11*). When the amino acid sequences of Bence-Jones proteins from different individuals were compared, it was observed that the amino-terminal half of the chain consisting of 110 amino acids was found to vary among different Bence-Jones proteins. This region was called the variable region designated as V.

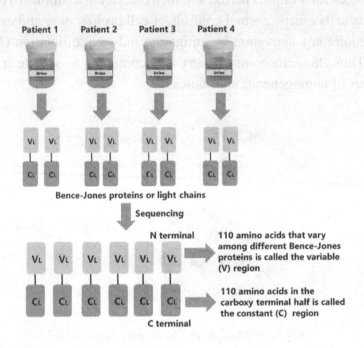

Bence-Jones proteins or light chains

Sequencing

N terminal

110 amino acids that vary among different Bence-Jones proteins is called the variable (V) region

110 amino acids in the carboxy terminal half is called the constant (C) region

C terminal

Fig 1-11: Sequencing of Bence-Jones proteins, or light chains isolated from the patients' urine

On the other hand, the other 110 amino acids in the carboxy-terminal half of the molecule comprise the light chain's constant region.

The constant region's amino acid sequencing revealed two sequence patterns based on the subtle differences in the amino acid sequences. And based on these differences in amino acid sequences of constant regions, the light chain can be divided into two types: kappa (κ) chain and lambda (λ) chain (*Fig 1-12*). These are similar in structure and function but are coded by different genes. The genes coding for Kappa chains are present on chromosome 2, and the genes coding for lambda chains are present on chromosome 22.

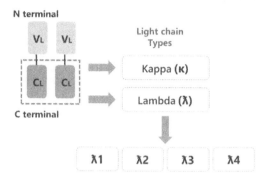

Fig 1-12: Types of light chains

It is important to note that each antibody molecule produced by a plasma cell will either have a kappa or lambda light chain but can never have both. 60% of the light chains are kappa in humans, and 40% are lambda. Further, the amino acid sequences of the constant region of lambda light chains also show minor differences. Thus, lambda light chain can be classified into subtypes; in humans, there are four subtypes of lambda light chain λ1, λ2, λ3, and λ4.

1.7. Types of heavy chains

To know the different types of heavy chains of antibody molecules, antibodies produced by cancerous plasma cells were reduced with mercaptoethanol. The resulting heavy chains were separated by gel filtration. When the amino acid sequences of several heavy chains were compared, a pattern similar to that of the light chains emerged. The amino-terminal part, or variable region consisting of 110 amino acids, showed significant sequence variation among the heavy chains.

By contrast, the amino acid sequencing of the regions beyond the variable region called the constant region of heavy chains revealed five basic sequence patterns based on the differences in the amino acid sequences. Based on the amino acid differences in the constant regions, the heavy chains can be divided into five types, named as δ, γ, α, μ, and ε heavy chains (*Fig 1-13*). Each of the five different heavy chains is called an isotype. The length of the constant regions in δ, γ, and α heavy chains is approximately 330 amino acids, and the length of the constant regions is 440 amino acids for μ and ε heavy chains.

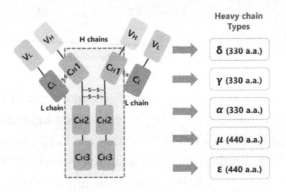

Fig 1-13: Types of heavy chains

The presence of the specific type of heavy chain determines the class of that antibody: IgD (δ), IgG (γ), IgA (α), IgM (μ), or IgE (ε). Further, each class of antibody can have either kappa or lambda light chains.

Minor differences in the amino acid sequences of the α and γ heavy chains lead to the further classification of heavy chains into subisotypes that determine the subclass of antibody molecules they constitute (*Fig 1-14*). In humans, there are two sub isotypes of α heavy chain α1 and α2 and thus two subclasses of IgA- IgA1 and IgA2 whereas there are four subclasses of IgG: IgG1, IgG2, IgG3, and IgG4 based on four subisotypes of heavy chain: $\gamma 1$, $\gamma 2$, $\gamma 3$, and $\gamma 4$.

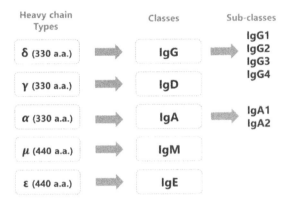

Fig 1-14: Classes and subclasses of antibodies

Chapter 2: Detailed structure of Antibodies

The immunoglobulin structure is determined by the protein's primary, secondary, tertiary, and quaternary organization (*Fig 2-1*). The primary structure of the immunoglobulin refers to the sequence of amino acids in the variable and constant regions of the heavy and light polypeptide chains. The secondary structure of immunoglobulin refers to the folding of the immunoglobulin polypeptide chain back and forth upon itself to form a β pleated sheet. The tertiary structure refers to the folding of the polypeptide chain into compact globular domains. And the globular domains of adjacent heavy and light polypeptide chains interact to form a quaternary structure, which eventually creates the functional immunoglobulin molecule that can specifically interact with the antigen and perform several biological functions.

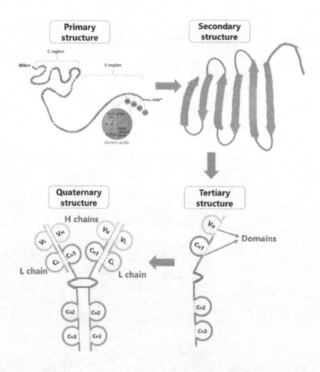

Fig 2-1: Levels of protein organization

2.1. Immunoglobulin Domains

The heavy and light polypeptide chains contain several homologous units of 110 amino acid residues, and each unit is termed as a domain (*Fig 2-2*). An intrachain disulfide bond is present in each domain, forming a loop of about 60 amino acids. In the case of light chains of the antibody, there is one variable domain (V_L) and one constant domain (C_L), and in the case of the heavy chains, there is one variable domain V_H and either 3 or 4 constant domains designated as C_H1, C_H2, C_H3, and C_H4.

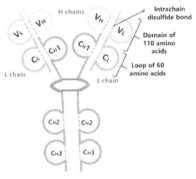

Fig 2-2: Domains in H and L chains

The overall shape of the immunoglobulin domain can be defined as the sandwich of two β pleated sheets, each containing antiparallel β strands of amino acid residues connected by loops of various lengths (*Fig 2-3*).

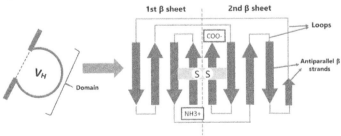

Fig 2-3: Structure of Immunoglobulin Domain

The β strands within the β pleated sheet are stabilized by hydrogen bonds that connect the amino group in one strand with the carbonyl group of an adjacent strand. The two β pleated sheets are stabilized by hydrophobic interactions between them and by the conserved disulfide bond. An analogy of the structure of the immunoglobulin domain can be made to two slices of bread, butter between them, and a toothpick holding the slices together (*Fig 2-4*). The two slices of bread are β pleated sheets; butter represents hydrophobic interactions, and toothpick represents the intrachain disulfide bond.

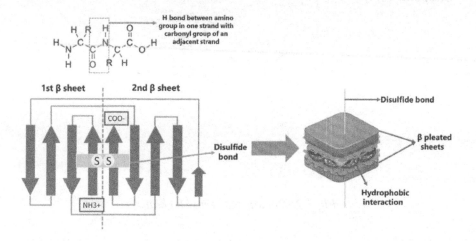

Fig 2-4: Analogy of the structure of the immunoglobulin domain to two slices of bread, butter between them, and toothpick holding the slices together

The variable (V) and constant (C) domains of immunoglobulins differ in the number and regularity of the β strands forming the β pleated sheets. For instance, the constant domain of the light chain is built up from seven β strands arranged such that four strands form one β sheet and three strands form the second β sheet. In contrast, the V domains contain nine β strands instead of seven, four strands form one β sheet, and five strands form the second sheet (*Fig 2-5*).

Thus, the V domain is slightly longer than the C domain because of the two extra β strands and the extra loop connecting these strands.

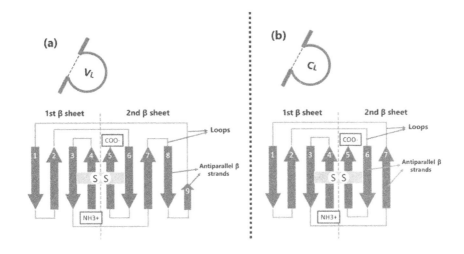

Fig 2-5: In a light chain, (a) V domain contains nine β strands and (b) C domain is built up from seven β strands

Non-covalent interactions form links between the identical domains of heavy chains and between non-identical domains of heavy and light chains.

2.2. Complementarity determining regions (CDRs)

The specific regions within the variable region in each light and heavy chain responsible for generating the antigen-binding site of the antibody are termed complementarity determining regions abbreviated as CDRs. As already discussed, the variable regions in the light and heavy chains form the antigen-binding site. There are two antigen-binding sites in an antibody molecule. Also, the heavy and light polypeptide chains contain several homologous units of 110 amino acid residues. Each unit is termed a domain, which is a sandwich of two β pleated sheets, each sheet containing antiparallel β strands of amino acid residues connected by loops of varied lengths.

The exciting thing is that the maximum variation in the variable domain of heavy and light chains is present in the amino acid sequences of loops that join the β strands. These loop regions are called **hypervariable regions** (*Fig 2-6*).

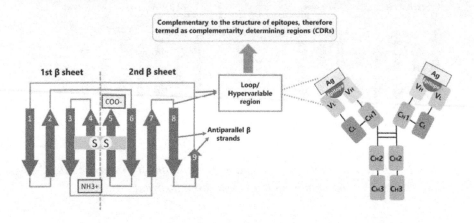

Fig 2-6: Complementarity Determining Regions (CDRs)

The light and heavy variable domains fold in a manner that brings the hypervariable regions of both chains together to create the antigen-binding site or paratope.

The surface of the antigen-binding site formed by the hypervariable regions is complementary to the structure of epitopes to generate antigen specificity. An epitope is the specific part of an antigen to which the antibody binds. Since the hypervariable regions are complementary to the structure of epitopes, they are called complementarity determining regions or CDRs.

Within the variable domain of each heavy and light chain, there are 3 CDRs. The antigen-binding site is formed by pairing the variable domain of one light chain with the variable domain of one heavy chain.

Each domain contributes to three complementarity-determining regions, CDR-L1, CDR-L2, and CDR-L3, in the light chain variable region and CDR-H1, CDR-H2, and CDR-H3 in the variable region of the heavy chain (*Fig 2-7*). Since the CDRs form the antigen-binding site of an antibody molecule, thus a total of 6 CDRs constitute one antigen-binding site. In addition, because CDRs from both V_H and V_L domains contribute to the antigen-binding site, it is the combination of the heavy and the light chain, and not either alone, that determines the final antigen specificity.

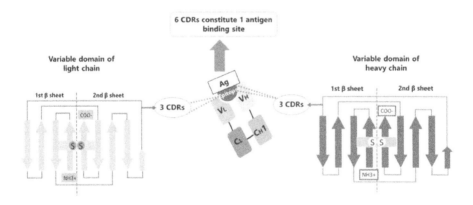

Fig 2-7: Six CDRs constitute one antigen-binding site

Similarly, the second antigen-binding site is formed by pairing variable domains of the other light chain and heavy chain. Thus, the second antigen-binding site will also be created by another 6 CDRs. Therefore, a single antibody molecule contains a total of 12 CDRs (*Fig 2-8*).

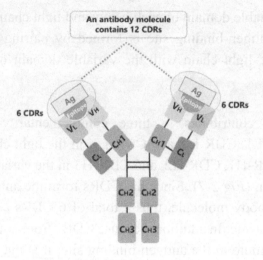

Fig 2-8: A single antibody molecule contains a total of 12 CDRs

The antigen specificity of an antibody determines its ability to distinguish the subtle differences among antigens. Since the CDRs are the antigen-binding sites, they allow the antibody to bind to the specific antigen only and account for the diversity of antigens that a repertoire of antibodies can recognize.

2.3. Framework region

Variable domains of both heavy and light chains can be divided into two regions: complementarity determining regions that have been discussed and framework regions abbreviated as FRs. Unlike the complementarity determining regions (CDRs) which show maximum variation in the amino acid sequences, framework regions are conserved regions of variable regions and show less variation in the amino acid sequences. These regions support the binding of CDRs to the antigen. In other words, the framework regions serve as a scaffold to hold the CDRs in position to contact antigen so that the CDRs can take the correct orientation and position to bind to the antigen. The framework regions are present in the variable domains of both heavy and light chains.

The CDRs are present on the loops that join the β strands in the variable domains of both heavy and light chains. In contrast, the β-sheet structure is a framework region that serves as a scaffold to hold the CDRs in position to contact antigen (*Fig 2-9*).

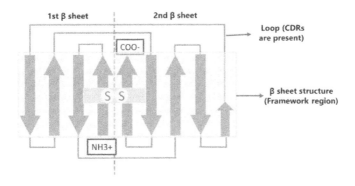

Fig 2-9: β sheet structure constitutes the framework region

2.4. Binding of antigen to CDRs

As already discussed, the CDRs generate the antigen-binding site of the antibody, and the antigen-binding site of an antibody is complementary to the structure of epitopes to generate antigen specificity. Clearly, as the amino acid sequences of the CDRs are different in different antibodies, so are the shapes of the surfaces created by these CDRs; thus, different antibodies bind with different antigens. Therefore, as a general principle, antibodies bind antigens whose surfaces are complementary to that of the antibody (*Fig 2-10*).

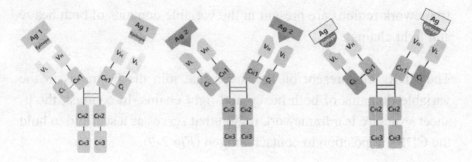

Fig 2-10: Antigen-binding site of an antibody is complementary to the structure of epitopes

The antigen can bind to the antigen-binding site formed by CDRs in 3 possible ways.

- Suppose the antigen is a large globular protein, for instance, viral coat proteins or polysaccharide coats of pathogens; in that case, the contact between this antigen and the antibody occurs over a broad, flat, and undulating surface created by the CDRs (*Fig 2-11*). In the area of contact, protrusions or depressions present on the antigen are likely to match complementary depressions or protrusions present on the antibody molecule. In this scenario, around 15–22 amino acids in the CDRs of antibody contact the same number of residues in the protein antigen.

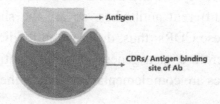

Fig 2-11: Protrusions or depressions on large globular protein match complementary depressions or protrusions on the Ab molecule

- In smaller antigens such as small haptens, antigen-antibody interaction occurs in narrow and deep pockets created by the CDRs (*Fig 2-12*).

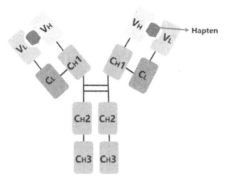

Fig 2-12: Binding of hapten in narrow & deep pockets created by CDRs

- In some cases, antigen binding to the antibody induces a conformational change in antibody, antigen, or both (*Fig 2-13*). This conformational change results in a closer fit between the epitope and antigen-binding site of the antibody.

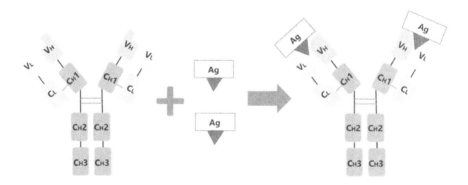

Fig 2-13: Binding of antigen induces a conformational change in antibody

Further X-ray studies have confirmed that more residues in the heavy-chain CDRs appear to contact antigen than in the light-chain CDRs. Thus the variable domain of the heavy chain often contributes more than the variable domain of the light chain. However, it is not the conclusion that the light chain is irrelevant because the antigen-binding site is only formed when the light and heavy variable domains fold in a manner that brings the CDRs of both chains together to create the Ag binding site or paratope.

Thus, the combination of the heavy and the light chain, not alone, determines the final antigen specificity. Even in some antigen-antibody interactions, studies have shown that the light chain makes the more significant contribution.

2.5. Hinge Region

Out of the five heavy chains, γ, δ and α heavy chains contain an extended amino acid sequence between the C_H1 and C_H2 domains that has no homology with the other domains. This region is called the hinge region (*Fig 2-14*).

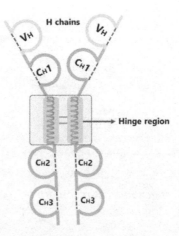

Fig 2-14: Hinge region in γ, δ and α heavy chains

Hinge is a flexible amino acid stretch that provides flexibility to IgG, IgD, and IgA and allows independent movement of the Fab fragments. As a result, the two Fab arms can move relative to each other, leading to better interaction with the antigen. Proline and cysteine are the two prominent amino acids present in the hinge region.

A large number of proline residues in the hinge region makes the antibody vulnerable to getting cleaved by proteolytic enzymes such as papain or pepsin. On the other hand, the cysteine residues present in the hinge region form interchain disulfide bonds, enabling the two heavy chains to bind together.

The number of interchain disulfide bonds in the hinge region varies significantly among different classes of antibodies.

μ and ε heavy chains lack a hinge region, but they have an additional domain of 110 amino acids with hinge-like features (*Fig 2-15*).

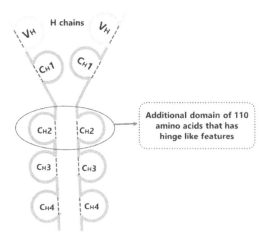

Fig 2-15: Lack of hinge region in μ and ε heavy chains

Thus, there are four constant domains in IgM and IgE Abs because of the absence of hinge region, whereas there are three constant domains in IgG, IgD, and IgA antibodies because of the presence of the hinge region (*Fig 2-16*).

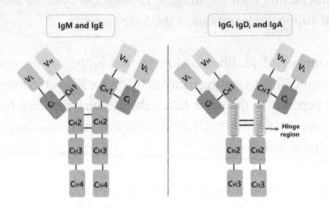

Fig 2-16: 4 constant domains in IgM and IgE; and 3 constant domains in IgG, IgD, and IgA antibodies

Chapter 3. Antibody classes and their biological activities

There are five different classes of antibodies: IgG, IgM, IgA, IgE, and IgD. Each class of antibody is distinguished by the unique amino acids present in the constant region of the heavy chain that confer structural and functional properties to the antibodies.

3.1. Immunoglobulin G or IgG

First is Immunoglobulin G, designated as IgG. It is the most abundant antibody in serum and constitutes about 75-80% of the immunoglobulin serum. IgG molecule consists of two γ heavy chains and either two κ light chains or two λ light chains. But can never have both of the light chains.

There are four different IgG subclasses: IgG1, IgG2, IgG3, and IgG4 that are distinguished by subtle differences in amino acid sequences in the constant region of γ heavy chains. Besides differences in amino acid sequences, few structural differences distinguish one subclass from another (*Fig 3-1*). These are differences:

- in the size of the hinge region
- And the number of interchain disulfide bonds between the heavy chains. For instance, IgG1 has two interchain disulfide bonds; IgG2 and IgG4 have four interchain disulfide bonds, whereas IgG3 has 11 interchain disulfide bonds.

Immunoglobulin G has many biological roles.

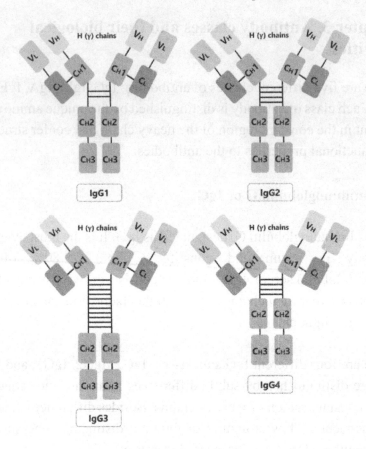

Fig 3-1: Subclasses of IgG

The differences in amino acids between subclasses of IgG also affect their biological activity. For instance,

1. IgG is the only class of Ig that can cross the placenta in humans and enter the fetal circulation, and it is mainly responsible for the protection of the newborn during the first months of life. The transfer of IgG from mother to fetus is a form of **passive immunization**, which means the acquisition of immunity by receiving preformed antibodies of the mother by the fetus rather than by active production of antibodies after exposure

to antigen. Among all the subclasses, IgG1, IgG3, and IgG4 can readily cross the placenta and play an essential role in protecting the fetus.

2. Another important role of IgG is that IgG molecules can react with Fcγ receptors present on the surface of macrophages, neutrophils, and natural killer cells (*Fig 3-2*). These cells phagocytose the particles or pathogens coated with IgG antibodies and thus is a vital mechanism that cells use to kill the microorganisms. This process is called opsonization. Among the subclasses of IgG, IgG1 and IgG3 bind with high affinity to Fc receptors and are most efficient in mediating opsonization, whereas IgG4 antibody has an intermediate affinity and IgG2 antibody has an extremely low affinity for Fc receptors.

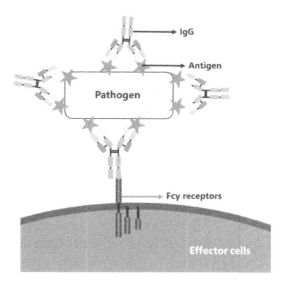

Fig 3-2: Effector cells phagocytose pathogens coated with IgG antibodies

31

3. The third important role of IgG is that it activates the complement system. The complement system comprises proteins that can perforate the cell membrane of the microorganisms, thus killing them. The collaboration between the antibody and the complement system is essential for the inactivation, removal, and killing of pathogens. The complement system is discussed in detail in the next chapter. Among the subclasses of IgG, IgG3 is the most effective complement activator, followed by IgG1. On the other hand, IgG2 is less efficient in activating the complement system, whereas IgG4 cannot activate the complement system.

3.2. Immunoglobulin A or IgA

The IgA antibody constitutes only 10-15% of total serum immunoglobulins. But is the predominant immunoglobulin found in body secretions such as breast milk, tears, saliva, and mucous membranes of the respiratory, digestive, and genitourinary systems. Structurally IgA molecule consists of two α heavy chains and either two κ light chains or two λ light chains. There are two different IgA subclasses IgA1 and IgA2 that are distinguished by subtle differences in amino acid sequences in the constant region of α heavy chains. However, besides differences in amino acid sequences, few structural differences distinguish one subclass from another. These are differences in the size of the hinge region.

- The hinge region of IgA1 is longer than that of IgA2 (*Fig 3-3*). The IgA1 hinge region consists of 16-18 amino acids, whereas the IgA2 hinge region contains around 5 amino acids.
- The extended hinge region of IgA1 also has glycosylation sites.

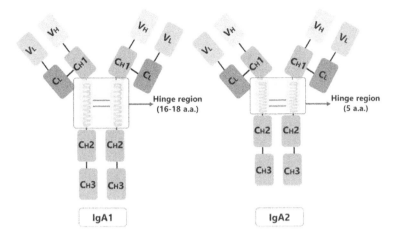

Fig 3-3: Hinge region of IgA1 is longer than that of IgA2

Based on their presence in serum and body secretions, IgA can be divided into two forms:
- serum IgA
- and secretory IgA (sIgA)

Serum IgA is predominantly found in serum. In contrast, the secretory IgA is present in body secretions like breast milk, saliva, tears, and mucous membranes.

Additionally, serum IgA generally exists as a **monomer,** and its polymeric form is rarely found. On the other hand, secretory IgA occurs in **polymeric form** and consists of either dimer or tetramer. The IgA monomers are held together by Fc-linked polypeptide called the joining chain designated as J chain (*Fig 3-4*). The J chain is disulfide-bonded to the carboxyl-terminal cysteine residue of the two subunits of polymeric IgA. The function of the J chain is to facilitate the polymerization of the monomers to form polymeric IgA.

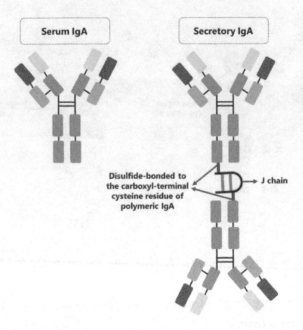

Fig 3-4: Monomeric form of serum IgA and dimeric form of secretory IgA

IgA also contains another polypeptide called the secretory component (*Fig 3-5*).

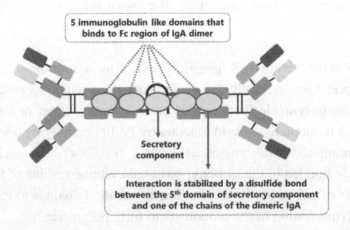

Fig 3-5: Secretory component of IgA dimer

The secretory component consists of 5 Ig-like domains that bind to the Fc region of IgA dimer. The interaction is stabilized by a disulfide bond between the fifth domain of the secretory component and one of the chains of dimeric IgA.

Polymeric IgA secreting plasma cells get concentrated along the mucous membrane surfaces. IgA binds to the polymeric Ig receptor (or poly Ig receptor), which recognizes and interacts with the J chain of polymeric IgA antibodies (*Fig 3-6*). The poly Ig receptor is expressed on the epithelial cells of the mucous membrane.

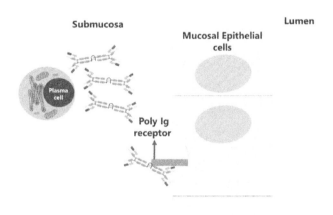

Fig 3-6: Poly Ig receptor interacts with J chain of IgA and then transports it across the epithelial cells of the mucous membrane

Once the polymeric IgA is bound to poly Ig receptor, endocytosis of receptor-IgA complex occurs. After endocytosis, cleavage of the poly Ig receptor occurs. The cleaved poly Ig receptor becomes the secretory component of IgA, and then the IgA bound with the secretory component is released into the mucous secretions (*Fig 3-7*). The released IgA antibody is called the secretory IgA (sIgA) antibody. The secretory component of sIgA is essential as it masks the protease cleavage sites in the hinge region of the IgA molecule, thus protecting immunoglobulin from getting degraded by proteolytic enzymes and allowing the polymeric IgA to exist longer in the environment.

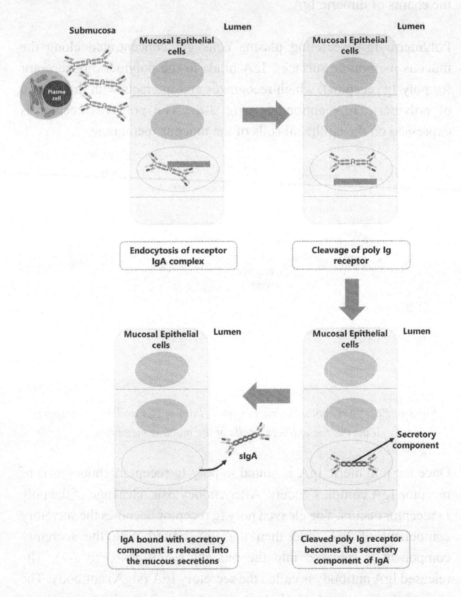

Fig 3-7: Mechanism of transport of IgA into the mucous secretions

Secretory IgA serves a vital function at mucous membrane surfaces, which are the potential entry sites of most pathogenic organisms. The binding of secretory IgA to the membranes of pathogens prevents their attachment to the mucosal membranes, thus inhibiting viral and bacterial infection (*Fig 3-8*). For instance, secretory IgA provides defense against bacteria like *Salmonella, Vibrio cholerae,* and viruses such as polio, influenza, etc.

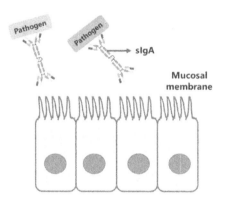

Fig 3-8: sIgA prevents attachment of pathogens to mucosal membranes

Breast milk containing secretory IgA helps protect the newborn against infections during the initial months of their life and provides them the required immunity until their own immune system becomes fully functional.

3.3. Immunoglobulin M or IgM

Of the five major classes of immunoglobulins, the immunoglobulin M (IgM) antibody is the largest antibody and is the first immunoglobulin class to be produced in a primary response to an antigen. Also, it is the first immunoglobulin to be synthesized by neonates. Structurally IgM molecule consists of two μ heavy chains and either two κ light chains or two λ light chains. It accounts for 5–10% of the total serum immunoglobulins and has two forms: monomeric IgM and pentameric IgM (*Fig 3-9*).

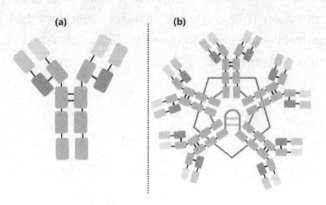

Fig 3-9: (a) Monomeric IgM and (b) Pentameric IgM

As a monomer, IgM is present on the surface of B cells (*Fig 3-10a*). Thus, monomeric IgM is called membrane-bound IgM designated as mIgM. In contrast, the IgM secreted by plasma cells is in the pentameric form (*Fig 3-10b*). The pentameric form of IgM is present in blood and body secretions.

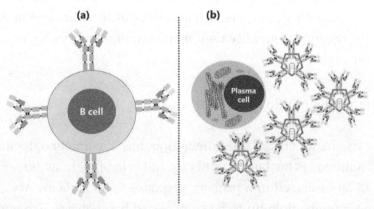

Fig 3-10: (a) Monomeric IgM is membrane-bound, and (b) pentameric IgM is secreted by plasma cells

The five monomer subunits of pentameric IgM are arranged with their Fc regions in the center of the pentamer and the ten antigen-binding sites on the periphery of the molecule. The five monomer units are held together by disulfide bonds that link their carboxyl-terminal, i.e., Cµ4 and the Cµ3 heavy chain domains (*Fig 3-11*). Pentamer IgM contains an additional Fc-linked polypeptide called the joining chain designated as J chain, similar to that found in the case of IgA, and is added just before the secretion of the pentamer.

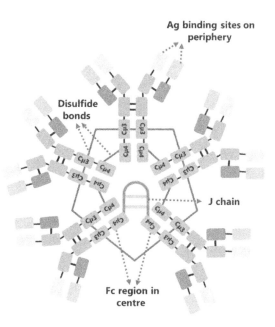

Fig 3-11: Structure of pentameric IgM

Since each original monomer of immunoglobulin has two antigen-binding sites, therefore each pentameric complex of IgM should be able to bind to 10 identical antigens simultaneously. However, although an IgM molecule can bind to 10 antigen molecules, because of **lack of flexibility in the hinge region and steric hindrance** that occurs on larger antigens, only five or fewer molecules of antigens can bind simultaneously.

Due to its high valency, pentameric IgM is more efficient than other antibody classes in binding antigens with many repeating epitopes such as antigens of red blood cells (RBCs) and viral particles. For example, IgM antibodies are mainly responsible for the clumping or agglutination of red blood cells if the recipient of a blood transfusion receives blood that is not compatible with their blood type (*Fig 3-12*). Interestingly it takes 100 to 1000 times more IgG molecules than IgM to achieve the same level of agglutination.

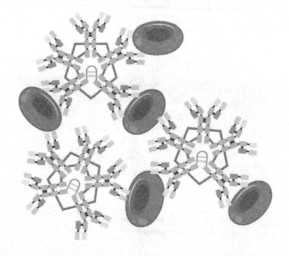

Fig 3-12: Clumping or agglutination of RBCs by pentameric IgM antibodies

Similarly, less IgM than IgG is required to neutralize viral infectivity.

Additionally, IgM is the most efficient antibody in activating the complement system. Since the complement activation requires at least two Fc regions in close proximity, the pentameric structure of a single molecule of IgM fulfills this requirement (discussed in Chapter 4).

The J chain present allows IgM to bind to receptors on epithelial cells on the mucous membrane, which transport it across the epithelial membrane to enter the mucous secretions. The pentameric IgM is transported to mucous secretions through a phenomenon similar to that of IgA that has been already discussed. However, because of its large size, IgM does not diffuse well. Therefore, it is found in very low concentrations in the mucous secretions and is also restricted from crossing the placenta. Although IgM is present in the body secretion, the predominant immunoglobulin class in the secretions is IgA.

3.4. Immunoglobulin E or IgE

Structurally IgE is a monomer consisting of two ε heavy chains and either two κ light chains or two λ light chains. IgE is found in trace amounts in serum, with its concentration in serum being around 0.3 µg/ml. It constitutes less than 1% of serum immunoglobulins. IgE antibody does not participate in complement activation, opsonization, etc., but it plays a crucial role in allergic reactions and defense against parasitic worms.

IgE in defense against parasitic worms such as helminths etc.: When there is an invasion by parasitic worms, the T helper cells secrete the cytokines such as IL-4 and stimulate B cells to secrete IgE antibodies.

The IgE antibodies then coat the surface of the parasitic worm by binding to its surface antigens. These bound IgE antibodies are then recognized by specific Fcε receptors present on the eosinophils, which bind to the Fc region of IgE bound to worms (*Fig 3-13*).

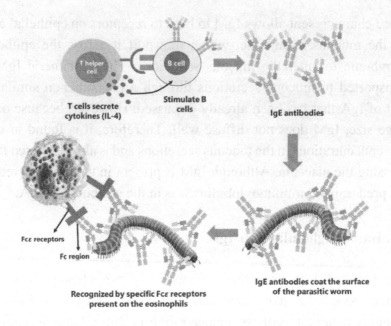

Fig 3-13: Role of IgE in defense against parasitic worms

Once bound, the eosinophils undergo translocation of their granules to the plasma membrane, followed by the release of contents of the granules to the extracellular environment. This release of granular content is known as degranulation. The released granule content then destroys the parasitic worms (*Fig 3-14*).

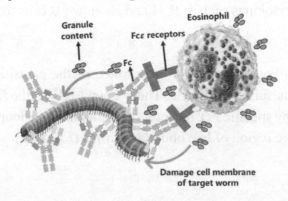

Fig 3-14: Degranulation of eosinophils destroys the parasitic worms

Role of IgE in allergic reactions: IgE antibodies also mediate allergic reactions in the body that are responsible for the symptoms of asthma, hay fever, hives, and anaphylactic shock. Some people's immune system is sensitive to some substances such as pollen, nuts, dust, etc. These substances are known as allergens. These substances are harmless to most people, but the immune system of people allergic to them recognizes them as dangerous. For example, let's assume that a person is allergic to pollen. On his first exposure to pollen, the B cells of this allergic person get activated. Once activated, the B cells then differentiate into IgE-producing plasma cells (*Fig 3-15*).

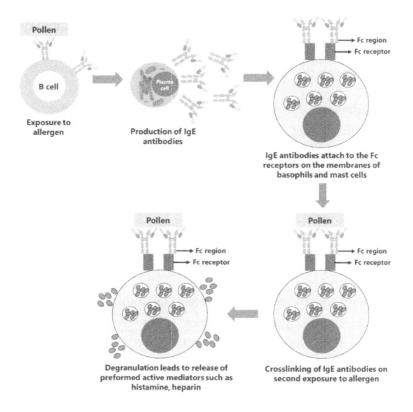

Fig 3-15: Role of IgE in allergic reactions

These IgE antibodies then attach themselves to the Fc receptors on the membranes of basophils and mast cells by their Fc regions. Now, the antigen-binding sites of these IgE antibodies are free. When there is a second exposure of the allergic person to allergen pollen, the allergen binds to the IgE antibodies attached to Fc receptors of mast cells and basophils. This binding of allergen to IgE antibodies results in crosslinking of IgE antibodies.

This crosslinking then sends the signal to the basophils and mast cells to translocate their granules to the plasma membrane and release the granule contents to the extracellular environment by a process known as degranulation. As a result of degranulation, there is a rapid release of preformed active mediators from the granules, such as histamine, heparin, etc.

These mediators act on a person's eyes, nose, throat, lungs, skin, or gastrointestinal tract, causing allergy symptoms like watery eyes, itching, sneezing, runny nose, rashes, abnormal heart rate, etc. Thus, the elevated levels of IgE antibodies in the body also have a diagnostic significance. It indicates the possibility of either allergic reaction or parasitic infection.

3.5. Immunoglobulin D or IgD

IgD antibody constitutes about 0.25% of the total immunoglobulins in serum. Structurally IgD is a monomer. It has two δ heavy chains and either two κ light chains or two λ light chains.

IgD can both be membrane-bound and secreted. IgD, together with IgM, is the major membrane-bound antibody expressed by the mature B cells (*Fig 3-16*). IgD signals the B cells to get activated. By being activated, B cells are ready to take part in the body's defense as part of the immune system. The exact function of IgD antibodies is still unclear. Some studies have also suggested that secreted IgD has essential roles in respiratory mucosal immune defense. It binds to microbial virulence factors as well as pathogenic respiratory bacteria and viruses.

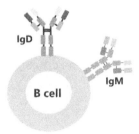

Fig 3-16: Both IgD and IgM are expressed by mature B cells

Few studies have also suggested that IgD may have a role in allergic responses as well. Although the nature of the IgD receptor remains elusive, the cross-linking of IgD on basophils stimulates the release of immune-activating, proinflammatory, and antimicrobial mediators.

Chapter 4. Complement activation

4.1. Introduction to the complement system

The complement system is a part of the immune system that enhances the ability of the antibodies and phagocytic cells to clear microbes and damaged cells from the body. The word "complement" is used because the complement system enhances or complements our immunity.

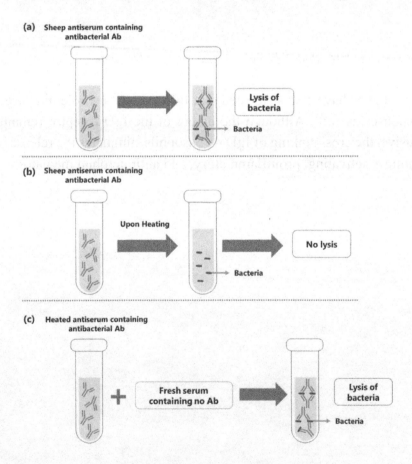

Fig 4-1: Jules Bordet experiment

Jules Bordet first discovered the complement system as a heat-labile component of plasma that causes the killing of bacteria (*Fig 4-1*). Jules Bordet showed that the sheep antiserum caused the lysis of bacterium *Vibrio cholerae*, and upon heating the antiserum, its bacteriolytic activity was destroyed. But the ability of the heated antiserum to lyse the bacteria was restored by adding the fresh serum that contained no antibodies directed against the bacterium.

The serum containing no antibodies was otherwise unable to kill bacteria by itself. Thus, Bordet observed that the bacteriolytic activity of antiserum was mediated by two components (*Fig 4-2*):

1. Specific antibacterial antibodies which were heat resistant
2. And the other component which was heat sensitive

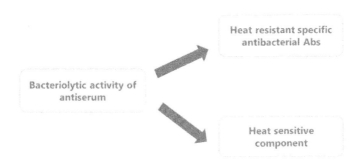

Fig 4-2: Components of bacteriolytic activity of antiserum

Later, scientist Paul Ehrlich coined the term 'complement' for the heat-sensitive component, defining it as the activity of the blood serum that completes the action of antibodies. The complement system refers to a series of more than 20 proteins circulating in the blood and tissue fluids. The complement proteins are synthesized mainly by liver hepatocytes, although significant amounts are also produced by tissue macrophages, blood monocytes, and epithelial cells of the gastrointestinal and genitourinary tracts.

Most of the complement proteins that circulate in the serum are in functionally inactive forms as proenzymes or zymogens, and they come into effect only when activated. In response to the recognition of microorganisms, the complement proteins get sequentially activated in an enzyme cascade which means the activation of one protein enzymatically cleaves and activates the next protein in the cascade (*Fig 4-3*).

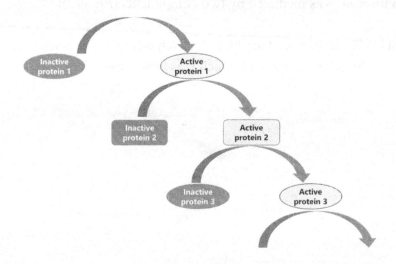

Fig 4-3: Complement proteins get sequentially activated in an enzyme cascade

4.2. Nomenclature of complement proteins

Complement proteins are designated by capital letter C followed by a number from 1 to 9, for example, C1, C2, C3, till C9. The numbers in the names of complement proteins C1-C9 represent the order of their discovery. Some complement proteins are also designated by letter symbols, like Factor B and Factor D. Also, the complement proteins circulate in serum in inactive forms, and they come into effect only once activated. For the activation, the complement protein is cleaved, and the resulting peptide fragments are denoted by adding a lower suffix a and b. In most cases, the smaller fragment resulting from the cleavage of complement protein is designated as "a," and the larger fragment is designated as "b" (*Fig 4-4*).

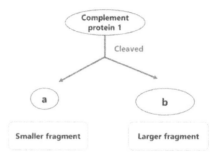

Fig 4-4: Cleavage of complement protein yields two fragments

For instance, C3 on activation produces two peptide fragments C3a and C3b. In this case, C3a is the smaller fragment, and C3b is the larger fragment (*Fig 4-5*).

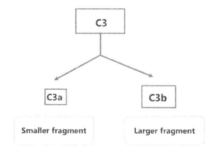

Fig 4-5: C3 on activation produces C3a (smaller) and C3b (larger) fragments

Note that among all the complement proteins, C2 is an exception because the cleaved fragment C2a is the larger fragment and C2b is the smaller fragment (*Fig 4-6*).

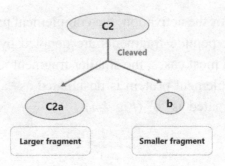

Fig 4-6: C2 on activation produces C2a (larger) and C2b (smaller) fragments

The larger fragment of the complement proteins binds to the target sites and contributes to the activation of other complement proteins in the cascade. At the same time, the smaller fragment of the complement proteins diffuses from the site and can initiate localized inflammatory responses by binding to the specific receptors. The larger complement fragments of different complement proteins interact with one another to form functional complexes leading to activation of the complement system.

Pathways of complement activation

The complement system can be activated by three pathways: the classical pathway, the alternative pathway, and the lectin pathway.

4.3. Classical pathway

Complement activation by the classical pathway begins with the formation of the Ag-Ab complex. In other words, the complement activation occurs upon binding of Ab to the Ag on a target such as a bacterial cell. The classical complement system is generally activated by IgM and certain IgG subclasses such as IgG1, IgG2, and IgG3.

There are primarily four complement proteins that participate in activating the classical complement pathway- C1, C2, C3, and C4. All these proteins are present in a functionally inactive form in plasma.

The numbers in the names of complement proteins C1, C2, C3, and C4 do not reflect the order in which they react; instead, they represent the order of their discovery. The formation of the Ag-Ab complex induces the conformational change in the Fc region of the IgM Ab that exposes a binding site for the C1 component of the complement system.

C1 protein is a macromolecular complex consisting of one molecule of C1q and two molecules each of C1r and C1s held together to form the C1qr$_2$s$_2$ complex stabilized by Ca^{2+}(*Fig 4-7*). C1q molecule comprises 18 polypeptide chains that associate to form six collagen-like triple-helical arms and the globular heads.

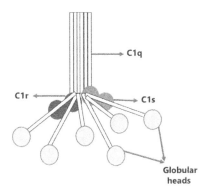

Fig 4-7: Structure of C1 protein

The globular heads of C1q bind to the exposed C1q binding sites in the C$_H$2 domain of the Ab molecule. Each C1 molecule must bind by its C1q globular heads to at least two Fc sites for a stable C1-Ab interaction to occur. Therefore, when attached to the Ag on a target, pentameric IgM assumes staple conformation in which at least three binding sites for C1q are exposed (*Fig 4-8*).

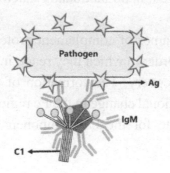

Fig 4-8: When pentameric IgM is bound to Ag, at least three binding sites for C1q are exposed

On the contrary, an IgG molecule contains only a single C1q binding site in the CH2 domain of the Fc region. Therefore, for a stable C1-IgG interaction to occur, at least two IgG molecules should be in close proximity on a target surface to provide two attachment sites for C1q (*Fig 4-9*).

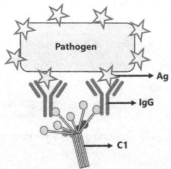

Fig 4-9: 2 IgG molecules are required for a stable C1-IgG interaction

Because of this reason, a single molecule of pentameric IgM bound to a red blood cell is sufficient to activate the classical complement pathway and lyse the cell. In contrast, some 1000 molecules of IgG are required to ensure that two IgG molecules are close enough to each other on the cell surface to initiate C1q binding.

1. When C1q binds to Fc sites of Ab, a conformation change is induced in C1r that converts C1r into an active serine protease C1r, which cleaves C1s to convert it into an active serine protease enzyme C1s. So now, the active C1s has two substrates C2 and C4 (*Fig 4-10*).

2. C4 complement protein has three polypeptide chains- α, β, and γ. When active C1s hydrolyses a small fragment C4a from the amino terminus of the α chain of C4, the resulting C4b fragment becomes active.

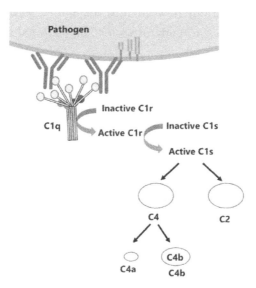

Fig 4-10: C4 protein is cleaved to produce active C4b fragment

The binding site for C2 on C4b is now exposed, and C4b binds to the target surface in vicinity of C1. Then C2 proenzyme binds to the exposed binding site on C4b, followed by cleaving C2 into C2a and

C2b by C1s active enzyme. The smaller fragment C2b diffuses away (*Fig 4-11*).

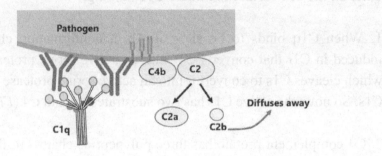

Fig 4-11: Activation of C2 protein

3. The resulting C4b2a complex is called C3 convertase, which can convert C3 complement protein into an active form (*Fig 4-12*). A single C3 convertase can generate over 200 molecules of active C3b.

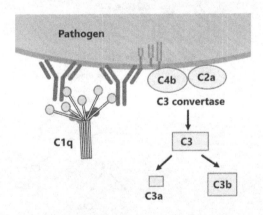

Fig 4-12: C3 convertase cleaves C3 to produce active fragment C3b

Some of the C3b binds to C4b2a to form a trimolecular complex C4b2a3b, which is now called C5 convertase. C5 convertase can further activate C5 complement protein by cleaving C5 into C5a and C5b (*Fig 4-13*).

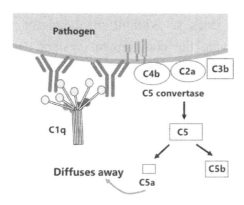

Fig 4-13: C5 convertase cleaves C5 to produce active fragment C5b

C5a diffuses away, and C5b attaches to C6 and initiates the formation of the membrane attack complex (*Fig 4-14*). The complete sequence of membrane attack complex formation is described in section 4.6.

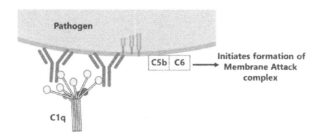

Fig 4-14: C5b attaches to C6 and initiates the formation of membrane attack complex

4.4. Alternative pathway

The second pathway by which the complement system can be activated is the alternative pathway. Like the classical pathway, the alternative pathway also culminates in the formation of C5b, which then initiates the formation of a membrane attack complex to lyse the target cell. But it does so without the need for antigen-antibody complexes to activate the complement system. Because no Ab is required, the alternative pathway is considered a component of the innate immune system. This complement activation pathway involves four proteins- C3, Factor B, Factor D, and properdin.

Generally, this pathway is initiated by cell surface components that are foreign to the host, such as lipopolysaccharides from gram-negative bacteria cell walls, teichoic acids from gram-positive bacteria cell walls, and zymosan from fungal and yeast cell walls. Additionally, some viruses, parasites, virus-infected cells, tumor cells, etc., can also activate the alternative pathway of the complement system. In the classical pathway, C3 is cleaved into C3a and C3b by C3 convertase. But in the alternative pathway, the thioester bond of serum C3 undergoes slow spontaneous hydrolysis to yield C3a and C3b (*Fig 4-15*).

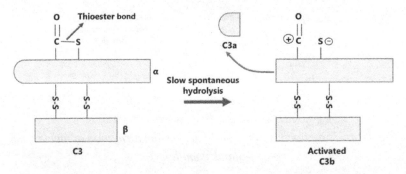

Fig 4-15: Slow spontaneous hydrolysis of C3 to yield C3a and C3b

Now, this C3b component can bind to foreign surface Ags and not just foreign antigens; it can even bind on the host's own cells. But the membrane of mammalian cells has high levels of sialic acid, which enables the rapid inactivation of C3b molecules on the host cells. Thus, the binding of C3b molecules on host cells rarely leads to activation of the complement system. On the other hand, foreign antigenic surfaces like bacterial and yeast cell walls, viral envelopes, etc., have low sialic acid levels; therefore, C3b bound to them remains active and can activate the complement system (*Fig 4-16*).

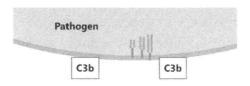

Fig 4-16: C3b component binds to foreign surface Ags

1. The C3b present on the surface of foreign cells binds to another serum protein called factor B, stabilized by Mg^{2+}.

2. Binding to C3b exposes a site on factor B that makes factor B accessible to be cleaved by another serum protein called factor D. Factor D cleaves Factor B, generating two fragments. The smaller fragment Ba diffuses away, and the other larger fragment Bb makes a complex with C3b, and the complex C3bBb has C3 convertase activity (*Fig 4-17*).

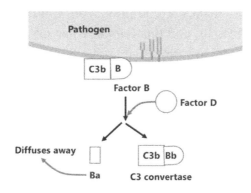

Fig 4-17: Larger fragment Bb makes a complex with C3b to form C3bBb that has C3 convertase activity

3. This activity is analogous to the C4b2a complex of classical pathways. C3bBb complex has a half-life of 5 minutes unless the serum protein properdin binds to it, stabilizing the C3bBb complex, thus extending its half-life to 30 minutes. The C3bBb generated can activate unhydrolyzed C3 to generate more C3b (*Fig 4-18*). As a result, initial steps of the alternative pathway are again activated and amplified from binding of C3b to foreign cell surface to the formation of C3bBb to generate more C3b.

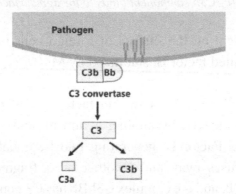

Fig 4-18: Activation of C3 by C3Bb complex

4. C3b generated makes a complex with C3bBb resulting in the formation of C3bBb3b, and this complex has C5 convertase activity (*Fig 4-19*) analogous to C4b2a3b complex in the classical pathway.

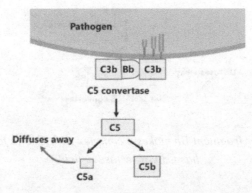

Fig 4-19: Activation of C5 by C3bBb3b complex

C5 convertase can further activate C5 complement protein by cleaving C5 into C5a and C5b. The resulting C5a component diffuses away while the C5b component attaches to C6 and initiates the membrane attack complex formation.

4.5. Lectin Pathway

The third pathway by which the complement system can be activated is the lectin pathway. As the name indicates, the lectin pathway of complement activation is initiated by the lectins. Lectins are the proteins that can recognize and bind to the specific carbohydrate residues on the target cells. The lectin that activates the complement system binds to mannose residues; therefore, this pathway is also named the MBLectin pathway or Mannan binding lectin pathway (*Fig 4-20*). Like the alternative pathway, the lectin pathway does not depend on Ab for its activation.

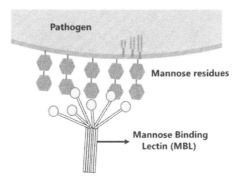

Fig 4-20: Lectin pathway is activated by binding of mannose-binding lectin to mannose residues

1. The lectin pathway is activated when mannose-binding lectin (MBL) binds to the mannose residues on glycoproteins or carbohydrates on the surface of microorganisms like Salmonella,

Neisseria, Listeria strains, *Candida albicans,* etc. Additionally, the mannose-binding lectin protein has activity analogous to the C1q protein of the classical pathway.

2. After MBL binds to the surface of a pathogen, MBL associated serine proteases bind to mannose-binding lectin. These MBL associated serine proteases are MASP-1 and MASP-2 (*Fig 4-21*).

3. The active complex formed by the MASP-1 and MASP-2 proteins causes cleavage and activation of C4 and C2 proteins. MASP-1 and MASP-2 have activity similar to C1r and C1s of the classical pathway. C4 is cleaved into C4a and C4b; and, C2 is cleaved into C2a and C2b.

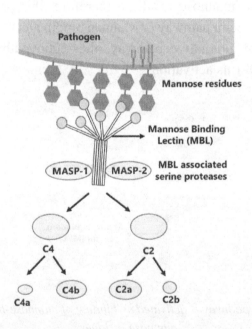

Fig 4-21: Cleavage of C4 and C2 proteins to generate active C4b and C2a

4. C4b2a complex has C3 convertase activity, which cleaves and activates C3 (*Fig 4-22*).

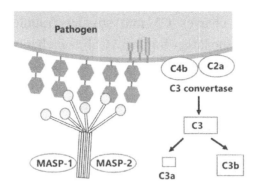

Fig 4-22: C3 convertase cleaves and activates C3

5. Further, like the classical pathway, the C4b2a3b complex is formed, with C5 convertase activity resulting in the formation of C5b (*Fig 4-23*). C5b attaches to C6 and initiates the formation of the membrane attack complex.

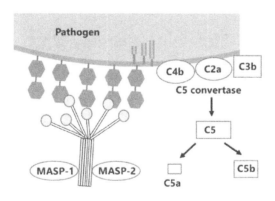

Fig 4-23: C5 convertase cleaves and activates C5

4.6. Membrane Attack Complex

The end result of all the three complement pathways: classical, alternative & lectin pathway is the production of an active C5 convertase which cleaves C5 into smaller fragment C5a, which diffuses away, and the larger fragment C5b, which binds to the surface of the target cell. Now, this C5b component provides a binding site for the subsequent components C6, C7, C8, and C9, which interact sequentially to form a macromolecular structure called Membrane Attack complex abbreviated as MAC (*Fig 4-24*). MAC creates a large channel through the membrane of the target cell, enabling ions and small molecules to diffuse freely across the membrane, thus disrupting the cell membrane of the target cells, which in turn leads to cell lysis and death of these cells.

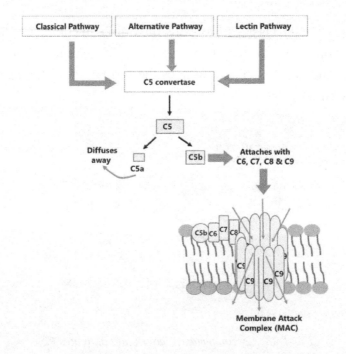

Fig 4-24: C5b component attaches with C6, C7, C8 and to form a MAC Attack

1. The C5b component is highly labile and becomes inactive within 2 minutes unless C6 binds to it and stabilizes its activity.

2. All the complementation reactions, till the binding of C6 to C5b, take place on the hydrophilic surface of the target membrane. But as soon as C5b6 binds to C7, the resulting complex undergoes a hydrophilic amphiphilic structural transition to expose the hydrophobic site on the C5b67 complex, which mediates its binding to the phospholipid bilayer of the target cells (*Fig 4-25*). As a result, the C5b67 gets inserted into the phospholipid bilayer of the target cell.

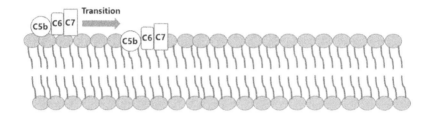

Fig 4-25: Hydrophilic amphiphilic structural transition of C5b67 complex

3. Binding of C8 to the inserted C5b67 complex also induces a conformational change in C8 such that C8 also undergoes a hydrophilic-amphiphilic structural transition. It exposes its hydrophobic region, which mediates the insertion of C8 into the phospholipid bilayer of the target cell (*Fig 4-26*). After insertion of C8, the C5b678 complex creates a small pore of diameter 10 Å in the target cell.

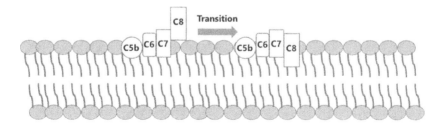

Fig 4-26: Hydrophilic amphiphilic structural transition of C8 protein

4. The final step of membrane attack complex formation involves the binding and polymerization of C9 molecules to the C5b678 complex. Around 10-17 molecules of C9 can bind and get polymerized by a single C5b678 complex (*Fig 4-27*). During polymerization, C9 molecules also undergo a hydrophilic-amphiphilic transition, thus exposing their hydrophobic region, which facilitates the insertion of C9 molecules into the target cell's membrane. The whole $C5b678(9)_{10-17}$ complex is known as the membrane attack complex.

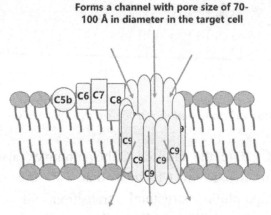

Fig 4-27: C9 molecules polymerize to C5b678 complex and form membrane attack complex (MAC)

5. The complete membrane attack complex forms a channel with a pore size of 70-100 Å in diameter in the target cell, through which small ions and molecules can diffuse freely. Membrane attack complexes create such pores all over the microbial cell membrane (*Fig 4-28*). These pores, in turn, compromise the membrane integrity of the pathogen. The creation of these pores leads to the loss of essential electrolytes from the microbial cell. Simultaneously these pores also allow the inflow of extracellular fluid like water, ions, and other small molecules into the microbial cell, because of which the microbial cell can not maintain its osmotic stability and eventually gets lysed and killed. So, this is the complete mechanism of how the

complement proteins kill pathogens or other target cells such as tumor cells.

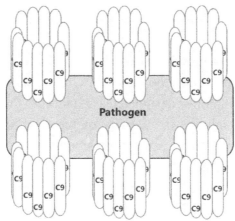

Fig 4-28: Membrane attack complexes create pores all over the microbial cell membrane

4.7. Regulation of the complement system

Undoubtedly the complement system serves as an essential and effective defense mechanism to destroy the invading microorganisms. But there are many elements of the complement system that are capable of attacking not only the foreign cells and pathogens but also the host cells. It leads to the lysis and killing of host cells. For instance, the C5b67 complex, if it gets released from the target cells, poses a threat to nearby healthy cells by lysing and killing them. Thus, several regulatory proteins in the body restrict the complement activity to the target cells only.

The regulation of the complement system occurs at three stages:

1. The first stage is regulation before the assembly of C3 convertase

2. The second stage is regulation after the assembly of C3 convertase

3. And the third stage is regulation at the assembly of the Membrane attack complex.

1. Regulation before the assembly of C3 convertase

(a) Prevents activation of C2 and C4 proteins:

The first regulatory protein in the classical pathway of complement activation that prevents the assembly of C3 convertase is the glycoprotein C1 inhibitor designated as C1Inh. As the name indicates, the C1 inhibitor inhibits the activity of the C1 protein. As already discussed, C1 in serum is a macromolecular complex consisting of C1q, and two molecules of C1r and C1s are held together in a complex stabilized by Ca^{2+}. When C1q binds to Fc sites of Ab, a conformation change is induced in C1r that converts C1r into an active serine protease C1r, which then cleaves C1s to convert it into an active serine protease enzyme C1s. Now the active C1s cleaves the substrate C4 into C4a and C4b. The smaller fragment C4a diffuses away while, the larger fragment C4b becomes active (*Fig 4-29*).

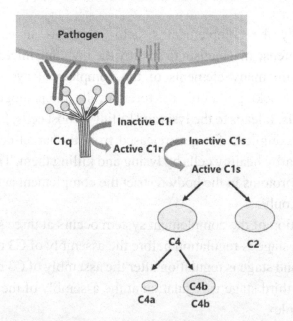

Fig 4-29: Classical pathway of complement activation

Then the C4b binds to the C2 proenzyme, followed by cleaving C2 by C1s active enzyme. The resulting C4b2a complex is called C3 convertase, which can convert C3 complement protein into an active form (*Fig 4-30*).

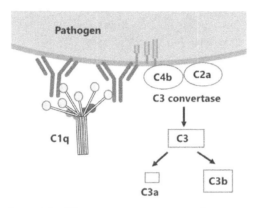

Fig 4-30: C3 convertase activates C3 protein

This step is highly regulated so that C3 convertase is activated only when the body sees any foreign pathogen or some damaged or tumor cells that are required to be destroyed by the immune system. In the absence of regulation, the **spontaneous activation of C3 convertase can even kill the host cells**.

To regulate this step of the classical pathway of complement activation, the regulatory protein **C1 inhibitor** (C1Inh) forms a complex with $C1r_2s_2$, which in turn causes the $C1r_2s_2$ to dissociate from C1q (*Fig 4-31*).

The dissociated $C1r_2s_2$ loses the ability to activate C2 and C4 proteins. The inactivated C2 and C4 proteins then lose their ability to form C3 convertase, thus inhibiting the classical pathway of complement activation.

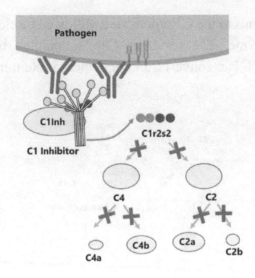

Fig 4-31: Binding of C1 inhibitor to C1r2s2 results in inactivation of C2 and C4 proteins

(b) Prevents assembly of C3 convertase:

Classical pathway: It has already been discussed that the reaction catalyzed by the C3 convertase enzyme of classical, alternative, and lectin pathway is the major amplification step in complement activation, generating hundreds of molecules of C3b.

C3b generated can bind to nearby healthy cells, mediating their damage either

- by causing their phagocytosis by C3b receptors bearing phagocytic cells
- or by causing their lysis by initiating the membrane attack complex formation.

As already discussed in the alternative pathway of complement activation, the membranes of mammalian cells have high levels of sialic acid. The presence of sialic acid leads to the rapid inactivation

68

of C3b molecules on the host cells; thus, the binding of C3b molecules on host cells rarely leads to the activation of the complement system.

The destruction of healthy host cells by C3b is further limited by a family of regulatory proteins, known as regulators of complement activation, abbreviated as RCA. The RCA proteins include C4b binding protein abbreviated as C4BP, complement receptor type I abbreviated as CR-1, and membrane cofactor protein abbreviated as MCP. Each of these regulatory proteins can bind to C4b and prevent the assembly of C3 convertase (*Fig 4-32*). Once these regulatory proteins are bound to C4b, another protein factor I cleaves C4b into C4d and C4c. As a result, the cleaved C4b is unable to associate with C2a to form a C3 convertase.

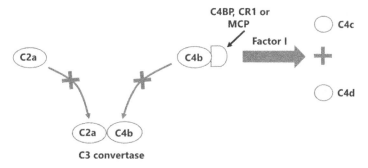

Fig 4-32: Regulatory proteins C4BP, CR-1, and MCP cleave C4b and prevents its association with C2a to form C3 convertase

Alternative pathway: In the case of the alternative pathway, a similar regulatory sequence prevents the assembly of C3 convertase C3bBb. CR1, MCP, or factor H binds to C3b and prevents its association with factor B. Once any of these regulatory proteins are bound to C3b, factor I cleaves C3b into iC3b and C3f fragments (*Fig 4-33*). Thus, the cleaved C3b is unable to associate with Factor Bb to form C3 convertase.

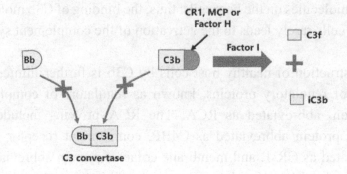

Fig 4-33: Regulatory proteins CR1, MCP, or factor H cleave C3b and prevents its association with factor B to form C3 convertase

2. Regulation after assembly of C3 convertase

The second stage of regulation of the complement system is after assembly of the C3 convertase. Several regulators of complement activation can also act on assembled C3 convertase causing it to dissociate. These include already mentioned RCA proteins C4BP, CR-1, and factor H and, in addition, decay-accelerating factor abbreviated as DAF. These proteins bind to the assembled C3 convertase (C3bBb) and then dissociate the complex. Once the dissociation of C3 convertase occurs, factor I cleaves C3b into iC3b and C3f fragments (*Fig 4-34*). The cleaved C3b fragments then lose the ability to associate with Bb proteins to form active C3 convertase.

On the other hand, in the case of the classical pathway, when RCA proteins bind to the assembled C3 convertase (C4b2a), they dissociate the C3 convertase. The released C4b is then cleaved by Factor I into C4c and C4d fragments. As a result, the cleaved fragments lose their ability to associate with C2a to form C3 convertase.

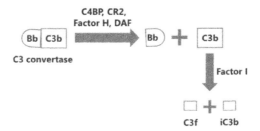

Fig 4-34: Regulation after assembly of C3 convertase

3. Regulation at the assembly of Membrane Attack Complex (MAC)

(a) The third stage of regulation of the complement system is at the level of membrane attack complex. If the C5b67 complex of MAC gets released from target cells, it can pose a threat to nearby healthy cells as it can mediate their lysis. But the regulatory proteins prevent this event from occurring. A regulatory serum protein known as S protein binds to the released C5b67 complex (*Fig 4-35*). It induces hydrophilic transition in the complex, thus preventing the insertion of the C5b67 complex into the membrane of the nearby cells.

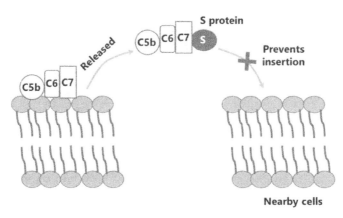

Fig 4-35: S protein prevents insertion of C5b67 complex into the membrane of the nearby cells

(b) The other regulatory proteins, homologous restriction factor, abbreviated as HRF, and membrane inhibitor of reactive lysis abbreviated as MIRL, protect cells from non-specific complement-mediated lysis. These proteins bind to C5b678 and prevent the assembly of poly-C9, which in turn blocks the formation of MAC (*Fig 4-36*). It is how our body regulates the activation of the complement system to kill specific target cells and prevent the non-specific killing of host cells.

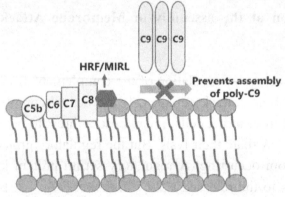

Fig 4-36: HRF and MIRL prevents assembly of poly-C9

4.8. Other functions of complement proteins

Though the complement system has an enormous role in the lysis and killing o f pathogens and damaged cells, various peptides produced during complement activation play other essential functions.

1. Opsonization: First is opsonization that is facilitated by C3b larger fragments. Opsonization is the process by which pathogens, or other target cells, are marked for ingestion and are then eliminated by the phagocytes like macrophages and neutrophils. The molecules that promote opsonization are called opsonins.

C3b is the major opsonin of the complement system, although C4b and iC3b also have opsonization activity. Phagocytic cells express complement receptors CR1, CR3, and CR4 that bind to C3b, C4b, and iC3b, respectively.

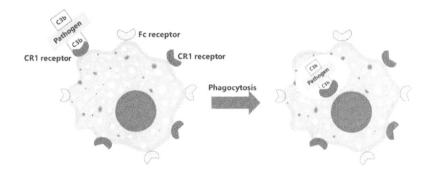

Fig 4-37: Phagocytosis of antigen-coated with C3b molecules

Antigen coated with C3b molecules binds to phagocytic cells bearing CR1 receptors. Once bound, phagocytosis of C3b coated Ag occurs by the phagocytic cells. This process is called opsonization (*Fig 4-37*).

2. Inflammation: The second role of complement components is in inflammation. The cleaved products of complement components can mediate inflammation and secretion of immunomodulatory molecules. For instance, the smaller fragments C3a, C4a, and C5a resulted from the cleavage of C3, C4, and C5 proteins, respectively, are called anaphylatoxins (*Fig 4-38*). These bind to receptors on mast cells and basophils and then induce degranulation. As a result, histamine and other pharmacological active mediators are released, mediating a local inflammatory response.

Anaphylatoxins can also cause smooth muscle contraction and increased vascular permeability, which results in the influx of fluid that carries Abs and phagocytic cells to the site of antigen entry.

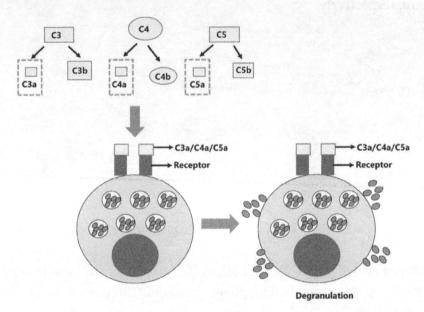

Fig 4-38: C3a, C4a, and C5a molecules are anaphylatoxins

3. Clearance of immune complexes: The third important function of complement components is to clear immune complexes from circulation. C3b molecules can attach to the Fc regions of the antigen-bound antibodies. The immune complexes coated with C3b are then able to bind to the CR1 receptors on erythrocytes (*Fig 4-39*). The erythrocytes carry these immune complexes to the spleen and liver. In the spleen and liver, these immune complexes are removed from the red blood cells, which are then phagocytosed by phagocytic cells such as macrophages and neutrophils, thus preventing their deposition in the tissues.

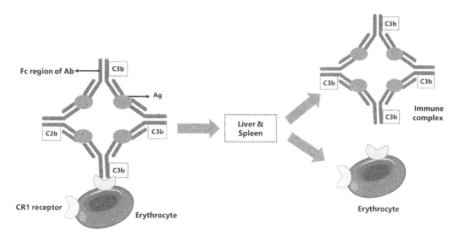

Fig 4-39: Clearance of immune complexes by complement components

In the case of complement deficiencies, immune complexes don't get cleared from the circulation and instead get deposited into tissues, thus leading to tissue damage. Moreover, the complement deficiencies can also predispose an individual to autoimmune diseases.

Chapter 5: Other effector functions of antibodies

5.1. Neutralization of infectivity

Pathogens or toxins cause disease by binding to the specific receptors on the host cells to gain entry into the cells. But when the specific antibodies bind to the pathogens or toxins, they block their entry into the host cells. In other words, antibodies neutralize the pathogens' infectivity.

For instance, the Human Immunodeficiency Virus (HIV) weakens the immune system by infecting immune cells, i.e., CD4 T cells, eventually depleting them. The glycoproteins gp120 and gp41, present on the envelope, allow HIV to lock onto the CD4 receptor present on CD4 T cells to gain entry into the cells. The neutralizing antibodies raised by the immune system bind to the gp120 proteins, which block the attachment of the virus to the T cells, thus preventing its entry into the T cells *(Fig 5-1)*.

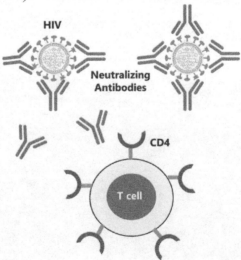

Fig 5-1: Virus neutralization by antibodies

Once a pathogen has been neutralized by the neutralizing antibodies, the pathogen-antibody complex is eventually taken up and degraded by the macrophages.

5.2. Opsonization

Opsonization is the process by which pathogens, immune complexes, tumor cells, apoptotic cells, etc., are marked for ingestion and then eliminated by the phagocytes like macrophages and neutrophils. The molecules that promote opsonization are called opsonins. The complement protein C3b (discussed in section 4.8) and the antibody are two main opsonins.

Additionally, the phagocytes have receptors (Fc receptors) for binding to the antigen-coated opsonins on their membranes. The Fab region of the antibody binds to the target antigen, whereas the Fc region of the antibody binds to the Fc receptor on the phagocyte. Once bound, phagocytosis of Ab bound Ag occurs by the phagocytic cells. This process is called opsonization *(Fig 5-2)*.

During the phagocytosis process, the membrane of the phagocyte cell induces membrane protrusions, called pseudopodia, to extend around the attached Ag-Ab complex. The fusion of the pseudopodia encloses the Ag-Ab complex within a membrane-bounded structure called a phagosome, which then enters the endocytic processing pathway. In this pathway, a phagosome fuses with a lysosome to form a phagolysosome. Lysosomes contain lysozyme and a variety of other hydrolytic enzymes that digest the ingested antigen. In this way, through phagocytosis, the internalized antigen is neutralized.

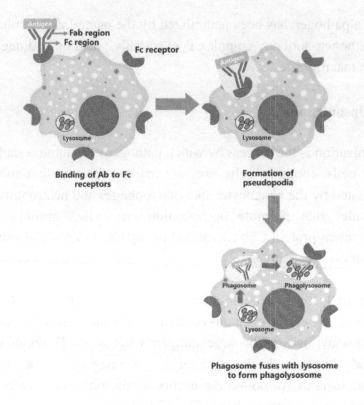

Fig 5-2: Phagocytosis by phagocytic cells

5.3. Antibody-dependent cell-mediated cytotoxicity (ADCC)

ADCC pathway is activated when

- there is an intracellular infection (e.g., tumor cell or if the virus has infected the cell)
- or when the invading pathogen is too large, e.g., parasitic worms.

In both cases, phagocytosis cannot eliminate the infected cell or parasites as it is challenging to internalize them by phagocytic cells. In such cases, the immune system activates the ADCC pathway.

Activation of ADCC involves the binding of antibodies to specific proteins (antigens) on the infected cell, tumor cell, or parasite. The Fc region of the bound antibodies then binds to the Fc receptors present on the effector cells of the immune system that have the cytotoxic function, like natural killer (NK) cells and eosinophils. Once bound, degranulation of the cytotoxic cells occurs. The released cytotoxic chemicals disrupt the cell membrane of the target cell, resulting in its lysis. For instance,

Natural killer (NK) cells: NK cells are generally involved in killing tumor cells and cells infected by viruses. Tumor cells and cells infected by viruses display antigens that are recognized as foreign by the immune system, against which the immune system generates antibodies, specifically IgG. The IgG antibodies then bind to the antigens displayed by tumor and virus-infected cells. NK cells express CD16, a membrane Fc receptor that binds to the Fc region of the bound IgG molecule. Once the Fc receptor binds to the Fc region of the bound antibodies, NK cells release cytotoxic factors like granzyme and perforin proteins, which cause the lysis of the target cells, thereby killing them *(Fig 5-3)*.

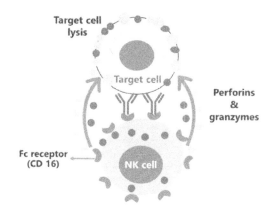

Fig 5-3: NK cell-mediated ADCC pathway

Eosinophils: Eosinophils are generally involved in recognizing parasites and killing them by releasing toxic substances. The IgE antibodies coat the surface of the parasitic worm by binding to its surface antigens. These bound IgE antibodies are then recognized by the eosinophils *(Fig 5-4)*. This recognition is mediated by specific Fcε receptors present on the eosinophils, which bind to the Fc region of IgE bound to worms. Once bound, the eosinophils undergo translocation of their granules to the plasma membrane, followed by the release of contents of the granules to the extracellular environment. The release of granular content is known as degranulation. The granule content is a source of various cytokines, chemokines, enzymes, cationic proteins, etc., that, when released, destroy the parasitic worms.

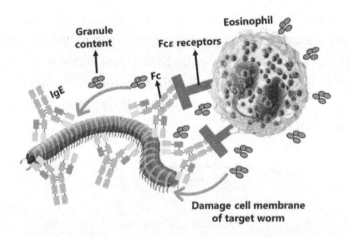

Fig 5-4: Eosinophil-mediated ADCC pathway

Practice Test 1

1. Antibodies/ Immunoglobulins are
(a) Glycoproteins
(b) Steroids
(c) Prostaglandins
(d) Lipoproteins

2. Antibody molecules are present in the
(a) albumin fraction of serum proteins
(b) alpha (α) globulin fraction of serum proteins
(c) beta (β) globulin fraction of serum proteins
(d) gamma (γ) globulin fraction of serum proteins

3. Which of the following cells are responsible for the production of immunoglobulin?
(a) Plasma cells
(b) T cells
(c) Dendritic cells
(d) Macrophages

4. Antibody structure is
(a) Z-shaped
(b) A-shaped
(c) Y-shaped
(d) B-shaped

5. Antibody structure contains
(a) One heavy and one light chain polypeptide
(b) Two heavy chains and two light chain polypeptides
(c) One heavy chain and two light chain polypeptides
(d) Two heavy chains and one light chain polypeptide

6. Which of the following are the two types of light chains?
(a) Kappa and lambda
(b) Kappa and omega

(c) Lambda and epsilon
(d) Lambda and delta

7. Cleavage of an antibody molecule by the protease papain produces:
(a) An antigen-binding site and two constant regions
(b) Two heavy chain-light chain dimers
(c) Two Fab fragments and one Fc fragment
(d) An antibody without its N linked oligosaccharide

8. Antigen binding sites of an immunoglobulin are located in:
(a) Light chain alone
(b) Heavy chain alone
(c) Fab region of the antibody
(d) Fc region of the antibody

9. How many antigen-binding sites are present in an antibody molecule?
(a) 1
(b) 2
(c) 3
(d) 4

10. Which region forms the basis of the classification of antibodies?
(a) Constant region of the light chain
(b) Constant region of the heavy chain
(c) Variable region of the light chain
(d) Variable region of the heavy chain

11. Five types of Immunoglobulins are:
(a) IgM, IgA, IgE, IgG and IgD
(b) IgB, IgF, IgA, IgE and IgD
(c) IgG, IgE, IgC, IgN and IgM
(d) IgH, IgN, IgA, IgK and IgE

12. The heavy chain and light chain in an antibody are linked by:

(a) Phosphodiester bonds
(b) Peptide bonds
(c) Disulfide bonds
(d) Ionic bonds

13. Which of the following statements are correct about the immunoglobulin domain?

(a) Each homologous unit of 110 amino acid residues in an antibody molecule is termed a domain
(b) Shape of the domain can be defined as the sandwich of two β pleated sheets, each containing antiparallel β strands of amino acid residues connected by loops of various lengths
(c) Within the variable domain of each heavy and light chain, there are 3 CDRs
(d) All of the above

14. How many CDRs are present in an antibody molecule?

(a) 6 CDRs
(b) 12 CDRs
(c) 3 CDRs
(d) 18 CDRs

15. What is the location of CDRs?

(a) Loops that join the β strands in the variable domains of both heavy and light chains
(b) Loops that join the β strands in the constant domains of both heavy and light chains
(c) On the β strands in the variable domains of both heavy and light chains
(d) On the β strands in the constant domains of both heavy and light chains

16. The CDRs in the variable heavy and light chain are responsible for generating the antigen recognition region. On the other hand, the framework region in V region:
(a) assists in generating antigen-binding site
(b) acts as a scaffold to support CDRs
(c) is highly variable
(d) none of the above

17. Antigens such as proteins have several different sites that can react with antibodies. These sites are called
(a) Paratopes
(b) Isotopes
(c) Epitopes
(d) Peritopes

18. What is the role of the hinge region?
(a) Provides flexibility to antibodies and allows independent movement of the Fab fragments
(b) Leads to better interaction with the antigen
(c) Both A and B
(d) None of the above

19. Which of the following heavy chains lack a hinge region?
(a) μ and ε
(b) δ and α
(c) γ and δ
(d) μ and δ
(e) α and ε

20. The class of immunoglobulins, which can cross the placenta is:
(a) IgG
(b) IgM

(c) IgA

(d) IgE

21. Which of the following statements are correct about IgM?

(a) Largest antibody

(b) First Ig class to be produced in a primary response to an antigen

(c) First Ig to be synthesized by the neonates

(d) All of the above

22. Which of the following antibodies is responsible for most allergic and hypersensitivity reactions?

(a) IgM

(b) IgG

(c) IgE

(d) IgA

23. Which is the most efficient complement activating class of antibodies?

(a) IgE

(b) IgM

(c) IgD

(d) IgA

24. The most abundant class of immunoglobulin in the body is

(a) IgM

(b) IgE

(c) IgG

(d) IgD

25. Which of the following is not a function of IgG?

(a) Provide passive immunization to the fetus

(b) First antibody type produced against an antigen during the primary antibody response

(c) Activates complement system

(d) Involved in opsonization and phagocytosis

26. The secretory component of sIgA is

(a) made by plasma cells that secrete dimeric IgA

(b) added to dimeric IgA by the M cell

(c) formed by cleavage of an epithelial cell receptor used to transport the dimeric IgA across the epithelial cell

(d) made by T cells

27. Which of the following immunoglobulins are secretory and are present in the milk?

(a) IgG

(b) IgA

(c) IgD

(d) IgM

28. Which of the following is not a function of IgA?

(a) Protect mucosal surfaces

(b) Activate complement system

(c) Protect eyes

(d) Agglutinate antigen

29. Which of the following class of Ig has pentameric structure?

(a) IgM

(b) IgA

(c) IgD

(d) IgE

30. Which of the following class of Ig has a dimeric structure?

(a) IgM

(b) IgA

(c) IgD

(d) IgE

31. The IgA and IgM antibodies consist of the following chain that allows their polymerization

(a) H chain

(b) L chain

(c) J chain

(d) V chain

32. Which of the following antibodies are expressed by the mature B cells?

(a) IgM and IgA

(b) IgM and IgD

(c) IgD and IgE

(d) IgD and IgA

33. Complement system

(a) Consists of 20 serum proteins

(b) Complement proteins get sequentially activated in an enzyme cascade

(c) Both A and B

(d) Is a set of antibodies

34. Complements are the proteins that are involved in the clearance of antigens/bacteria. Which of the following pathways is involved in the adaptive immune response?

(a) Classical Pathway

(b) Lectin Pathway

(c) Alternative Pathway

(d) All of the above

35. Classical Pathway of the complement system is activated by
(a) Antigen-antibody complexes
(b) Antigen
(c) Antigenic peptides
(d) Antigens bound to MHC complexes

36. Which of these pathways don't require antibodies for their activation
(a) Lectin Pathway
(b) Alternative Pathway
(c) Both A and B
(d) Classical Pathway

37. Which of the following subunits of C1 protein binds to the Ab-Ag complex and activates the classical pathway?
(a) C1q
(b) C1r
(c) C1s
(d) All of the above

38. Which of the following class of antibodies is a potent activator of the classical complement pathway?
(a) IgM
(b) IgA
(c) IgE
(d) IgG

39. Which of the following C1 subunits has the catalytic activity that cleaves C4 and C2 complement proteins?
(a) C1q

(b) C1r

(c) C1s

(d) None of the above

40. In the classical pathway, which of the following complement complexes serve as C3 convertase?

a) C4aC2a

b) C4bC2b

c) C4bC2a

d) C4aC2b

41. In the classical pathway, which of the following components is cleaved by C4bC2aC3b and initiate the formation of membrane attack complex

a) C5

b) C6

c) C7

d) C8

42. Which of the following proteins are the components of the alternative pathway except:

a) C1

b) Factor B

c) Factor D

d) Properdin

43. Which of the following carbohydrate moieties present in the mammalian cells inactivates C3b?

a) Sphingosine

b) Sialic acid

c) Mannose-6-phosphate

d) None of the above

44. Microorganism such as Salmonella, Listeria, Neisseria, consist of specific carbohydrate moieties on their cell surface that activate

a) Alternative Pathway

b) Classical Pathway

c) Lectin Binding Pathway

d) All of the above

45. Cell lysis in complement pathway is initiated by:

(a) Membrane destruction complex

(b) Membrane attack complex

(c) Membrane degrading complex

(d) Membrane lysis complex

46. Membrane attack complex (MAC) is:

(a) C5b6789 complex

(b) C5b678 complex

(c) C5b5789 complex

(d) C5b578 complex

47. The MAC consists of five complement proteins C5, C6, C7, C8, and C9. Which of the following subunits bind to the surface and provide a binding site for a subsequent component?

a) C5a

b) C5b

c) Both of the above

d) None of the above

48. Which of the following complement protein polymerizes to form perforin-like structure that stabilizes membrane attack complexes?

a) C6

b) C7

c) C8

90

d) C9

49. Which of the following components of complement proteins enhances inflammation (anaphylatoxin)?
a) C3a
b) C5a
c) Both of the above
d) None of the above

50. Which of the following complement components facilitate opsonization and phagocytosis?
a) C3a
b) C3b
c) C5a
4) C5b

51. Which of the complement receptors activate phagocytosis by binding to C3b coated antigens?
a) CR1
b) CR2
c) CR3
d) CR4

52. Erythrocytes express the complement receptor help that helps transport and clear the immune complex from circulation. Which of the following complement receptors is expressed on the erythrocytes?
a) CR1
b) CR2
c) CR3
d) CR4

53. Which of the following regulatory protein prevents the assembly of C3 convertase?

(a) C2Inh

(b) C1Inh

(c) C3Inh

(d) C5Inh

54. Which of the following regulatory proteins prevent the destruction of healthy host cells by C3b?

(a) C4b binding protein (C4BP)

(b) Complement receptor type I (CR1)

(c) Membrane cofactor protein (MCP)

(d) All of the above

55. Which of the following regulatory proteins cause dissociation of assembled C3 convertase?

(a) Regulators of complement activation (RCA)

(b) Decay accelerating factor (DAF)

(c) Both of the above

(d) Factor D

56. Which of the following regulatory proteins prevent the host cells from the attack by the C5b67 complex?

(a) Factor B

(b) S protein

(c) HRF

(d) MIRL

57. Which of the following proteins block the formation of MAC?

(a) Homologous restriction factor (HRF)

(b) Membrane inhibitor of reactive lysis (MIRL)

(c) Both of the above

(d) None of the above

58. The effector function of the antibody is mediated by its Fc region. Which of the following is the effector function of the antibody?
a) Antigen binding to antibody promotes opsonization
b) Antigen binding to antibody activates the complement system
c) Antigen binding to antibody activates cell-mediated cytotoxicity
d) All of the above

Answer Key

1. (a) 2. (d) 3. (a) 4. (c) 5. (b) 6. (a) 7. (c) 8. (c) 9. (b) 10. (b) 11. (a) 12. (c) 13. (d) 14. (b) 15. (a) 16. (b) 17. (c) 18. (c) 19. (a) 20. (a) 21. (d) 22. (c) 23. (b) 24. (c) 25. (b) 26. (c) 27. (b) 28. (b) 29. (a) 30. (b) 31. (c) 32. (b) 33. (c) 34. (a) 35. (a) 36. (c) 37. (a) 38. (a) 39. (c) 40. (c) 41. (a) 42. (a) 43. (b) 44. (c) 45. (b) 46. (a) 47. (b) 48. (d) 49. (c) 50. (b) 51. (a) 52. (a) 53. (b) 54. (d) 55. (c) 56. (b) 57. (c) 58. (d)

Chapter 6: Organization of immunoglobulin genes

As already discussed, each antibody molecule comprises four polypeptide chains: two light chains and two heavy chains. Each light and heavy chain is made up of 2 regions: variable region and constant region. The variable region of a light chain and a heavy chain together form the antigen-binding site. We have a countless number of antibodies that can recognize a countless number of antigens. It is estimated that we can recognize more than 100 million different epitope sequences by our B cell receptors or immunoglobulins.

Each B cell can recognize and bind specific antigen, which triggers its activation, resulting in the generation of plasma cells that secrete antibodies *(Fig 6-1)*.

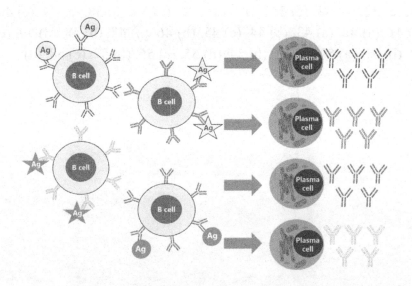

Fig 6-1: Generation of Ab secreting plasma cells

For several decades researchers sought to investigate a genetic mechanism that could explain the tremendous diversity of antibodies. Different theories were proposed more than 50 years ago.

6.1. Germline & somatic hypermutation Theory

1. First is the germline theory, which suggests that the genome contributed by the germ cells: egg and sperm contains an extensive repertoire of immunoglobulin genes that correspond to 100 million different specificities. This could not hold true because the body cannot invest such a large number of genes being dedicated only to the immune system and that also to B cells in specific.

2. So, the second theory proposed was somatic hypermutation, according to which genome contains a relatively smaller no of Ig genes, from which a large no of antibody specificities can be generated by mutation or recombination in the somatic cells. As more and more immunoglobulins were sequenced, it became evident to immunologists that there must be some mechanisms that not only account for generating antibody diversity but also for maintaining consistency.

Neither the germline nor somatic-mutation theory gives a reasonable explanation for the mechanism that could generate diversity in the variable region of heavy and light chains while preserving the amino acid sequences of constant regions of both the chains.

6.2. Dreyer and Bennett's theory

In 1963, Dreyer and Bennett proposed that two separate genes encode for a single heavy or light chain; one gene encodes for the variable region, and the second gene encodes for the constant region *(Fig 6-2)*. Thus, the two genes must somehow come together at the DNA level to form a continuous message and get translated to form a single immunoglobulin heavy or light chain.

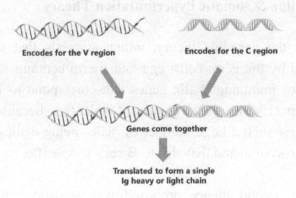

Fig 6-2: Dreyer and Bennett's theory

Additionally, they proposed that hundreds or thousands of Variable region genes and single gene copies of class and subclass of Constant region of antibodies were carried in the germline. This could account for the conserved constant region of immunoglobulins while allowing evolutionary diversification of variable region genes. But the suggestion that two genes encoded a single polypeptide contradicted the existing one gene-one polypeptide principle.

6.3. Tonegawa's Theory- Immunoglobulin genes rearrange

Thirteen years later, in 1976, two scientists named Tonegawa and Hozumi found the first direct evidence that separate genes encode V and C regions of immunoglobulins. They suggested that during the differentiation of lymphocytes from the embryonic state to the fully differentiated plasma stage, V and C genes undergo rearrangement. In the embryo, V and C genes are separated by a large DNA segment containing restriction endonuclease sites. But during the B cell differentiation, the V and C genes are brought closer together and are rearranged *(Fig 6-3)*.

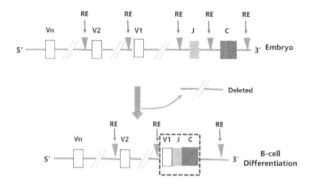

Fig 6-3: Rearrangement of V and C genes

Let us look at the experiment they carried out.

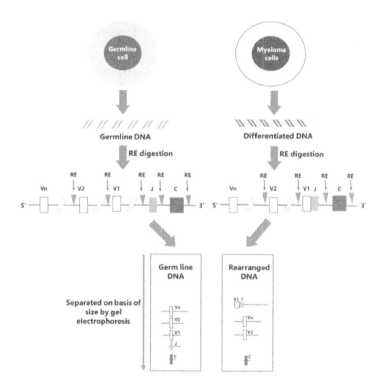

Fig 6-4: Electrophoresis of RE digested germline DNA and myeloma DNA

They took DNA from two types of cells. First was the embryonic cell that contributes germline DNA. The other source of DNA was the myeloma cell, which is a cancerous plasma cell. The DNA isolated from two cells was then digested with a restriction endonuclease enzyme. The DNA fragments obtained by digestion were electrophoresed separately *(Fig 6-4)*.

Electrophoresis is the technique to separate the DNA fragments by size. For this, the digested DNA is loaded into wells at one end of the gel, and then the electric current is applied. Since DNA fragments are negatively charged, they start migrating towards the positive elcctrode. Smaller DNA fragments migrate through the gel more quickly and, therefore, travel further than larger fragments that migrate more slowly and travel a shorter distance *(Fig 6-5)*.

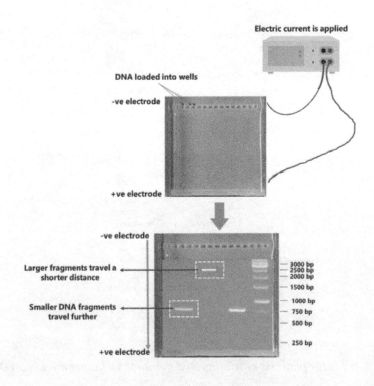

Fig 6-5: Principle of electrophoresis

As a result, the molecules are separated based on size by electrophoresis. Then the germline and myeloma DNA fragments separated by electrophoresis are analyzed by Southern Blotting. In the Southern Blotting technique, a radiolabelled probe (containing one of the Ig gene segments J) is allowed to hybridize to the electrophoresed fragments of DNA isolated from both cells.

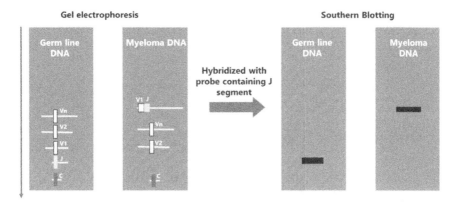

Fig 6-6: Analysis of electrophoresed fragments by Southern Blotting

The pattern obtained from restriction digestion followed by hybridization was different in the DNA of 2 cells. The hybridized restricted fragment of myeloma DNA is of larger size than that of germline DNA. This experiment suggested that there has been a change in the DNA of the myeloma cell *(Fig 6-6).*

It is because several coding sequences separated by non-coding sequences in the germline DNA are brought together at the DNA level during rearrangement in the myeloma cell. Thus, the size of the hybridized restricted fragment of myeloma DNA is larger than that of germline DNA *(Fig 6-7).* This experiment concluded that rearrangement of immunoglobulin genes occurs during B cell differentiation.

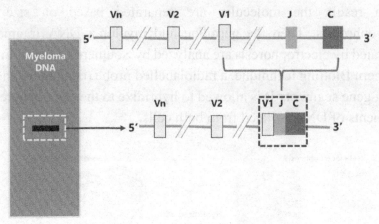

Fig 6-7: Rearrangement in myeloma DNA

6.4. Organization of Ig genes

The genes encoding the immunoglobulin chains are present as multiple gene segments and are present on different chromosomes. There are three immunoglobulin loci on human DNA. These are κ chain locus, λ chain locus, and heavy chain locus. Locus is defined as the specific and fixed position on a chromosome where a particular gene is found *(Fig 6-8)*.

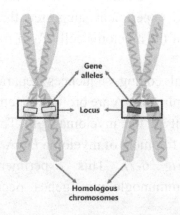

Fig 6-8: Locus on a chromosome

The κ chain locus is present on chromosome 2 and contains the gene segments encoding the κ chain. The λ chain locus is present on chromosome 22 and contains the gene segments encoding the λ chain, and the heavy chain locus is present on chromosome 14 and has the gene segments encoding the heavy chain.

Assume the bold black line represents germline DNA *(Fig 6-9)*. At the 5' end of any immunoglobulin locus on germline DNA, there is a cluster of variable gene segments. Variable gene segments are designated as V and are numbered from 1 to n. Each V gene segment is preceded at its 5' end by a leader sequence designated as L. The leader sequence encodes a leader peptide that facilitates the transport of growing immunoglobulin polypeptide chains into the endoplasmic reticulum.

At the 3' of the cluster of V gene segments, another cluster of J gene segments are present. J stands for joining. Like V gene segments, J gene segments are also numbered from 1 to n.

The C gene segments are located at the 3' of the J gene segments in each immunoglobulin loci. The number of gene segments varies in each immunoglobulin locus.

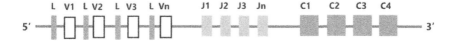

Fig 6-9: V, J, and C gene segments in light chain locus

In the case of heavy chain locus, additional D gene segments are present between V and J segments *(Fig 6-10)*. Here D stands for diversity. Therefore, light chain polypeptide is encoded by V, J, and

C gene segments. On the other hand, heavy chains are encoded by V, D, J, and C gene segments.

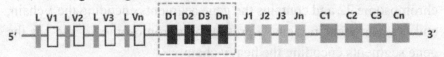

Fig 6-10: V, D, J, and C gene segments in heavy chain locus

During B cell maturation, these gene segments undergo rearrangement and are brought together to form a functional and continuous V region exon and C region exon. Exons are the coding sequences of the gene, which upon transcription and translation, produce Variable and Constant regions of the heavy and light chains of antibodies. It is essential to understand that though there are multiple copies of each type of gene segment in the germline DNA; still, only one gene segment is expressed at a time to synthesize one immunoglobulin molecule.

For instance, 1 V segment rearranges with 1 J segment to produce a VJ exon. This VJ exon encodes the variable region of the light chain *(Fig 6-11)*.

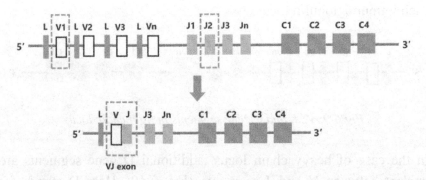

Fig 6-11: 1 V segment rearranges with 1 J segment to produce a VJ exon

And on the other hand, 1 V segment rearranges with 1 D and 1 J segment to produce a VDJ exon *(Fig 6-12)*. This VDJ exon encodes the variable region of the heavy chain of the antibody. The C gene segments encode the constant regions of the antibody.

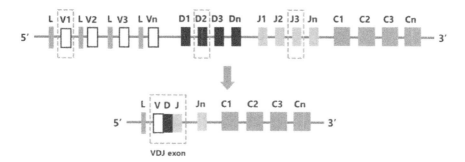

Fig 6-12: 1 V segment rearranges with 1 D and 1 J segment to produce a VDJ exon

The gene segments V, J, D, and C, along with the L sequence, are the coding sequences; therefore, they are also called exons. These exons are separated by some non-coding sequences, which are referred to as introns. This entire process of rearrangement and organization of the gene segments gives our immune system its capabilities to generate a repertoire of antibodies that are able to recognize and respond to a variety of antigens.

6.5. Organization of gene segments encoding light chains

Organization of gene segments encoding the λ chain: In humans, the λ light chain locus, present on chromosome 22, contains 31 Vλ gene segments *(Fig 6-13)*. Each Vλ gene segment is preceded at the 5' end by a leader sequence that encodes a leader peptide designated as L. The leader peptide transports the growing λ polypeptide chain into the endoplasmic reticulum. Leader peptides are later cleaved; therefore, they are not present in the mature λ chain.

The cluster of 4 Jλ segments is present at the 3' of the Vλ gene segments. The rearranged VλJλ segment encodes the variable region of λ light chain.

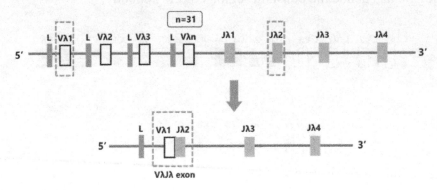

Fig 6-13: Rearranged VλJλ segment encodes the V region of λ light chain

As already discussed, the variable region comprises 110 amino acids. The Vλ gene segment encodes the first 97 amino acids, and Jλ encodes the remaining 13 amino acid residues of the variable region.

Additionally, 4 Cλ gene segments are located at the 3' of the Jλ gene segments *(Fig 6-14)*. Each Jλ gene segment is associated with 1 Cλ gene segment. The presence of multiple Cλ gene segments gives rise to the four subtypes of λ light chain λ1, λ2, λ3, and λ4.

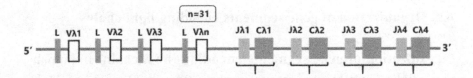

Fig 6-14: Each Jλ gene segment is associated with 1 Cλ gene segment

Organization of gene segments encoding the κ chain: The κ light chain locus present on chromosome 2 contains 40 Vκ gene segments *(Fig 6-15)*. Similar to Vλ gene segments, each Vκ gene segment is preceded by a leader sequence at the 5' end. The 5 Jκ segments are
104

present at 3' of Vκ gene segments. Out of 5 Jκ gene segments, 4 Jκ gene segments are functional. The non-functional Jκ segment is represented by Ψ. The rearranged VκJκ segment encodes the variable region of the κ light chain. The Vκ gene segment encodes the first 97 amino acids, and Jκ encodes the remaining 13 amino acid residues of the variable region.

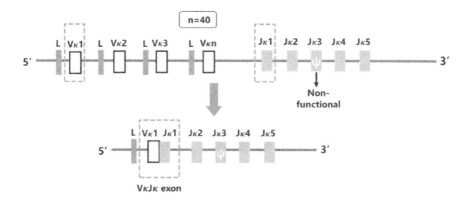

Fig 6-15: Rearranged VκJκ segment encodes the V region of κ light chain

The κ light chain locus has a single Cκ gene segment present at the 3' of the Jκ gene segments *(Fig 6-16)*. The single Cκ gene segment encodes for the entire constant region of the κ light chain. Since there is only one C gene segment, therefore, no subtypes of κ light chains are present.

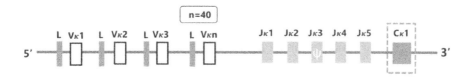

Fig 6-16: Single Cκ gene segment encodes for the C region of the κ light chain

6.6. Heavy chain multigene family

The organization of immunoglobulin heavy chain genes is similar to κ and λ light chain genes but is more complex. Here in the case of heavy chains, D gene segments are also present in addition to V, J, and C gene segments. In other words, the heavy chain family contains V_H, D_H, J_H, and C_H gene segments. In humans, there are 51 V_H, 27 D_H, 6 J_H, and 8 C_H gene segments *(Fig 6-17)*. The rearranged $V_H D_H J_H$ gene segments encode the variable region of the heavy chain of an antibody.

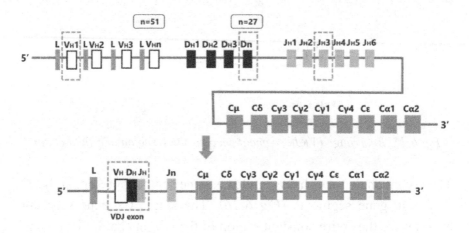

Fig 6-17: Rearranged VDJ segment encodes the V region of the heavy chain

The V_H gene segment encodes 1-94 amino acids, the D_H gene segment encodes 95-97 amino acids, and the J_H segment encodes 98-113 amino acids of the variable region of the heavy chain.

We have already discussed that within the variable domain of each heavy and light chain, there are 3 CDRs. The CDRs from both V_H and V_L domains contribute to the antigen-binding site. In this case, the **D_H segment encodes amino acids within the third complementarity**

determining region CDR3 of the antigen-binding site of the antibody *(Fig 6-18)*.

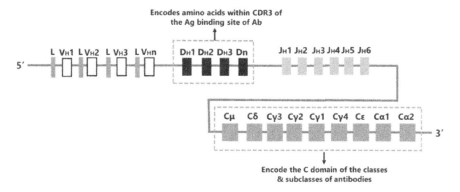

Fig 6-18: D$_H$ segment encodes amino acids within CRD3, and C$_H$ gene segments encode C domain of classes and subclasses of antibodies

Also, the CDRs within the variable region account for the diversity of antigens that a repertoire of antibodies can recognize. Since the D$_H$ segment encodes amino acids within the third complementarity determining region CDR3, thus the segment D$_H$ is designated D because of its contribution to the generation of antibody diversity. The C$_H$ gene segments are arranged in the order Cμ, Cδ, Cγ3, Cγ2, Cγ1, Cγ4, Cε, Cα1, and Cα2. The constant gene segments encode the constant domain of the classes and subclasses of antibodies—for instance, Cμ gene segment codes for the constant domain of IgM antibody.

During the B cell maturation, the heavy chain variable region gene segments rearrange first, then the light chain variable region rearranges *(Fig 6-19)*. After the rearrangement, each B cell contains a single functional variable region DNA sequence for its heavy chain and another for its light chain. Then the B cell becomes committed to produce a membrane-bound antibody with a unique antigen-binding site encoded by a particular sequence of its rearranged variable region genes. Later, the rearrangements of heavy chain constant region genes occur. The rearrangements in the gene segments of the heavy chain constant region generate changes in the immunoglobulin class or isotype expressed by a cell. These changes, however, do not affect the cell's antigenic specificity. It is explained in detail in subsequent chapters.

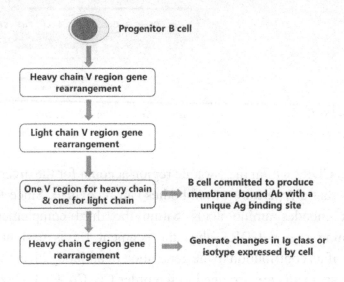

Fig 6-19: Ig gene rearrangement during B cell maturation

Chapter 7: V(D)J Recombination

7.1. VJ recombination in κ light chain DNA

As discussed, the variable region of each of the light chains of an immunoglobulin molecule is encoded by multiple V and J gene segments. These gene segments are first rearranged to form an exon VJ segment that encodes the variable region of the light chain. Though there are multiple copies of each type of gene segment in the germline DNA, only one gene segment is expressed. In the case of the κ light chain, during the process of VJ recombination, any of the Vκ gene segments out of 40 segments can join with any of the functional Jκ gene segments.

In *Fig 7-1*, assume the 2nd Vκ gene segment has to join with the 4th Jκ gene segment. This VκJκ joining creates an exon that encodes the whole variable region of the κ light chain. In the rearranged DNA, a leader sequence is present at the 5' end of the joined VκJκ gene segment. Upstream from each of the leader sequences, a promoter is present.

The RNA polymerase binds on the promoter present upstream of the leader sequence at the 5' end of the joined VκJκ gene segment. Once bound, RNA polymerase initiates the transcription from the L sequence through the C segment to the stop signal, generating a κ light chain primary RNA transcript. Next, the non-coding sequences referred to as introns present in the light chain primary RNA transcript are removed by RNA processing enzymes. This process is called RNA splicing. It creates the joining of the variable region VκJκ exon to the constant region exon to form VκJκCκ exon.

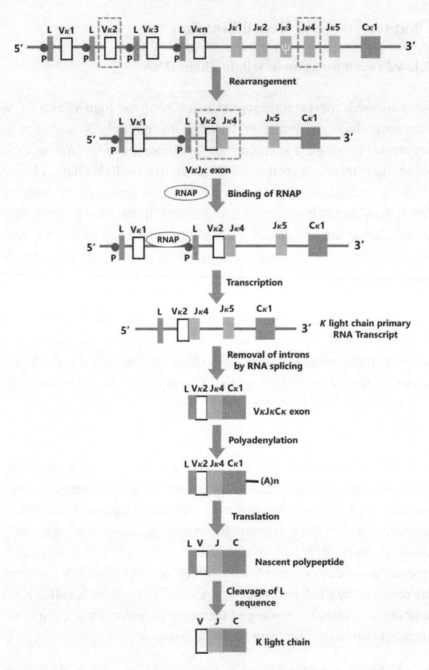

Fig 7-1: Generation of κ light chain

The polyA tail is then added at 3', resulting in the formation of messenger RNA, also written as mRNA. This resulting light chain messenger RNA exits from the nucleus, binds to the ribosome, and is translated into the light chain polypeptide. The leader sequence present at the amino terminus of the polypeptide pulls the growing polypeptide chain into the endoplasmic reticulum and is then cleaved. Therefore, the leader sequence is not present in the finished light chain protein product. This is how the gene arrangements occur to generate a functional κ light chain. To summarize, the variable region V_L of the κ light chain is formed by Vκ and Jκ gene segments, and Cκ gene segments form the C region.

7.2. VJ recombination in λ light chain DNA

The VJ rearrangement of gene segments in λ light chain is slightly different from that of the κ light chain. In the case of the κ light chain, during VJ recombination, any of the Vκ gene segments out of 40 segments can join with any of the functional Jκ gene segments. But in the case of λ light chain, any of the Vλ gene segment out of 31 segments can join with any of the Jλ-Cλ gene segment combination *(Fig 7-2)*. Since the λ light chain locus contains multiple Cλ gene segments and each Jλ gene segment is associated with 1 Cλ gene segment. Therefore, to form a functional VλJλ segment that encodes the variable region of λ light chain, functional Vλ gene segment combines with any of the Jλ-Cλ gene segment combinations.

Then the RNA polymerase binds on the promoter present upstream of the leader sequence at the 5' end of the joined VλJλCλ gene segment. Once bound, RNA polymerase initiates the transcription of the gene segment from the L sequence through the C segment to the stop signal, generating a λ light chain primary RNA transcript.

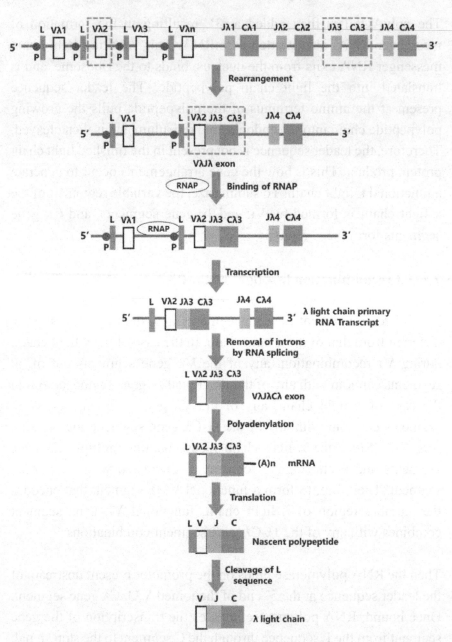

Fig 7-2: Generation of λ light chain

In the next step, the non-coding sequences, also known as introns present in the light chain primary RNA transcript, are removed by RNA processing enzymes. The polyA tail is then added at 3', resulting in the formation of messenger RNA. This resulting λ light chain messenger RNA exits from the nucleus binds to the ribosome and is translated into the light chain polypeptide.

The leader sequence present at the amino terminus of the polypeptide pulls the growing λ polypeptide chain into the endoplasmic reticulum and is then cleaved. This is how the gene arrangements occur to generate a functional λ light chain. To summarize, the variable region V_L of the λ light chain is formed by Vλ and Jλ gene segments, and Cλ gene segments form the C region.

Another essential point to know is that the **presence of multiple Cλ gene segments** in the germline DNA gives rise to the four subtypes of lambda light chain λ1, λ2, λ3, and λ4.

7.3. VDJ recombination in heavy chain DNA

Similar to light chains, the rearrangements occur in gene segments of heavy chain DNA to generate a functional heavy chain. The rearrangements occur sequentially. First, any of the D_H segments can join any of the J_H gene segments to form the $D_H J_H$ segment. Assume in *Fig 7-3* D_H2 segment has to join the J_H3 gene segment to form the $D_H J_H$ segment. In the next rearrangement step, the resulting $D_H J_H$ segment can join with any of the randomly selected V_H gene segments, say V_H1 gene segment, to generate a $V_H D_H J_H$ unit. This $V_H D_H J_H$ segment encodes the entire variable region of the heavy chain of an antibody molecule.

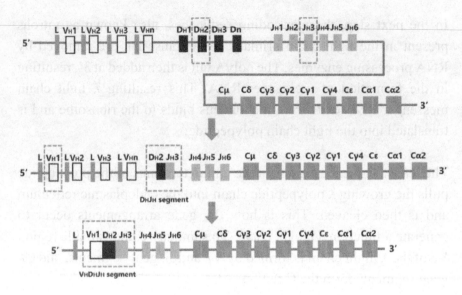

Fig 7-3: VHDHJH rearrangement in the heavy chain

As with the light chain, the heavy chain gene also contains a leader sequence that is present at the 5' end of the joined VHDHJH segment, followed by the J segments that were not joined to V and D, and then the series of C gene segments at the 3' end. In addition, a promoter sequence is located upstream of the leader sequence. Thus, once the heavy chain gene rearrangements are accomplished, RNA polymerase can bind to the promoter region and transcribe the entire heavy chain gene, including introns *(Fig 7-4)*. Initially, both Cμ and Cδ gene segments are transcribed. Then the introns are removed, and the V region exon is joined to the Cμ and Cδ exons.

After that, polyadenylation of the RNA transcript occurs to generate two mRNAs; one mRNA contains Cμ, while the other mRNA contains Cδ transcribed gene segment. These two mRNAs are then translated into μ and δ heavy chains. The leader peptide present in the nascent polypeptides is cleaved, generating finished μ and δ heavy chains.

114

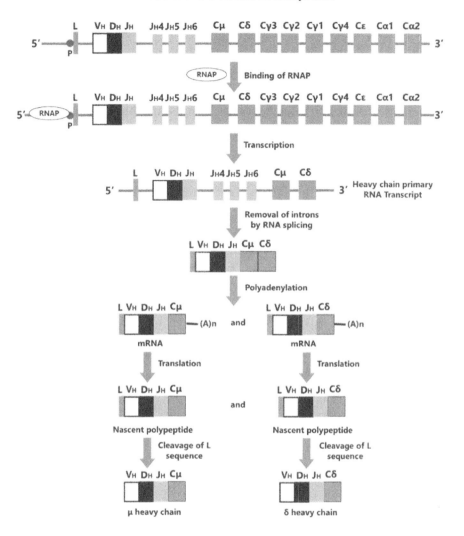

Fig 7-4: Generation of μ and δ heavy chains

Thus, the production of two different heavy chains allows a mature immunocompetent B cell to express both IgM and IgD immunoglobulins with identical antigen specificity on its surface.

7.4. Mechanism of variable region DNA rearrangement

Each germline segment V, D, and J is flanked by recombination signal sequences, abbreviated as RSS *(Fig 7-5)*. Recombination signal sequences are present adjacent to the points at which recombination takes place. Therefore, one RSS is located 3' to each V gene segment, one RSS is located 5' to each J segment, and two RSS are present on both 5' and 3' of D segment.

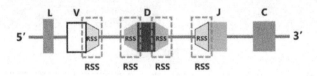

Fig 7-5: Each germline segment V, D, and J is flanked by RSS

The RSS sequences function as signals for the recombination process that rearranges the gene segments. Each RSS contains a conserved palindromic heptamer and a conserved AT-rich nonamer separated by an intervening sequence of 12 or 23 base pairs *(Fig 7-6)*.

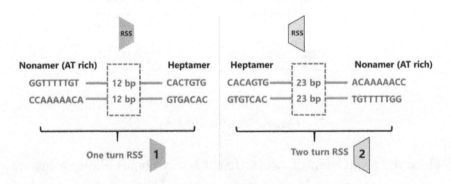

Fig 7-6: One turn and two turn RSS

If the intervening sequence is 12 base pairs, RSS is called a one turn recombination signal sequence. If the intervening sequence is of 23 base pairs, then RSS is called a two turn recombination signal sequence.

In the case of the κ light chain, the Vκ gene segment RSS is one turn spacer, and the Jκ signal sequence has a two turn spacer *(Fig 7-7)*.

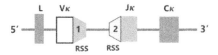

Fig 7-7: RSS in κ light chain

Whereas in the case of λ light chain, the order is reversed Vλ gene segment gene signal has a two turn spacer, and the Jλ signal sequence has one turn spacer *(Fig 7-8)*.

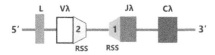

Fig 7-8: RSS in λ light chain

In heavy chain DNA, VH and JH gene segments have two turn spacer signal sequences, and signals on either side of the DH gene segment have one turn spacers *(Fig 7-9)*.

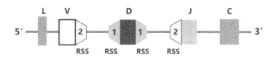

Fig 7-9: RSS in heavy chain

117

The most important rule in gene rearrangements is that a gene segment containing a signal sequence with one turn spacer can join only the gene segments with a two-turn spacer. Thus, it is also called the one turn/two turn joining rule *(Fig 7-10)*. For example, the joining rule ensures Vκ segment joins only to a Jκ segment but not to another Vκ segment.

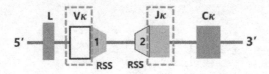

Fig 7-10: One turn/two turn joining rule in the light chain

The rule likewise ensures that Vн, Dн, and Jн segments of heavy chain join in the proper order *(Fig 7-11)*.

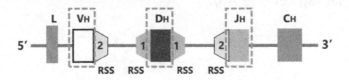

Fig 7-11: One turn/two turn joining rule in the heavy chain

VJ or VDJ recombination is catalyzed by the recombinase enzyme and terminal deoxynucleotidyl transferase enzyme. There are two types of recombinase enzymes: RAG-1 and RAG-2. The recombination of the variable region gene segments involves the following steps:

1. Firstly, the recombinase enzymes recognize the recombination signal sequences or RSS of the gene segments V and J, then bring the two signal sequences and the adjacent coding sequences in proximity *(Fig 7-12)*.

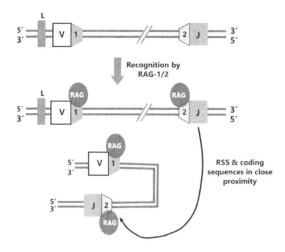

Fig 7-12: Recognition of RSS by RAG-1 and RAG-2

2. RAG-1 and RAG-2 then cleave one strand of DNA *(Fig 7-13)*. This cleavage occurs at the juncture between RSS and the coding sequence of V and J segments. Mutations or defects in RAG-1 and RAG-2 enzymes do not allow rearrangement of immunoglobulin genes, leading to a lack of generation of B cells.

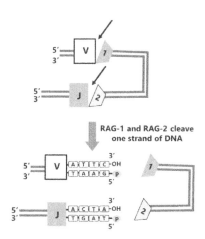

Fig 7-13: RAG-1 and RAG-2 cleave one strand of DNA

3. After single-strand cleavage by recombinase enzyme, the free 3'OH group on the cut DNA strand attacks the phosphodiester bond linking the opposite strand to the signal sequence. Thus forming a hairpin-like structure at the V and J segment *(Fig 7-14)*.

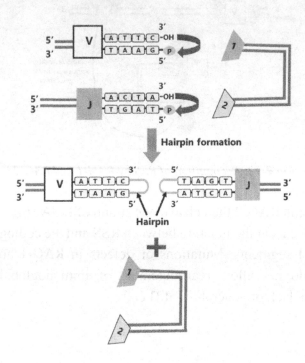

Fig 7-14: Formation of hairpin like structure

4. Further, a specific endonuclease enzyme known as Artemis cleaves the hairpin loops. This endonuclease does not recognize any specific sequence. Instead, it recognizes the hairpin structure. As a result, the nicking of DNA occurs randomly on both hairpin structures, after which a series of palindromic or 'P' nucleotides are added *(Fig 7-15)*.

5. Then, the enzyme terminal deoxynucleotidyl transferase or TdT adds up to 15 nucleotides at the cut ends of V, D, and J coding

sequences of the heavy chain, but not on the light chain. Tdt is one of the marker enzymes present in B cells.

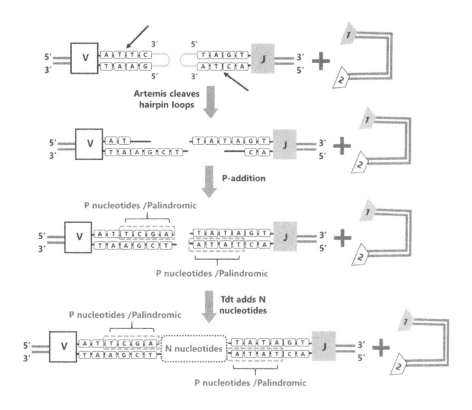

Fig 7-15: Addition of P and N nucleotides

6. After adding P and N nucleotides, ligation occurs, which joins the coding sequences and the signal sequences. It is performed by the double-strand break repair enzymes abbreviated as DSBR enzymes. Thus, the recombination event results in a coding joint formed by the combination of V and J coding gene segments and a signal joint formed by joining 2 RSS *(Fig 7-16)*.

121

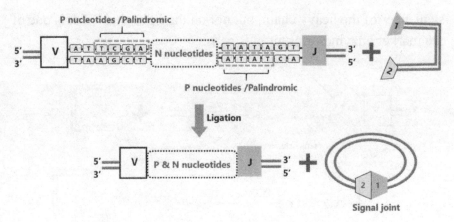

Fig 7-16: Ligation of coding and signal sequences

It is important to note that if the two gene segments are in the same transcriptional orientation, the joining of the gene segments results in the deletion of the signal joint, and the intervening DNA is obtained as a circular excision product *(Fig 7-17)*.

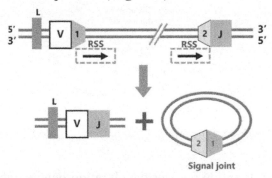

Fig 7-17: Deletion of signal joint if two gene segments are in the same transcriptional orientation

But if the two gene segments are in reverse orientation, their joining results in retention of both the coding joint and the signal joint on the chromosome *(Fig 7-18)*. For instance, this occurs in the human κ locus, where about half of the Vκ gene segments are in reverse orientation with respect to the Jκ gene segments.

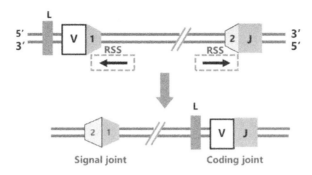

Fig 7-18: Retention of both the coding joint and the signal joint if two gene segments are in reverse transcriptional orientation

Chapter 8: Generation of antibody diversity

As already discussed, the antibody repertoire has the specificity to recognize more than 100 million different antigen molecules. There are various sources that generate diversity in antibody molecules because of which they can do so.

8.1. Combinatorial VJ and VDJ joining

The first source is the presence of multiple V, D, and J segments in germline DNA. In humans, there are 51 V_H, 27 D_H and 6 J_H gene segments for immunoglobulin heavy chain variable region and 31 $V\lambda$, 4 $J\lambda$, 40 $V\kappa$ and 5 $J\kappa$ gene segments for immunoglobulin light chain variable regions.

The presence of multiple germline V, D and J gene segments and their random rearrangement contribute to the diversity of antigen-binding sites in an antibody molecule. For instance, in the heavy chain locus, 51 V_H gene segments can combine with any of the 27 D_H gene segments and any of the 6 J_H gene segments. It allows 51*27*6= 8262 possible combinations of the heavy chain variable region that significantly contributes to the generation of the heavy chain diversity *(Fig 8-1)*. Similarly, in κ light chain, 40 $V\kappa$ gene segments can randomly combine with any of the 5 $J\kappa$ gene segments and therefore has the potential to generate 40*5=200 possible combinations of κ light chain variable region. On the other hand, the 31 $V\lambda$ gene segments can combine with any of the 4 $J\lambda$ gene segments to generate 31*4=124 possible combinations of the λ light chain variable region.

Since it is the variable region in the light and heavy chain that together form the antigen-binding site, combining a heavy chain with any of the two light chains further leads to diversity in an antibody. As a result of this combination, 8262*200*124, which approximately equates to 10^8 different antigen-binding sites, can be generated.

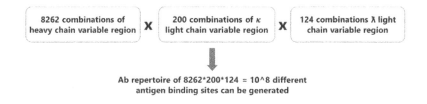

Fig 8-1: Combinatorial VJ and VDJ joining

8.2. Junctional Flexibility

The second source that generates antibody diversity is junctional flexibility. The enormous diversity generated through V, D, and J combinations is further augmented by junctional flexibility. As already discussed, the joining of V and J segments involves joining recombination signal sequences and coding sequences. However, the joining of these coding sequences is often imprecise. For example, let's analyze the joining of Vκ21 and Jκ1 coding sequences in 4 B cell lines.

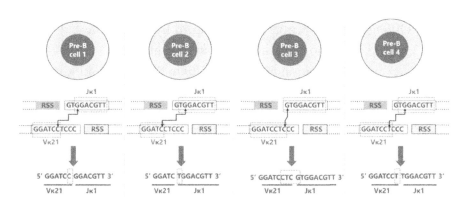

Fig 8-2: B cell lines exhibit sequence variability in their coding sequences

125

After joining V and J gene segments by recombination process, different B cell lines exhibit sequence variability in their coding sequences *(Fig 8-2)*.

This is called **junctional flexibility** & because of junctional flexibility, VJ segments encode alternate amino acids sequences in different cell lines, thus increasing antibody diversity *(Fig 8-3)*.

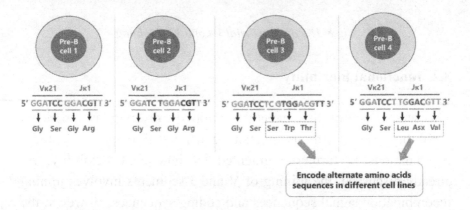

Fig 8-3: Because of junctional flexibility, VJ segments encode alternate amino acids sequences in different cell lines

The amino acid sequence variation generated by junctional flexibility in the coding joints is primarily in the third hypervariable region, or CDR3 in the immunoglobulin heavy and light chain. Since CDR3 makes a major contribution to the diversity in the antigen-binding site of the antibody molecule, amino acid changes in CDR3 generated by junctional flexibility lead to the generation of further antibody diversity. Sometimes, the junctional flexibility can also cause non-productive rearrangements in some of the B cell lines. If V, D, and J gene segments are joined out of phase, it leads to the occurrence of stop codons in the resulting VJ or VDJ unit *(Fig 8-4)*.

These stop codons are TAG, TGA, and TAA (in RNA, stop codons are designated as UAG, UGA, and UAA). The stop codons signal the end of the light or heavy chain polypeptide synthesis, thus leading to the death of B cells by apoptosis.

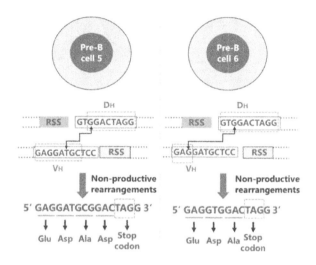

Fig 8-4: Non-productive rearrangements in B cell lines

8.3. P-addition

The third source that generates antibody diversity is P-addition. As already discussed, during recombination of VJ gene segments, RAG-1 and RAG-2 recognize the recombination signal sequences or RSS of the gene segments V and J, followed by bringing the two signal sequences and the adjacent coding sequences in proximity. Then RAG-1 and RAG-2 cause single-stranded DNA cleavage at the junctures of signal sequences and coding sequences *(Fig 8-5)*.

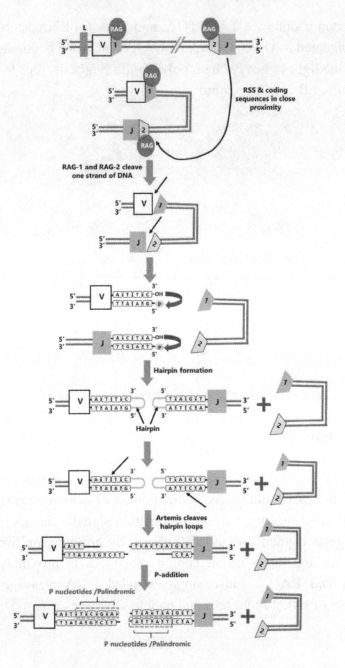

Fig 8-5: Addition of P-nucleotides

After that, the free 3'OH group of the cut DNA attacks the phosphodiester bond linking the opposite strand to the signal sequence, thus forming a hairpin-like structure at the cut end of the coding sequence of the V and J segment. The hairpin structure is then cleaved by the endonuclease. Remember that the nicking of DNA occurs randomly on both hairpin structures. This cleavage of the hairpin structure leaves a short strand at one end of both V and J gene segments. To this short strand, the repair enzymes add the nucleotides complementary to the nucleotides of the opposite strand.

This addition of complementary nucleotides generates a palindrome sequence in the coding joint, because of which these added nucleotides are called P nucleotides.

The term palindrome refers to a string of letters with the same meaning whether you read it from left or from the right. For example, some palindrome words are "CIVIC," "LEVEL," "NOON," "ROTOR," etc. Palindrome examples also exist in phrases or sentences where punctuation, capitals, and spacing are ignored. For instance, in the case of "NEVER ODD OR EVEN." The sequence of letters remains the same whether read from right to left or from left to right.

Similar is the case with palindromic repeat sequences in double-stranded DNA. A sequence of nucleotides is said to be palindromic if the sequence on one DNA strand is identical to the opposite strand's sequence when both are read in their respective 5' to 3' directions. An example of a palindromic sequence is 5'-GGATCC-3', which has a complementary strand, 3'-CCTAGG-5'. When either strand is read from the 5' to 3' direction, the nucleotide sequence remains the same, i.e., GGATCC *(Fig 8-6)*.

Fig 8-6: Palindrome sequence

Similarly, the sequence of P nucleotides added to the coding joint after the endonuclease activity on the hairpin structure remains the same when either strand is read from the 5' to 3' direction. For instance, the sequence of nucleotides added to the V segment remains TCGA when either strand is read from 5'-3' direction. On the other hand, the sequence of nucleotides added to the J segment remains TATA when either strand is read from 5'-3' direction. Thus, these added nucleotides are called P or palindromic nucleotides *(Fig 8-7)*.

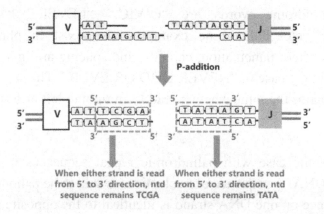

Fig 8-7: Addition of P- nucleotides to the V and J segments

Further, the endonuclease enzyme that cleaves the hairpin structure does not recognize any specific sequence; instead, it recognizes the hairpin structure. Because of this, nicking of DNA occurs randomly on both hairpin structures *(Fig 8-8)*.

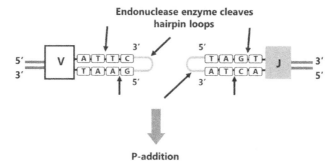

Fig 8-8: Variation in the position at which endonuclease cuts the hairpin structure and addition of P-nucleotides leads to diversity in the V region

Therefore, the variation in the position at which endonuclease cuts the hairpin structure and further addition of different P nucleotides by the repair enzymes in the coding joint leads to variations in the sequence of the coding joint, thus leading to the diversity in the variable region of the antibody molecule.

8.4. N-addition

The fourth source that generates antibody diversity is N-addition. N-addition generates additional diversity in the variable region coding joint $V_H D_H J_H$ in the rearranged heavy chains. The mechanism of VDJ recombination is similar to that of VJ recombination.

First, any of the D_H segments join any of the J_H gene segments to form the $D_H J_H$ segment. Then the resulting $D_H J_H$ segment joins with any of the randomly selected V_H gene segments to form the $V_H D_H J_H$ segment. Let's take the scenario of recombination of the $D_H J_H$ segment. RAG-1 and RAG-2 recognize the recombination signal sequences or RSS of the gene segments D and J, followed by bringing the two signal sequences and the adjacent coding sequences in proximity. Then RAG-1 and RAG-2 cause single-stranded DNA cleavage at the junctures of signal sequences and coding sequence of D and J segments *(Fig 8-9)*.

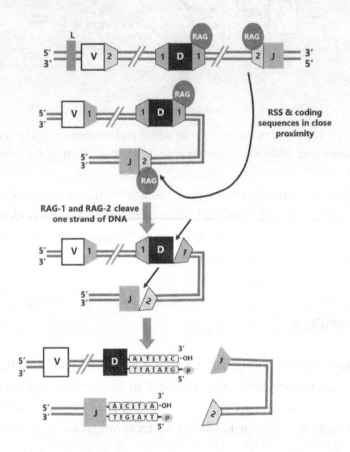

Fig 8-9: RAG-1 and RAG-2 cleave at the juncture between RSS and the coding sequence of D and J segments

Then the free 3'OH group of the cut DNA attacks the phosphodiester bond linking the opposite strand to the signal sequence, thus forming a hairpin-like structure at the cut end of the coding sequence of the D and J segment *(Fig 8-10)*. The hairpin structure is then cleaved by the endonuclease. This cleavage of the hairpin structure leaves a short strand at one end of both D and J gene segments. To this short strand, the repair enzymes add the nucleotides complementary to nucleotides of the opposite strand. This addition of complementary nucleotides generate a palindrome sequence in the coding joint, because of which these added nucleotides are called P nucleotides.

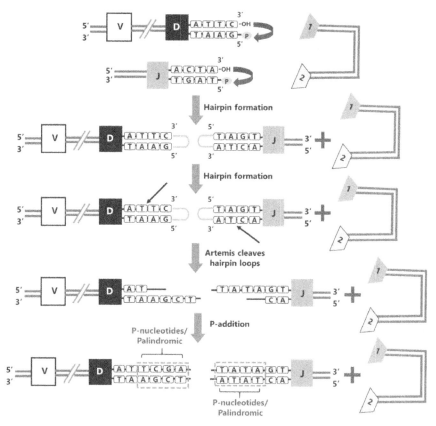

Fig 8-10: P nucleotides addition at D and J gene segments

After adding P nucleotides by repair enzymes, the enzyme terminal deoxynucleotidyl transferase, abbreviated as TdT, adds up to 15 nucleotides at the $D_H J_H$ coding joints *(Fig 8-11)*. Then the resulting $D_H J_H$ segment joins with any of the randomly selected V_H gene segments through a similar mechanism. Also, the enzyme terminal deoxynucleotidyl transferase adds up to 15 nucleotides at the $V_H D_H J_H$ coding joints. Therefore, the diversity generated by adding N nucleotides is quite large because of the addition of random nucleotide sequences at the coding joints.

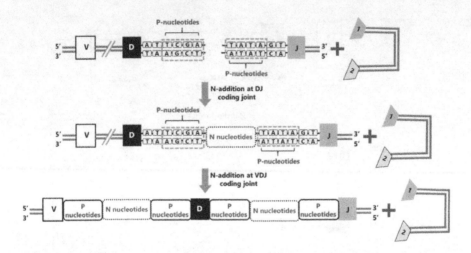

Fig 8-11: N nucleotides addition at DJ and VDJ coding joint

The diversity generated by N-addition at the VDJ joints is localized in the CDR3 region of the heavy chain.

The addition of N-nucleotides is not found in the V_L-J_L coding joints.

8.5. Somatic Hypermutation

The fifth source that generates antibody diversity is somatic hypermutation. Somatic hypermutation is a process in which mutations accumulate in the rearranged VDJ or VJ gene segments that encode the variable regions of heavy and light chains of an antibody molecule.

The mutations may lead to amino acid changes in the variable region of the antibody molecules that increase the antibody's affinity for antigen. Most of these mutations are nucleotide substitutions, with deletions or insertions being less common.

Nucleotide substitution is a type of mutation where one base pair is replaced by a different base pair. For instance, A is replaced with T. This may lead to replacing one amino acid in a protein with another amino acid *(Fig 8-12)*.

Fig 8-12: Nucleotide substitution

These mutations mainly occur within the CDRs of the V_H and V_L domains, where they most likely influence the affinity of antibodies for antigens.

When a B cell contacts antigen through the B cell receptor (BCR), the B cell proliferates. During the proliferation of B cells, the somatic hypermutation process generates mutations in the genes encoding the variable regions of both heavy and light chains of an antibody molecule *(Fig 8-13)*. The introduction of mutations in the proliferating B cells leads to the production of thousands of B cells that possess slightly different B cell receptors and varying affinity for the antigen.

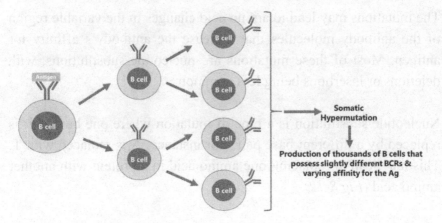

Fig 8-13: Somatic hypermutation process leads to the production of B cells with slightly different BCRs and varying affinity for the antigen

Then the B cells with the highest affinities for the antigen are selected. After this, the selected B cells with the highest affinity differentiate into plasma cells producing antibody and long-lived memory B cells with high-affinity B cell receptors *(Fig 8-14)*. The memory B cells then provide enhanced immune responses upon reinfection.

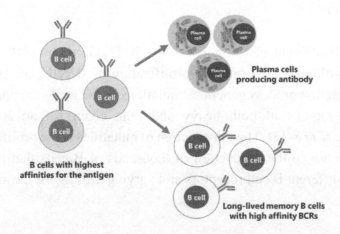

Fig 8-14: B cells with the highest affinity differentiate into plasma cells producing antibody and long-lived memory B cells

Let's understand it through an experiment that was conducted on a rabbit. On day 1, the rabbit was injected with an antigen. After a lag phase of 7 days, antibodies were generated against the antigen. Then, when the antibody titers came down, the rabbit was again immunized, and then the secondary response to Ag was developed in the rabbit. Similarly, when the antibody titers came down during secondary immune response, the rabbit was again immunized with the same antigen a third time, thus generating the tertiary immune response against the Ag *(Fig 8-15)*.

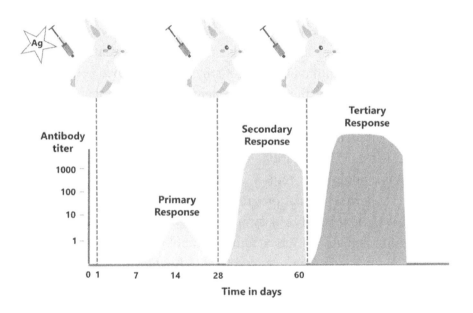

Fig 8-15: Primary, secondary, and tertiary immune response upon immunizing rabbit

It was observed that the amplitude of antibody titer during a primary immune response was small. In contrast, the secondary immune response showed a larger amplitude of antibody titer than that of the primary immune response. The antibody titer amplitude was even larger than that of the secondary immune response during the third immune response. It is because, during the primary immune response to antigen, the memory cells were generated, thus on second exposure to antigen, memory cells formed during the primary response begin to proliferate without any lag phase. Therefore antibody titer was higher than that of the primary immune response. The same was the case during the tertiary immune response. The memory cells formed during secondary immune response proliferated without any lag phase, thus resulting in a high antibody titer during the tertiary immune response.

When the scientists compared the B cell receptors on memory cells versus those on the naive B cells, they observed that the B cell receptors present on the naive B cells have a predefined sequence of CDRs determined by the rearrangement of VDJ segments. On the other hand, it was observed that mutations occurred in the B cell receptors of the memory cells after the secondary and tertiary immune response. Most of the mutations were clustered within the CDR region or antigen-binding site region of the antibodies. The number of somatic hypermutations progressively increases following the primary, secondary and tertiary immunizations, thus contributing to the overall increase in the affinity of antibodies for that antigen. During the tertiary immune response, the affinity of antibodies increases even 100-1000 fold.

Thus, it can be concluded from the experiment that **during subsequent exposure to antigens, the affinity of the antibodies increases**.

To summarize, the presence of numerous germline VDJ gene segments, combinatorial joining of VJ and VDJ gene segments, junctional flexibility, P and N region nucleotide addition, and somatic hypermutation contribute to overall antibody diversity.

Chapter 9: Expression of immunoglobulin genes

9.1. Class switching

As already discussed, there are five classes of antibodies: IgM, IgA, IgG, IgE, and IgD based on the type of heavy chain they have μ, α, γ, ε and δ respectively. Each of these five different heavy chains is called an isotype. The antibody class of a B cell changes during B cell development and activation. The immature naive B cells, which have never been exposed to an antigen before, express only membrane-bound IgM antibodies. But the mature naive B cells express both membrane-bound IgM and IgD. The coexpression of IgM and IgD antibodies makes the mature B cells ready to recognize and bind to an antigen. Upon binding to an antigen, B cells get activated. The activated B cells begin to divide and differentiate into antibody-producing plasma cells.

If these activated B cells encounter specific signals, they undergo antibody class switching to produce IgG, IgA, or IgE antibodies that have defined roles in the immune system *(Fig 9-1)*.

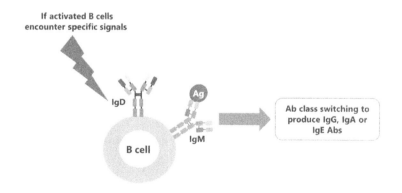

Fig 9-1: When activated B cells encounter specific signals, they undergo antibody class switching

In this process, the heavy chain DNA can undergo a further rearrangement in which the V$_H$D$_H$J$_H$ rearranged unit can combine with any constant gene segment *(Fig 9-2)*.

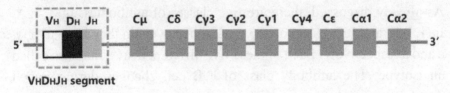

Fig 9-2: V$_H$D$_H$J$_H$ rearranged unit can combine with any C gene segment

Therefore, antibody class switching is defined as the process that changes a B cell's antibody production from one class to another, such as from the class IgM to class IgG. During the class switching process, the constant region of the antibody's heavy chain is changed, but the variable region of the heavy chain stays the same *(Fig 9-3)*.

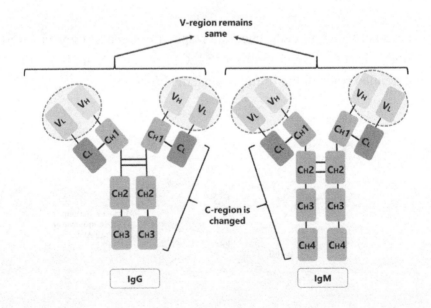

Fig 9-3: During class switching, the C- region of the heavy chain is changed, but the V- region stays the same

Since the variable region does not change, therefore, class switching does not affect the antigen specificity of a B cell. Instead, the antibody retains affinity for the same antigens but can interact with different effector molecules. It has already been discussed that the unique amino acids present in the constant region of the heavy chains of different classes of antibodies confer structural and functional properties to the antibodies. For instance, secretory IgA is present in body secretions and prevents the attachment of pathogens to mucosal membranes. IgG antibody crosses the placenta and provides protection to the fetus. IgM antibody is most efficient in activating the complement system. IgE antibody plays a very crucial role in allergic reactions and defense against parasitic worms. And IgD antibody signals B cells to get activated. Thus, the specific functions of each class of an antibody can be attributed to the unique amino acids present in the constant region of the respective heavy chains.

9.2 Mechanism of class switching

1. Class switching process requires the switch sequences present on the 5' side of each of the C_H domain gene segments. Note that there is no switch region between the $C\mu$ and $C\delta$ (Fig 9-4).

Fig 9-4: Switch sequences are present on the 5' side of each of the C_H domain

These switch sequences are designated as $S\mu$, $S\gamma3$, $S\gamma2$, $S\gamma1$, $S\gamma4$, $S\epsilon$, $S\alpha1$ and $S\alpha2$. The switch sequences are 5-10 kb long and are composed of multiple copies of short repeats of GAGCT and

TGGGG. The switch region Sμ needs to recombine with any of the switch regions Sγ, Sε, and Sα for the class switching.

2. Class switching is mediated by an enzyme called switch recombinase that recognizes these switch sequences and carries out recombination. Then the switch sequences are cleaved by an enzyme named Activation Induced Deaminase, abbreviated as AID, followed by repair and ligation of broken DNA ends by a non-homologous end-joining repair system.

Let's take a scenario where the cell wants to undergo isotype switching from Cμ to Cγ2 *(Fig 9-5)*. The switch recombinase enzyme recognizes the switch regions Sμ and Sγ2 and then carries out the recombination between these switch regions. During the process of recombination, looping of all the sequences that are between Sμ and Sγ2 occurs.

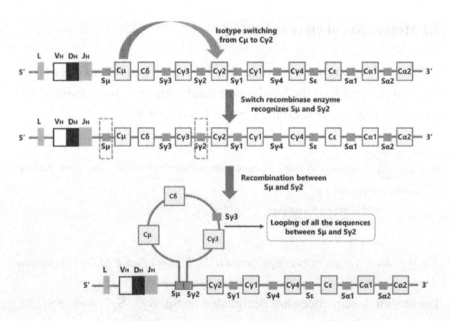

Fig 9-5: Recombination between the switch regions Sμ and Sγ2

Then the enzyme activation-induced deaminase AID cleaves the switch sequences Sμ and Sγ2 causing the deletion of all the sequences which are in between Sμ and Sγ2 in the form of circular excision product *(Fig 9-6)*. Since Cμ, Cδ, and Cγ3 are excised out therefore, the cell is now unable to produce IgM, IgD, or IgG3 antibodies. The constant region domains which come after Cγ2 continue to be present.

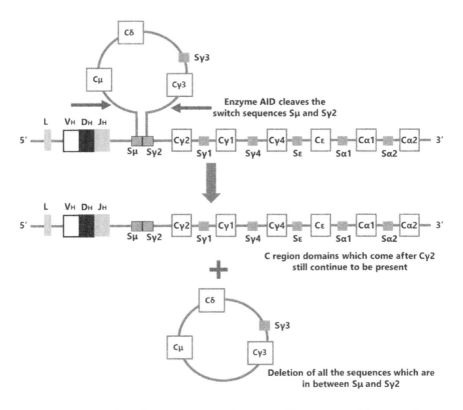

Fig 9-6: Cμ, Cδ, and Cγ3 are excised out; B cell is now unable to produce IgM, IgD or IgG3 antibodies

Then the repair and ligation of broken DNA ends occur by a non-homologous end-joining repair system. The recombination product then undergoes transcription and splicing to form γ2 primary RNA transcript, which upon polyadenylation, forms mRNA *(Fig 9-7)*. The mRNA is then translated into γ2 heavy chains. Finally, the leader peptide present in the nascent polypeptide is cleaved, generating finished γ2 heavy chains. The γ2 heavy chains then interact with two light chains to form an IgG2 antibody.

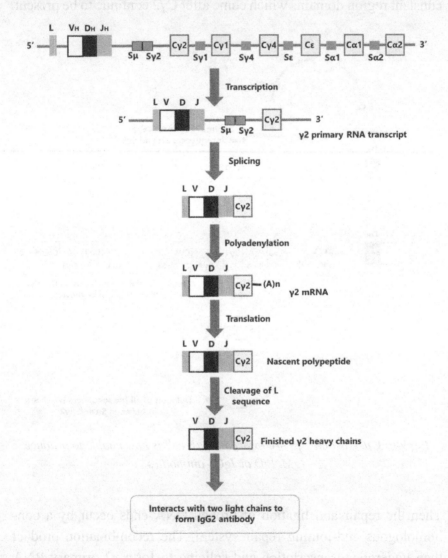

Fig 9-7: Transcription, splicing, and translation to form γ2 heavy chains

If the cell has undergone switching to IgG2, it can further undergo class switching to IgA1. For this, again, the recombination between switch regions Sγ2 and Sα1 occurs *(Fig 9-8)*.

During the process of recombination, looping of the sequences which are between Sγ2 and Sα1 occurs followed by the excision of the constant region and switch sequences that are between Sγ2 and Sα1. Since the constant region of IgG2 gets excised out, therefore, the cell can no longer be able to make IgG2.

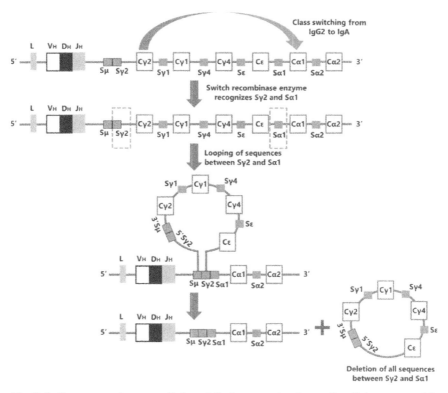

Fig 9-8: Sequences between Sγ2 and Sα1 are excised out; B cell is now unable to produce IgG2 antibody

The recombination product then undergoes transcription and splicing to form α1 primary RNA transcript, which upon polyadenylation, forms mRNA *(Fig 9-9)*. The mRNA is then translated into α1 heavy chains.

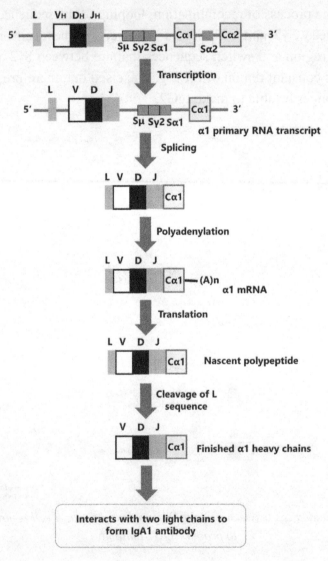

Fig 9-9: Transcription, splicing, and translation to form α1 heavy chains

The leader peptide present in the nascent polypeptide is cleaved, generating finished α1 heavy chains. The α1 heavy chains then interact with two light chains to form an IgA1 antibody. Thus, in the class switching process, the constant region of the antibodies changed, but the variable region remained the same.

9.3. Factors that govern class switching

1. For class switching to take place, it is essential that CD40 and CD40 Ligand interaction takes place *(Fig 9-10)*. CD40 receptor is constitutively expressed on B cells. To activate B cells, CD40 must interact with the CD40 ligand (CD40L) present on the surface of helper T cells. If there is no CD40-CD40 ligand interaction, class switching does not take place.

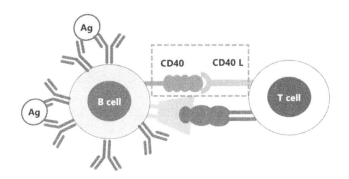

Fig 9-10: CD40-CD40L interaction is required for class switching

2. Certain regulatory proteins such as cytokines act as switch factors and determine the particular immunoglobulin class to be expressed during switching. For example, cytokine IL-4 induces class switching from IgM to IgG1 or IgE. In this case, the class switching will be done successively. Firstly, class switching will be from IgM to IgG1, followed by class switching to IgE.

3. Class switching also depends on the types of antigens encountered. For instance, stimulation of B cells by virus induces the generation of IgG2 antibodies, and on the other hand, helminths or allergens induce IgE antibody production, etc. It is because of the difference in the affinity of the antibodies that bind to these antigens. For example, IgG2 antibodies are induced in response to the virus because the Fc region of IgG2 can bind to natural killer cells and activate the ADCC pathway to destroy the virus-infected cells. And allergens induce class switching to IgE because IgE induces mast cell degranulation and releases active mediators to mediate allergic response.

4. Another factor governing class switching could also be the microenvironment of the plasma cells. For example, the activated plasma cells leaving Peyer's patches in the intestine exhibit class switching to IgA because IgA is the predominant antibody present in the mucous secretions of the digestive tract. IgA can bind to the membranes of the pathogens, thus preventing the attachment of pathogens to the mucosal cells.

Therefore, we can say that class switching happens so that the immune system gets better and better at eradicating almost all types of pathogens or other substances that are foreign to our body.

Chapter 10: Membrane-bound Igs and BCR

Immunoglobulins can exist in 2 forms: secreted immunoglobulin (sIg) and membrane-bound immunoglobulin (mIg). The five classes of antibodies IgG, IgA, IgD, IgE, and IgM can be expressed either as secreted immunoglobulin or membrane-bound immunoglobulin.

10.1. Structure of secreted and membrane-bound Ig

The basic structure of secreted immunoglobulin or membrane-bound immunoglobulin is the same. But their carboxyl-terminal domains differ in both structure and function. For instance, the carboxyl-terminal domain of each heavy chain of secreted immunoglobulin has a hydrophilic amino acid sequence of about 20 amino acids at the carboxyl-terminal end *(Fig 10-1a)*.

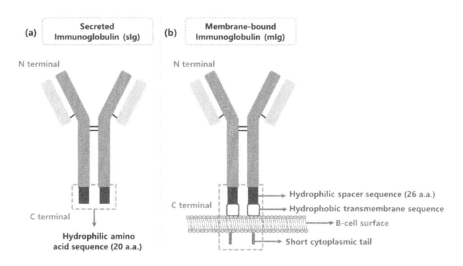

Fig 10-1: Structure of (a) secreted immunoglobulin and (b) membrane-bound immunoglobulin

But in membrane-bound immunoglobulin (mIg), the carboxyl-terminal domain of each heavy chain contains three regions that anchor the mIg on the surface of B cell *(Fig 10-1b)*:

1. An extracellular hydrophilic "spacer" sequence composed of 26 amino acid residues
2. A hydrophobic transmembrane sequence
3. And a short cytoplasmic tail

The length of the transmembrane sequence is constant among all immunoglobulin isotypes, whereas the lengths of the extracellular spacer sequence and the cytoplasmic tail vary among the isotypes. For instance, the mIgM and mIgD cytoplasmic tails contain only 3 amino acids, mIgA has a cytoplasmic tail of 14 amino acids. On the other hand, the mIgE and mIgG contain a cytoplasmic tail of 28 amino acids.

The function of the membrane-bound Ig is to recognize and bind to a specific antigen. For B cell activation, the B cell should get the signal that the specific antigen has been recognized. But in each isotype of membrane-bound Ig, the cytoplasmic tail is too short to deliver the activation signal to B cell after binding to a specific antigen.

Therefore, the activation signal to the B cell is delivered by the two accessory proteins associated with the membrane-bound Ig. These accessory proteins are Ig-α and Ig-β *(Fig 10-2)*.

These proteins together form a heterodimer Ig-α/Ig-β held together by a disulfide bond. Thus, the membrane-bound Ig alone does not constitute the entire B cell receptor on B cells. Instead, the B cell receptor (BCR) is composed of 2 components. One is membrane-bound Ig, and the other component is Ig-α/Ig-β. The Ig-α chain has a longer cytoplasmic tail of 61 amino acids, and the cytoplasmic tail of Ig-β contains 48 amino acids.

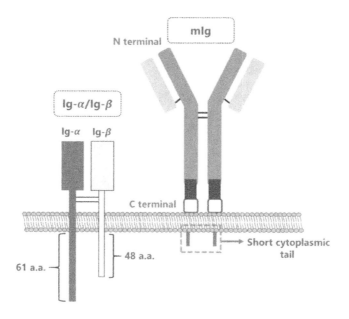

Fig 10-2: B cell receptor (BCR) is composed of membrane-bound Ig and Ig-α/Ig-β

The tails in both Ig-α/Ig-β are long enough to interact with the signaling molecules to induce the B cell activation.

Thus, to summarize the mechanism of B cell activation, upon the contact of mIg with specific antigen, the mIg delivers signals to Ig-α/Ig-β. Ig-α/Ig-β then interacts with signaling molecules to induce B cell activation. Once activated, the B cells proliferate and differentiate into effector B cells and memory B cells *(Fig 10-3)*.

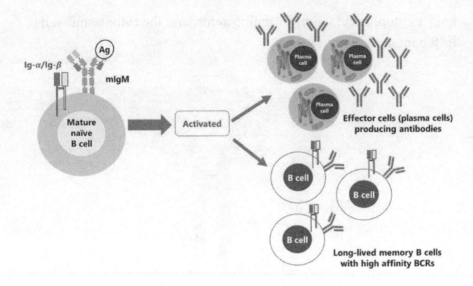

Fig 10-3: B cell activation

Effector B cells are known as plasma cells which secrete antibodies. The plasma cells produce and secrete antibodies specific to the antigen recognized by the B cell receptors. The secreted antibodies then bind to the pathogens or antigens and activate defense mechanisms that lead to the destruction of the pathogen.

The membrane-bound antibodies present on the B cells are components of B-cell receptors. And on the other hand, antibodies secreted by plasma cells are called secreted immunoglobulins.

10.2. Expression of membrane or secreted Immunoglobulin

The two forms of immunoglobulins: membrane-bound or secreted form, differ in the amino acid sequence of the heavy chain carboxyl-terminal domains. The secreted form of antibody has a hydrophilic sequence of about 20 amino acids in the carboxyl-terminal domain. In contrast, in the case of membrane-bound antibody, the carboxyl-terminal domain of each heavy chain contains an extracellular hydrophilic sequence, a hydrophobic transmembrane segment, and a short hydrophilic cytoplasmic tail at the carboxyl-terminal that extends into the cytoplasm.

Also, multiple constant gene segments encode the constant domain of the classes and subclasses of antibodies. C_H gene segments are arranged in the order $C\mu$, $C\delta$, $C\gamma3$, $C\gamma2$, $C\gamma1$, $C\gamma4$, $C\varepsilon$, $C\alpha1$, and $C\alpha2$. Constant region gene segments are organized as a series of coding exons and non-coding introns. For instance, the $C\mu$ gene segment that encodes the constant region of IgM contains four exons $C\mu1$, $C\mu2$, $C\mu3$, and $C\mu4$ *(Fig 10-4)*. These four exons correspond to the C_H1, C_H2, C_H3, and C_H4 domains of the heavy chain of an IgM antibody.

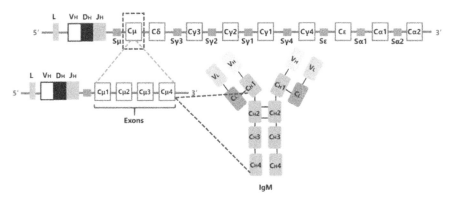

Fig 10-4: $C\mu1$, $C\mu2$, $C\mu3$, and $C\mu4$ exons correspond to the C_H1, C_H2, C_H3, and C_H4 domains of the heavy chain of an IgM antibody

$C\mu4$ exon contains a nucleotide sequence represented as S at its 3'end that encodes the hydrophilic sequence in the C_H4 domain of secreted IgM *(Fig 10-5)*.

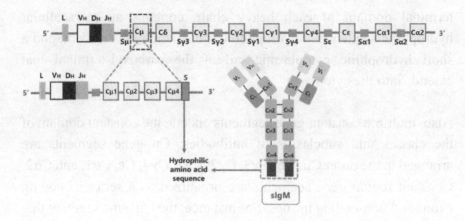

Fig 10-5: S sequence encodes the hydrophilic sequence in the CH4 domain

Apart from the S sequence, there are two additional exons M1 and M2, present downstream from the 3' end of the Cμ4 exon *(Fig 10-6)*. The M1 exon encodes for the transmembrane domain, and the M2 exon encodes for the hydrophilic cytoplasmic tail of the CH4 domain of membrane-bound IgM.

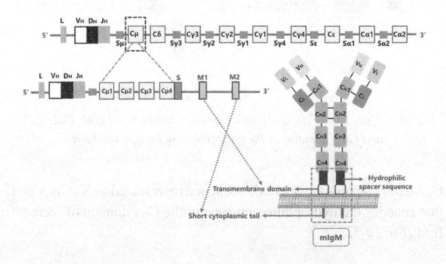

Fig 10-6: M1 exon encodes for the transmembrane domain, and M2 exon encodes for the hydrophilic cytoplasmic tail of CH4 domain of mIgM

When a primary transcript of IgM molecule is formed by transcription of rearranged μ heavy chain gene, it contains two polyadenylation signal sequences or poly-A sites in the Cμ gene segment.

Site 1 is located at the 3' end of S sequence, and site 2 is located at the 3' end of the M2 exon. Therefore, if polyadenylation occurs at site 1, then the M1 and M2 exons are lost; thus, excision of introns and splicing of primary transcript produces mRNA that encodes for the secretory form of μ chain *(Fig 10-7)*.

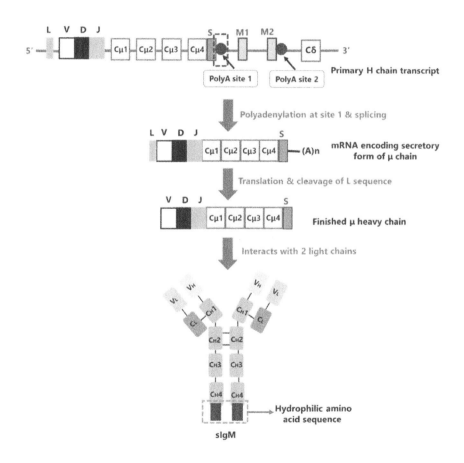

Fig 10-7: Polyadenylation at site 1 results in the production of sIgM

On the contrary, if the polyadenylation occurs on the second poly-A site, then, in this case, splicing removes S site at 3'end of Cμ4 exon *(Fig 10-8)*, that encodes for hydrophilic carboxyl-terminal end of the secreted form and joins the remainder of Cμ4 exon with M1 and M2 exons, thus producing mRNA that encodes for the membrane-bound μ chain.

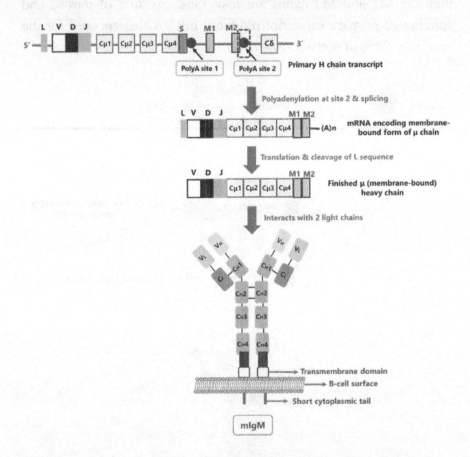

Fig 10-8: Polyadenylation at site 2 results in the production of mIgM

Therefore, differential processing of a primary transcript determines whether the secreted antibody or membrane-bound antibody will be produced. The mature naive B cells, which have never been exposed to an antigen, produce membrane-bound antibodies IgM and IgD. But upon recognizing and binding to a specific antigen, the naive B cells proliferate and get differentiated into plasma and memory B cells. The plasma cells then produce secreted forms of antibodies. On the other hand, the antibodies present on the surface of memory B cells are membrane-bound.

10.3. Simultaneous expression of IgM and IgD

In the case of heavy chain locus, Cμ and Cδ gene segments are present close together, and there is no switch sequence present between them. Therefore the entire VDJCμCδ rearranged gene will be transcribed into a single primary RNA transcript. IgM antibody has four constant domains because the hinge region is absent in it; therefore, there are four exons for the Cμ gene segment. On the other hand, the IgD antibody has three constant domains; therefore, there are three exons for the Cδ gene segment *(Fig 10-9)*. Also, there are 2 poly-A sites for one C gene segment.

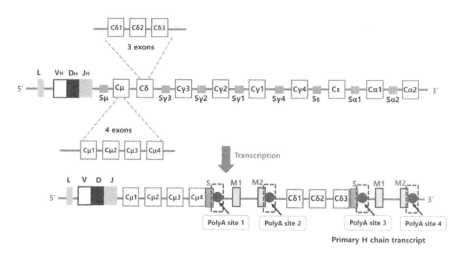

Fig 10-9: 4 exons for Cμ gene segment and 3 exons for Cδ gene segment

Therefore, the RNA transcript that contains Cμ and Cδ gene segments has 4 poly-A sites. Poly-A sites 1 and 2 are associated with Cμ, and poly-A sites 3 and 4 are associated with the Cδ gene segment. Therefore, if the polyadenylation occurs at site 2, present at 3'end of Cμ4 exon, then the mRNA formed after cleavage and splicing will encode the membrane-bound form of the IgM molecule *(Fig 10-10)*. Whereas if polyadenylation occurs at site 4, present at the 3' end of Cδ3, the RNA cleavage and splicing remove the Cμ exons and produce mRNA encoding the membrane-bound form of IgD molecule.

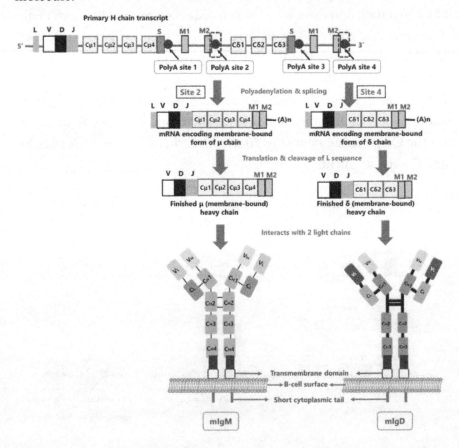

Fig 10-10: Polyadenylation at site 2 and site 4

In the case of mature B cells, both processes occur simultaneously. That is why mature B cells express both IgM and IgD on their membrane *(Fig 10-11)*.

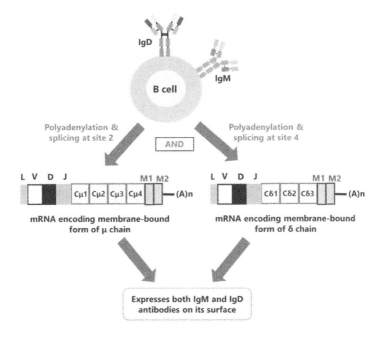

Fig 10-11: Simultaneous expression of mIgM and mIgD antibodies on B-cell surface

On the other hand, the polyadenylation of the VDJCμCδ primary RNA transcript at site 1 or site 3, followed by RNA cleavage and splicing in plasma cells, yields the secreted form of IgM or IgD antibodies *(Fig 10-12)*.

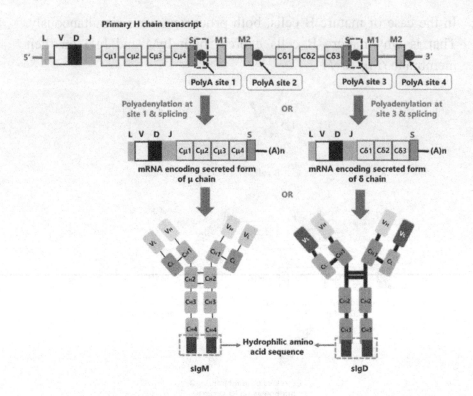

Fig 10-12: Polyadenylation at site 1 or site 3, yields the secreted form of IgM or IgD antibodies

Chapter 11: Regulation of Ig gene transcription

11.1. Regulatory sequences in DNA

The immunoglobulin genes are expressed only in B cells, and even in B cells, the genes are expressed at different rates during different developmental stages. As with other eukaryotic genes, there are three major classes of regulatory sequences present in immunoglobulin genes. These classes are Promoters, Enhancers, and Silencers

1. First and foremost is the promoter present 200 bp upstream from the transcription initiation site. Each V_H and V_L gene segment has a promoter located just upstream from the leader sequence (designated as L). In *Fig 11-1*, the promoter (designated as P) is shown in the black circle.

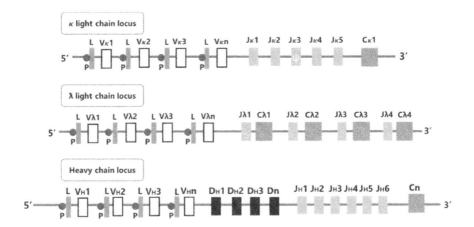

Fig 11-1: Each V_H and V_L gene segment has a promoter (P) located upstream from the leader (L) sequence

The immunoglobulin promoters contain a highly conserved AT-rich sequence called TATA box, which serves as a site for binding of RNA polymerase II to initiate transcription *(Fig 11-2)*. In addition, it also serves as a site for the binding of various transcription factors that regulate the transcription of immunoglobulin genes. For instance, Ig promoters contain a conserved octamer sequence, which binds to transcription factors oct-1 and oct-2.

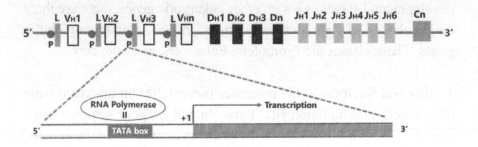

Fig 11-2: Promoters contain TATA box which serves as a site for binding of RNA polymerase II to initiate transcription

2. Apart from promoters, enhancers and silencers are also present on the immunoglobulin genes *(Fig 11-3)*. These are nucleotide sequences that regulate the transcription of Ig genes. Enhancers have binding sites for the proteins, like transcription factors that activate transcription from the promoter, and silencers have binding sites for the proteins like repressors that downregulate transcription from the promoter.

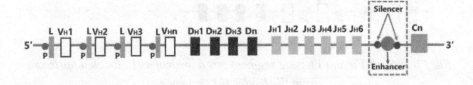

Fig 11-3: Enhancers activate transcription, and silencers downregulate transcription from the promoter

3. Another essential factor that regulates immunoglobulin transcription is immunoglobulin gene rearrangement.

In germline DNA, RNA polymerase II binds very weakly to the promoters associated with immunoglobulin V gene segments. Also, the variable region enhancers, which have binding sites for transcription factors to activate transcription from the promoters, are present around 200-300kb downstream from the promoters *(Fig 11-4)*. Since enhancers are quite distant from the promoters, they can hardly influence the transcription of the gene. For this reason, the transcription of V_H and V_L gene segments is negligible in germline DNA.

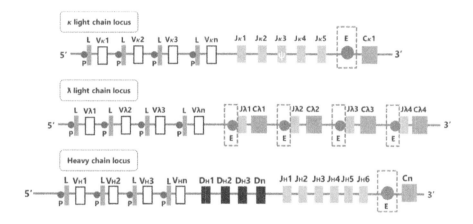

Fig 11-4: Enhancers (E) are quite distant from the promoters

At the same time, in the rearranged Ig gene segments, the promoter and enhancer are within a range of 2 kb distance from each other *(Fig 11-5)*. In this setting, they are close enough for the enhancer to activate the transcription from the promoter region. And as a result, the rate of transcription of rearranged VJ or VDJ unit is 10^4 times more than that of unarranged V_L or V_H gene segments.

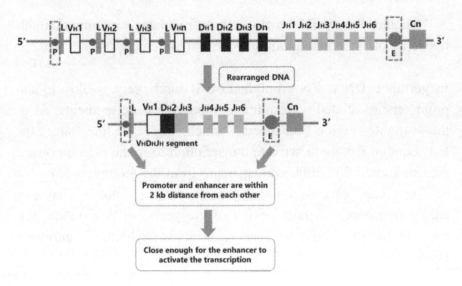

Fig 11-5: In the rearranged DNA, promoter and enhancer are close enough to
initiate transcription from the promoter region

11.2. Allelic exclusion

Allelic exclusion also regulates the expression of immunoglobulin
genes. It is a phenomenon that ensures that a mature B cell expresses
a single species of antibody with unique specificity for an antigen. But
before going into its details, it is important to understand the term
allele.

An individual has 23 pairs of chromosomes. And the two
chromosomes of a pair are said to be homologous because they are
very similar to one another and have the same size and shape. The
homologous pair of chromosomes in your genome is formed by
pairing of one homologous chromosome that came from your mother
and the other homologous chromosome that came from your father.
The pairing of homologous chromosomes is done in such a way that
the gene encoding for the same trait is always carried on a similar

place or position on both of the homologous chromosomes *(Fig 11-6)*. In other words, homologous chromosomes have the same type of genetic information: that is, each gene resides at the same specific locus on both the homologous chromosomes.

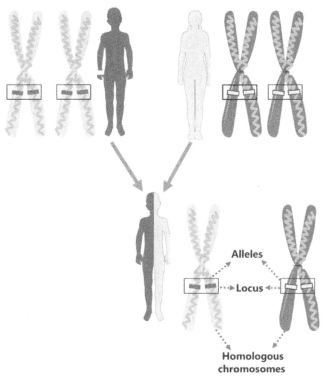

Fig 11-6: Alleles on homologous chromosomes

Though one copy of the gene is inherited from the mother and another from the father, it is not necessary that the individual will have the same versions of genes on the two homologous chromosomes of a pair. That's because he may have inherited two different gene versions from his mother and his father. If this is the situation where two copies of a gene differ from each other, they are known as alleles.

In other words, alleles can be defined as the **different versions or forms of the same gene**. For instance, the gene coding for eye color can have alleles for brown, blue, green, and other eye colors. Simply put, a gene specifies which trait is required to be expressed, say eye color, and the alleles of the "eye color" gene give directions for making eyes blue, green, brown, and so on. Additionally, a gene may have multiple different alleles, though only two alleles can be present at the gene's locus in any individual.

Like all somatic cells, B cells are also diploid. It means that each B cell has paired chromosomes: one from each parent. As already discussed, there are three types of immunoglobulin loci on human DNA. These are κ chain locus, λ chain locus, and heavy chain locus. Since the B cells are diploid, the immunoglobulin encoding genes are present on both maternal and paternal chromosomes. Or we can say, a B cell contains two heavy chain alleles, two kappa chain alleles, and two lambda light chain alleles *(Fig 11-7)*. So one heavy chain allele, one kappa chain allele, and one lambda chain allele are present on the maternal chromosome. The second heavy chain allele, kappa chain allele, and the lambda chain allele are present on the paternal chromosome.

Therefore, a B cell has two heavy chain loci and four-light chain loci in its genome. But suppose the immunoglobulin loci present on both the chromosomes are expressed. In that case, B cell might produce two different heavy chains and four different light chains, therefore resulting in B cell receptors or antibodies with 2*4=8 different antigen-binding specificities. But a B cell produces the B cell receptors or antibodies with only one particular antigen-binding specificity. Therefore, even though a B cell is diploid, it expresses rearranged heavy chain genes from only one chromosome. It also expresses light chain genes from only one chromosome, and that chromosome may either be paternal or maternal. The process by which this is accomplished is called **allelic exclusion.**

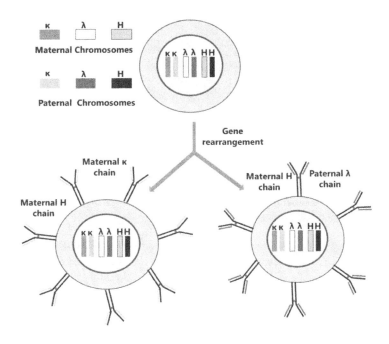

Fig 11-7: Allelic exclusion results in expression of rearranged heavy chain and light chain genes from only one chromosome, either paternal or maternal

Fig 11-7 shows that after rearrangement, the cell can express both the light and heavy chain genes encoded by the maternal chromosome or have heavy chain genes expressed from the maternal chromosome but light chain genes expressed from the paternal chromosome.

Allelic exclusion ensures that a single B cell does not contain more than one $V_HD_HJ_H$ unit and one V_LD_L unit. It is very critical for the antigen specificity of a B cell because expression of both alleles would render B cell multispecific. Because of allelic exclusion, once a productive $V_HD_HJ_H$ rearrangement and a productive V_LD_L

rearrangement have occurred, the recombination machinery is turned off, and then the heavy chain and light chain genes from the homologous chromosome are not expressed *(Fig 11-8)*.

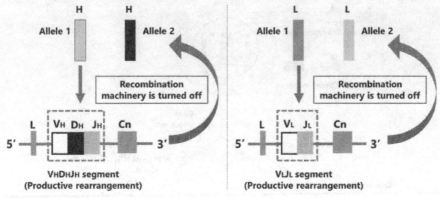

Fig 11-8: Once a productive VHDHJH and a VLDL rearrangement have occurred, the H chain and L chain genes from the homologous chromosome are not expressed

Allelic exclusion also limits the B cells to express either κ light chains or λ light chains. But never both of them *(Fig 11-9)*.

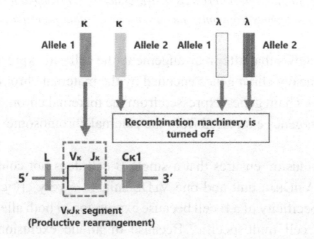

Fig 11-9: Once a productive VκJκ has occurred, then the κ chain and λ chain genes from the homologous chromosome are not expressed

11.3. Mechanism by which allelic exclusion occurs in B cells

Once the productive rearrangement of μ heavy chains is obtained from allele 1 in B cell, its encoded protein is expressed, and the presence of this protein signals the maturing B cell to turn off the rearrangement of other μ heavy chain allele and turn on the rearrangement of light chain gene *(Fig 11-10)*. Whereas if the productive rearrangement of μ heavy chain allele 1 is not obtained, then the expression of μ heavy chain allele 2 is turned on. And in case productive rearrangement is not obtained from any of the two alleles, then the cell undergoes death by apoptosis.

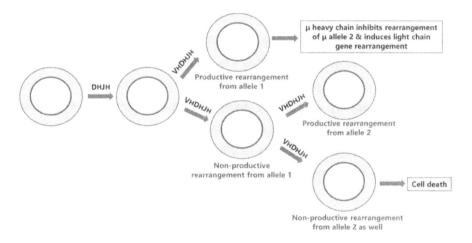

Fig 11-10: Productive μ heavy chain rearrangement by allelic exclusion

After this, the productive rearrangement of μ heavy chains turns on the rearrangement of κ light chain genes. If a productive κ rearrangement occurs, then κ light chains are produced that pair with μ heavy chains to form a complete antibody molecule *(Fig 11-11)*. The presence of this antibody molecule then turns off further light chain rearrangement from the other κ light chain allele as well as rearrangement from the λ allele.

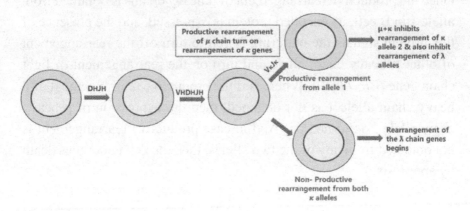

Fig 11-11: After the productive rearrangement of μ heavy chains, rearrangement of κ light chain genes begin

On the contrary, if κ rearrangement is non-productive for both κ alleles, then rearrangement of the λ chain genes begins *(Fig 11-12)*. If neither λ nor κ alleles rearrange productively, the B cell ceases to mature and soon dies by apoptosis.

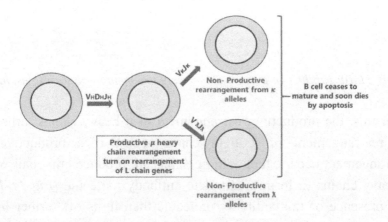

Fig 11-12: If neither λ nor κ alleles rearrange productively, then the B cell dies by apoptosis

Therefore, we can conclude that the recombination happens only in one of the alleles and never on both alleles simultaneously. The protein products encoded by rearranged heavy and light chain genes regulate rearrangement of the other allele, thus accounting for allelic exclusion.

Two studies with transgenic mice were done to prove that the protein products encoded by rearranged genes regulate the rearrangement of the remaining alleles. In one study, transgenic mice carrying a rearranged μ heavy chain transgene were prepared. The expressed rearranged μ heavy chain transgene protein then blocked the rearrangement of germline heavy chain genes of mice *(Fig 11-13)*.

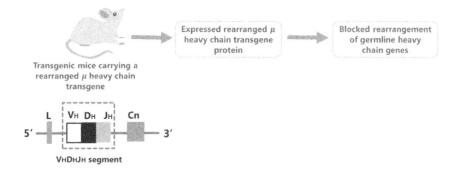

Fig 11-13: Study 1- Transgenic mice carrying rearranged μ heavy chain transgene

Similarly, the transgenic mice carrying a κ light chain transgene expressed the transgene κ light chain product, and this protein blocked the expression of germline κ light chain genes in mice *(Fig 11-14)*.

Additionally, transgene κ light chains were found to be associated with the heavy chains to form antibodies.

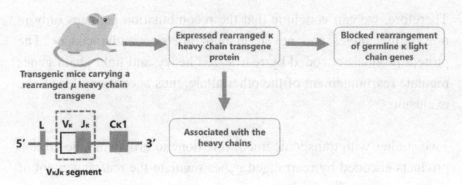

Fig 11-14: Study 2- Transgenic mice carrying rearranged κ light chain transgene

These studies suggest that the expression of heavy and light chain proteins prevents the gene rearrangement of the remaining alleles and thus accounts for allelic exclusion.

Chapter 12: Antigenic determinants/Epitopes on Igs

As already discussed, antigens are proteins that can induce an immune response. In other words, antibodies are generated against them. And since antibodies are glycoproteins, they can also induce an immune response (*Fig 12-1*). There are specific regions on antibodies that can induce the immune system to produce antibodies against them. These regions on antibodies are called antigenic determinants or epitopes.

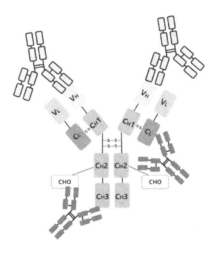

Fig 12-1: Antibodies generated against the antibodies

The epitopes or antigenic determinants of the antibody molecule fall into three major categories: Isotypic determinants, Allotypic determinants, and Idiotypic determinants

12.1. Isotypic determinants

The first type of antigenic determinant on Ig is the isotypic determinants. The prefix "iso" means the **same in all members of the same species**. Isotypic determinants are present in the constant region and define the class and subclass of each heavy chain and similarly define the type and subtype of each light chain of an immunoglobulin within a species. There are five different classes of antibodies; IgM, IgA, IgG, IgE, and IgD; based on the type of heavy chain, they have μ, α, γ, ε, and δ, respectively. Each of these five different heavy chains is called an isotype. And each isotype is encoded by a separate constant region gene.

Within a species, say in humans, each individual will carry the same constant region genes and express the same isotypes in a serum. In contrast, different species inherit different constant region genes and therefore express different isotypes. In other words, all individuals of the same species have the same isotype (*Fig 12-2*).

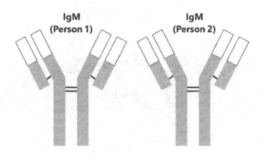

Fig 12-2: Individuals of the same species have the same isotype

But the isotypic determinants between different species are different (*Fig 12-3*).

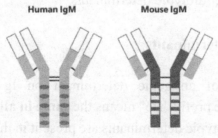

Fig 12-3: Human IgM is different from mouse IgM

This is the reason when an antibody, e.g., IgM from one species, say human, is injected into another species, say mouse, the isotypic determinants of human antibody are recognized as foreign by mouse. Thus, the mouse generates an antibody response or anti-antibodies to the isotypic determinants on the foreign human IgM antibody (*Fig 12-4*). And these anti-antibodies bind to the isotypic determinants in the constant region of injected human antibodies. The anti-antibodies generated are also called anti-isotype antibodies.

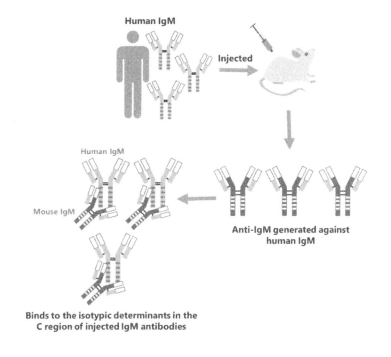

Fig 12-4: Anti-isotype antibodies (anti-antibodies) generated in mice against injected human IgM antibodies

These anti-antibodies are used in many immunological tests like immunofluorescence, enzyme-linked immunosorbent assays (ELISA), and western blots to quantify Ig classes and subclasses produced during an immune response in humans, characterization of

B cell leukemia, and in the diagnosis of various immunodeficiency diseases.

12.2. Role of anti-isotype antibodies in the detection of viral diseases

Suppose if the person is infected with HIV, then his immune system starts producing antibodies against HIV. Since HIV binds to CD4 cells via its envelope proteins, if the person is infected with HIV, his immune system makes antibodies to the HIV proteins, including envelope proteins (*Fig 12-5*).

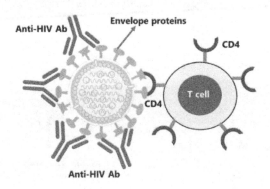

Fig 12-5: Anti-HIV antibodies against HIV proteins

To detect if the person is infected with HIV, ELISA can be done. For this, the HIV envelope protein is coated on the solid support, such as a microtiter plate (*Fig 12-6*). Then the blood of the patient is added to the microtiter plate. If antibodies against HIV are present in the blood sample, they bind to the viral antigen coated on the solid support. The bound anti-HIV antibodies are then detected using secondary antibodies.

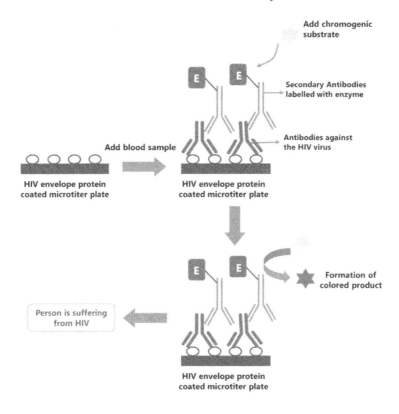

Fig 12-6: ELISA to detect if the person is suffering from HIV disease

The secondary antibodies are the antibodies that can bind to anti-HIV antibodies. These are raised in other species such as rabbits, mice, or goats by injecting them with anti-HIV antibodies. The animals of other species recognize anti-HIV antibodies as foreign and induce an immune response by producing antibodies against anti-HIV antibodies. Now, these anti-anti HIV antibodies act as secondary antibodies that are used for diagnostic purposes.

Suppose the patient's blood contains anti-HIV antibodies. In that case, the secondary antibody binds to the isotypic determinants in the constant region of the anti-HIV antibody present in the blood sample.

The secondary antibody is attached to an enzyme that catalyzes a color change when the substrate is added. If the substrate changes color, it indicates that the person is suffering from HIV. In this way, anti-antibodies can be used in the diagnosis of diseases.

12.3. Allotypic determinants

The second type of antigenic determinant on immunoglobulins is the allotypic determinants. The prefix "allo" means the difference in individuals of the same species. Individuals of the same species inherit the same set of genes for the constant region, hence having the same isotypic determinants. Yet within a species, multiple alleles may exist for certain isotypic genes. And these alleles encode for subtle differences in the amino acid sequences called allotypic determinants that occur in some but not all members of the species (*Fig 12-7*).

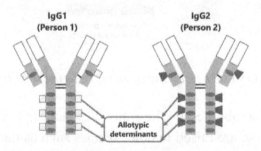

Fig 12-7: Allotypic determinants in humans

Consequently, some members within the same species have different antigenic determinants or allotypic determinants. The sum of the individual allotypic determinants displayed by an antibody determines its allotype. In humans, 25 different allotypes have been characterized for all four IgG subclasses, 2 allotypes for IgA2 subclass, and 3 allotypes for the kappa light chain. Each of these allotypic determinants represents differences in 1 to 4 amino acids of the constant region encoded by multiple alleles. Therefore, when antibodies from one member of a species, say from person 1 are injected into another member of the same species, say person 2, allotypic determinants of person 1 are recognized as foreign in person 2. Thus person 2 generates antibodies against the allotypic determinants of the injected antibodies of person 1 (*Fig 12-8*). The antibodies generated against the allotypic determinants are called anti-allotypic antibodies. These anti-allotypic antibodies then bind to the allotypic determinants in the constant region of injected Ab.

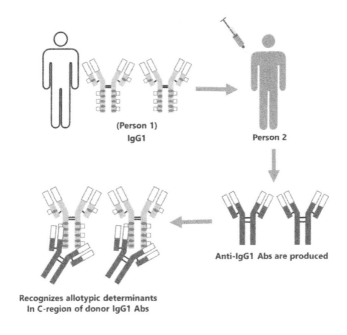

Fig 12-8: Anti-allotypic antibodies generated in person 2 binds to the allotypic determinants in the C- region of the donor person 1's IgG1 Ab

For instance, antibodies to allotypic determinants or anti-allotypic antibodies are sometimes produced by the mother during pregnancy in response to paternal allotypic determinants on the fetal immunoglobulins. Antibodies to allotypic determinants in a person can also arise from a blood transfusion.

12.4. Idiotypic determinants

The third type of antigenic determinant on immunoglobulins is idiotypic determinants. The unique amino acids of the domains of variable regions of heavy chain and light chain can function not only as antigen-binding site but also as a set of antigenic determinants or epitopes. Each individual antigenic determinant of a variable region of Ab is called an idiotope (*Fig 12-9*). In some cases, the idiotope may be the actual binding site of the antibody, also called paratope and in some cases, idiotope may comprise variable sequences outside of the antigen-binding site. Each antibody contains multiple idiotopes, and the combination of all idiotopes for each antibody is called idiotype of the antibody.

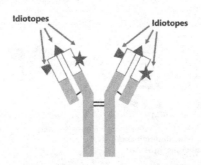

Fig 12-9: Idiotypic determinants on immunoglobulins

The antibodies produced by B cells derived from the same clone have an identical variable sequence, thus having the same idiotype (*Fig 12-10*).

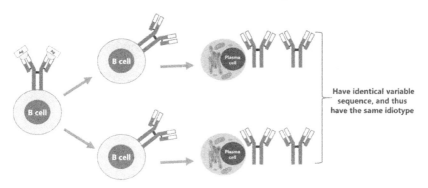

Fig 12-10: Antibodies produced by B cells derived from the same clone have the same idiotype

Suppose, if individual encounters two different antigens, i.e., Ag a and Ag b, and produce IgG1 antibody against both of these antigens, then, in this case, the idiotypic determinants for the IgG1 produced against Ag a will be different from the idiotypic determinants of IgG1 produced against Ag b (*Fig 12-11*).

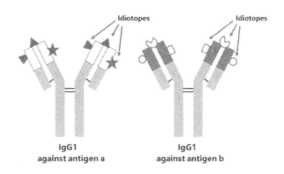

Fig 12-11: IgG1 antibodies with different idiotypic determinants

Further, when antibodies from a genetically identical donor are injected into a recipient, the recipient may induce the production of anti-idiotypic antibodies against the idiotype of donor antibodies. This is because in genetically identical twins, the isotype and allotype are the same, but the idiotype may be different. The antibodies generated against the idiotypic determinants of the antibody are called **anti-idiotypic antibodies** or written as anti-ID Ab.

12.5. Types of anti-ID antibodies

There are three classifications of anti-ID antibodies.

1. The first type of anti-ID antibody is an **antigen blocking anti-ID antibody**, which competes with the antigen to bind to the target antibody. It is because the paratope and idiotope of the target idiotypic antibody overlap with one another (*Fig 12-12a*). Paratope is the antigen-binding site of Ab and idiotope is the antigenic determinant or epitope of the Ab. Because of this overlapping of paratope and epitope of the target idiotypic antibody, the antibody's target antigen and the anti-ID antibody compete to bind to the target idiotypic antibody.

2. The second classification of anti-ID antibody is **non-blocking anti-ID antibody**, which can simultaneously bind to the target idiotypic antibody without affecting its antigen's binding capability (*Fig 12-12b*). This is because the target antibody's paratope and idiotope do not overlap. Because of this reason, the anti-ID antibody and the antigen can simultaneously bind to the target idiotypic antibody without affecting one another's binding capability.

3. The third classification of anti-ID antibody is a **complex specific anti-ID antibody**. This anti-ID antibody cannot bind to the target idiotypic antibody unless the target Ab is already bound to its antigen (*Fig 12-12c*).

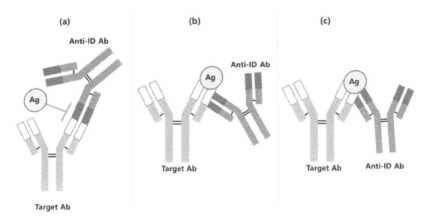

Fig 12-12: Types of anti-ID antibodies: (a) Antigen blocking anti-ID antibody (b) Non-blocking anti-ID antibody and (c) Complex specific anti-ID antibody

12.6. Applications of Anti-ID antibodies

Before studying the use of anti-ID antibodies, it is essential to get familiar with the term antibody-drug or antibody-drug conjugates. Antibody-drug is a highly potent biopharmaceutical drug composed of an antibody that is linked, via a chemical linker, to a biologically active drug or cytotoxic compound (*Fig 12-13*).

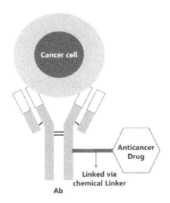

Fig 12-13: Tumor-specific antibody drug

For example, a tumor-specific antibody drug, in which anticancer drug is coupled to an antibody that specifically targets a specific tumor marker, e.g., a protein that ideally is only to be found in or on cancer cells. In this case, the antibody-drug will only bind and kill the targeted cancerous cell.

But after administering, it is essential to do the pharmacokinetic (PK) analysis of the antibody-drug. The pharmacokinetic analysis is the study of drug metabolism throughout the body.

It is critical in defining the absorption rates, distribution, half-life, and excretion rate of the antibody-drug. This analysis is essential to evaluate the dosage, toxicity, and efficacy of the antibody drug. To accomplish this, it is required to track and measure the antibody drugs which are bound or unbound to their designated target at various time points post administering them into the body.

For this, different types of anti-ID antibodies against the antibody-drug are used to detect and quantify the various forms of antibody drugs in patient serum, blood, urine, or other body fluids. For instance,

1. To examine if the antibody-drug is present in unbound form, i.e., not bound to its target antigen in the patient, then blocking anti-ID antibody is used, which is coated on the solid support (*Fig 12-14*). When antigen blocking anti-ID antibody is used, the antibody drug's target antigen and the anti-ID antibody will compete with one another to bind to the antibody-drug. Therefore, when the patient's sample like serum, blood, urine, or any other bodily fluid is added, the free or unbound antibody drugs present in an individual, i.e., antibody drugs that are not bound to their target antigens, will bind to the anti-ID antibodies coated on the substrate.

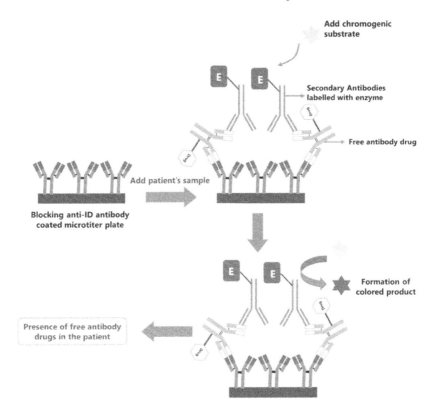

Fig 12-14: ELISA to detect the presence of free antibody drugs in the patient

Then these free antibody drugs bound to the coated anti-ID antibodies are detected using enzyme-tagged secondary anti-ID antibodies. After this, the chromogenic substrate is added, and the subsequent formation of a colored product indicates the presence of free antibody drugs in the patient. Thus, it establishes that antibody drugs in the patient are not bound to their target antigens.

2. The other type of non-blocking anti-ID antibody is used to detect both the antigen-bound and unbound antibody drug in the patient. In this case, the antibody drug's paratope and idiotope do not overlap. Therefore, the anti-ID antibody and the antigen can simultaneously

185

bind to the antibody-drug without affecting one another's binding capability. For detection in this case, non-blocking anti-ID antibodies are coated on the solid support followed by the addition of the patient's sample (*Fig 12-15*).

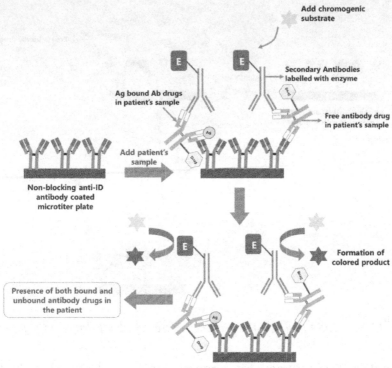

Fig 12-15: ELISA to detect the presence of both bound and unbound antibody drugs in the patient

Both unbound and bound antibody drugs present in the patient's sample will bind to the non-blocking anti-ID antibody coated on the substrate. Subsequently, antibody drugs bound to coated anti-ID antibodies are detected using enzyme-tagged secondary anti-ID antibodies. Thus, indicating that antibody drugs in the patient are both bound and unbound to their target antigens.

Once established, the ratio of unbound and bound antibody drugs in the patient's sample is evaluated in the subsequent steps.

3. To specifically detect if the antibody-drug is bound to its target antigen, the complex specific anti-ID antibodies coated on the solid support are used (*Fig 12-16*). The complex specific anti-ID antibody cannot bind to the antibody-drug unless the drug is already bound to its target antigen.

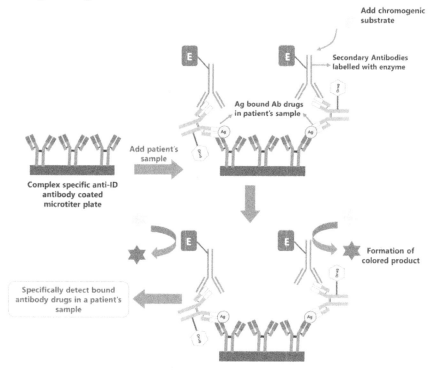

Fig 12-16: Complex specific anti-ID antibodies are used to detect the presence of bound antibody drugs in the patient

Therefore, complex specific anti-ID antibodies can specifically detect bound antibody drugs in a patient's sample.

Using a combination of three different types of anti-ID antibodies, it is possible to get overall information about the availability of antibody drugs in a patient. These anti-ID antibodies help to detect and track the state of antibody drugs, whether they are bound or unbound to their designated target at various time points post administering. And once the state of antibody drugs is established, the quantity and ratio of bound and unbound antibody drugs can also be calculated in the patient's serum, blood, urine, or any other body fluid.

Practice Test 2

1. Which theory provides the explanation for the tremendous diversity of antibodies?
(a) Germline Theory
(b) Somatic Hypermutation Theory
(c) Dreyer and Bennett Theory
(d) Tonegawa Theory

2. Which of the following statements are correct about Tonegawa's Theory?
(a) Separate genes encode V and C regions of Immunoglobulins
(b) During the B- cell differentiation, the V and C genes are brought closer together and are then rearranged
(c) Both of the above
(d) Genome contains a relatively smaller no of Ig genes, from which a large no of antibody specificities can be generated in the somatic cells by mutation or recombination

3. Immunoglobulin chains are encoded by ___ that is/are rearranged during ___ development to assemble a functional gene encoding either a heavy or a light chain.
(a) A single continuous DNA sequence; T cell
(b) A single continuous DNA sequence; B cell
(c) Sets of gene segments; B cell
(d) Sets of gene segments; T cell

4. The gene segments encoding for the variable and constant region of either kappa or lambda chain are arranged as:
a) J-V-C
b) V-J-C
c) C-J-V
d) None of the above

5. The gene segments encoding for the variable and constant region of the heavy chains are arranged as:
a) C-D-J-V
b) C-J-D-V
c) V-J-D-C
d) V-D-J-C

6. Which of the following is only contained in heavy chains and not in light chains?
(a) Leader (L) peptide
(b) Joining (J) gene segments
(c) Variable (V) gene segments
(d) Diversity (D) gene segments
(e) Constant (C) gene segments

7. Which gene segments give rise to the 4 subtypes of lambda light chain λ1, λ2, λ3, and λ4?
(a) Multiple Vλ gene segments
(b) Multiple Jλ gene segments
(c) Multiple Cλ gene segments

8. Why are there no subtypes of κ light chains?
(a) Because of single Cκ gene segment
(b) D gene segment is absent
(c) Both of the above
(d) None of the above

9. Why is the Dн gene segment named so?
(a) Dн segment encodes amino acids within the third complementarity determining region CDR3
(b) Contributes to the generation of antibody diversity
(c) Both of the above
(d) None of the above

10. During the gene expression, which of the following segments undergo the first gene arrangement?

a) Heavy chain constant region
b) Heavy chain variable region
c) Light chain constant region
d) Light chain variable region

11. Which gene segments encode the variable region of the light chain?

(a) V and D
(b) V and J
(c) V and C
(d) J and C

12. Which of the following is the sequential process of gene arrangement of the κ light chain of antibodies?

a) VJ joining --> Transcription --> RNA splicing --> VJC joining --> Translation --> Cleavage of leader peptide
b) Transcription --> VJ joining --> RNA splicing --> VJC joining --> Translation --> Cleavage of leader peptide
c) Transcription --> RNA splicing --> VJ joining --> VJC joining --> Translation --> Cleavage of leader peptide
d) None of the above

13. How does VJ recombination occur in the λ light chain?

(a) Any of the Vλ gene segment out of 31 segments join with any of the Jλ gene segment, then Vλ-Jλ joins with any of the Cλ gene segment
(b) Any of the Vλ gene segment out of 31 segments join with any of the Jλ-Cλ gene segment combinations
(c) Any of the Jλ gene segment joins with any of the Cλ, then Jλ-Cλ gene segment combination joins with any of the Vλ gene segment
(d) None of the above

14. Which gene segments encode the variable region of the heavy chain?

(a) V, J, C

(b) V, D, J

(c) V, D, C

(d) V, D, J, C

15. Which of the following is the sequential process of gene arrangement of the heavy chain of antibodies?

a) Transcription > DJ- joining > VDJ joining > RNA splicing > Translation

b) VJ- joining > VDJ joining > Transcription > RNA splicing > Translation

c) DJ- joining > VDJ joining > Transcription > RNA splicing > Translation

d) None of the above

16. Which of the following antibodies are co-expressed by the mature B-cells?

a) IgM and IgA

b) IgM and IgD

c) IgG and IgD

d) IgG and IgE

17. The joining of one V_L to one J_L is regulated by

(a) heptamer and nonamer sequences

(b) TdT binding site for DNA

(c) P-nucleotide addition sites

(d) 12 and 23 nucleotide spacers between heptamer and nonamer sequences

18. What is the one-turn/two-turn joining rule?

(a) Gene segment that contains a signal sequence with one turn spacer can join only with the gene segments that have a two-turn spacer

(b) Gene segment that contains a signal sequence with one turn spacer can join only with the gene segments that have a one-turn spacer

(c) Gene segment that contains a signal sequence with two turn spacer can join only with the gene segments that have a two-turn spacer

(d) All of the above

19. The complex of enzymes involved in recombination is called:
(a) RAG-1
(b) RAG-2
(c) Both of the above
(d) VDJ recombinase
(e) VDJ lyase

20. What is the function of RAG-1 & RAG-2 protein?
a) They catalyze the cleavage of one strand of the DNA
b) They catalyze the cleavage of both strands of the DNA
c) They catalyze the addition of 15 nucleotides in the junction
d) None of the above

21. Which is the marker enzyme present in B cells?
(a) Endonuclease (Artemis)
(b) Terminal deoxynucleotidyl transferase (TdT)
(c) RAG-1 and RAG-2
(d) Double-strand break repair (DSBR) enzymes

22. Which of the following contribute to antibody diversity?
(a) Numerous germline VDJ gene segments
(b) Combinatorial joining of VJ and VDJ gene segments
(c) Junctional flexibility
(d) P and N region nucleotide addition
(e) Somatic hypermutation
(f) All of the above

23. In the heavy chain locus, 51 functional V$_H$ gene segments can combine with any of the 27 D$_H$ gene segments and any of the 6 J$_H$ gene segments. The number of possible different combinations of the heavy chain variable region that could be made are
(a) 84

(b) 213

(c) 1383

(d) 8262

(e) 1200

24. The amino acid sequence variation generated by junctional flexibility is primarily located in

(a) all CDR equally

(b) CDR1

(c) CDR2

(d) CDR3

(e) FR3

25. Somatic hypermutation does NOT

(a) occur by somatic recombination

(b) occur by nucleotide substitution

(c) occur during B cell proliferation

(d) result in the death of some B cells which no longer bind antigen

(e) result in increased affinity of antibodies secreted later in immune responses

26. Where does somatic hypermutation occur?

(a) CDRs of V_H and V_L domains

(b) Light chain; Fab

(c) V_H, V_L, C_H, and C_L domains

(d) C_H and C_L domains

27. How does an antibody switch isotypes?

(a) By altering the constant domain of its light chain.

(b) By altering the variable domain of its heavy chain.

(c) By altering the variable domain of its light chain.

(d) By altering the constant domain of its heavy chain.

28. Which region of the heavy chains of different classes of antibodies confer structural and functional properties to the antibodies?
(a) Variable region of the light chain
(b) Variable region of the heavy chain
(c) Constant region of the light chain
(d) Constant region of the heavy chain

29. Which of the following statements are correct about switch sequences:
(a) Present on the 5' side of each of the C_H domain gene segments
(b) No switch region between the Cμ and Cδ
(c) Switch sequences are 5-10 kb long and are composed of multiple copies of short repeats of GAGCT and TGGGG
(d) Sμ needs to recombine with any of the switch regions Sγ, Sε and Sα for the class switching
(e) All of the above

30. Which of the following is the sequential process to undergo isotype switching from Cμ to Cγ2?
(a) Recombination between Sμ and Sγ2 > Cleavage of switch sequences by AID > Repair and ligation by non-homologous end-joining repair system > Transcription and splicing to form γ2 primary RNA transcript > Translation into γ2 heavy chains
(b) Cleavage of switch sequences by AID > Recombination between Sμ and Sγ2 > Repair and ligation by non-homologous end-joining repair system > Transcription and splicing to form γ2 primary RNA transcript > Translation into γ2 heavy chains
(c) Repair and ligation by non-homologous end-joining repair system > Recombination between Sμ and Sγ2 > Cleavage of switch sequences by AID > Transcription and splicing to form γ2 primary RNA transcript > Translation into γ2 heavy chains
(d) Repair and ligation by non-homologous end-joining repair system > Cleavage of switch sequences by AID > Recombination between Sμ

and Sγ2 > Transcription and splicing to form γ2 primary RNA transcript > Translation into γ2 heavy chains

31. Because of the order of the C$_H$ gene segments (Cμ, Cδ, Cγ3, Cγ2, Cγ1, Cγ4, Cε, Cα1, and Cα2), a human B cell which undergoes isotype switching from IgM to IgG2 can never produce which antibody in the future
(a) IgA
(b) IgE
(c) IgG3
(d) IgG4

32. Which of the following factors govern class switching?
(a) CD40 and CD40 Ligand interaction
(b) Cytokines
(c) Types of antigens encountered
(d) Microenvironment of plasma cells
(e) All of the above

33. What are the forms of immunoglobulins?
(a) Secreted
(b) Membrane-bound
(c) Both of the above
(d) None of the above

34. Membrane-bound Ig is a part of:
(a) BCR
(b) TCR
(c) MHC complex
(d) GPCR

35. A B cell can make membrane-bound and secreted versions of antibody using:
(a) Different gene pools

(b) Differential polyadenylation and splicing

(c) Somatic hypermutation

(d) Allelic exclusion

36. The cytoplasmic region of membrane-bound IgM consists of:

(a) A single H chain constant region domain

(b) Carbohydrate

(c) 110 amino acids

(d) 3 amino acids

37. The cytoplasmic region of the heavy chain of the secreted form of Ig consists of:

(a) Hydrophilic amino acid sequence of about 20 amino acids at the carboxyl-terminal end

(b) Hydrophilic amino acid sequence of about 20 amino acids at the amino-terminal end

(c) Hydrophobic amino acid sequence of about 20 amino acids at the carboxyl-terminal end

(d) Hydrophobic amino acid sequence of about 20 amino acids at the amino-terminal end

38. Which of the following statements are correct?

(a) Membrane-bound antibodies present on the B cells are components of B-cell receptors

(b) Antibodies secreted by plasma cells are called secreted immunoglobulins

(c) Both of the above

(d) None of the above

39. How many exons encode the constant region of IgM?

(a) 3 exons Cµ1, Cµ2, Cµ3

(b) 4 exons Cµ1, Cµ2, Cµ3, Cµ4

(c) 2 exons Cµ1, Cµ2

(d) Only 1 exon Cµ

40. In membrane-bound IgM, the transmembrane domain and cytoplasmic tail are encoded by which of the following exons
a) M1 and C1 exons
b) M1 and M2 exons
c) C_H3 & C_H4 exons
d) None of the above

41. Plasma cells produce which form of antibodies?
(a) Secreted
(b) Membrane-bound
(c) Both of the above
(d) None of the above

42. Which form of antibodies is present on the memory cells?
(a) Secreted
(b) Membrane-bound
(c) Both of the above
(d) None of the above

43. Which of these regulate the Ig gene transcription?
(a) Promoters, Enhancers, and Silencers
(b) Ig gene rearrangement
(c) Allelic exclusion
(d) All of the above

44. Which of the following transcription factor binds to the immunoglobulin promoter?
(a) E2B
(b) Myc
(c) Rb2
(d) Oct1

45. The ability of an individual B cell to express rearranged heavy chain genes from only one chromosome is called

(a) allelic exclusion

(b) co-dominant expression

(c) isotypic exclusion

(d) nonproductive rearrangement

(e) survival of the fittest

46. B cell expresses light chain from:

(a) Only one chromosome

(b) Both of the chromosomes

(c) Either one or both of the chromosomes

47. Allelic exclusion limits the B cells to express either κ light chains or λ light chains. But never both of them. Is it:

(a) True

(b) False

48. What do you mean by antigenic determinants on immunoglobulins?

(a) Specific regions on antibodies which can induce the immune system to produce antibodies against them

(b) Specific regions on antibodies that stimulate phagocytosis of antigens by macrophages

(c) Both of the above

(d) None of the above

49. Antibodies generated against isotypic determinants on the foreign antibodies bind to:

(a) Variable region of the foreign antibodies

(b) Constant region of the foreign antibodies

(c) Paratope of the foreign antibodies

(d) Both variable and constant regions of the antibodies

50. Which of the following statements is/are incorrect about allotypic determinants?

(a) Within a species, multiple alleles may exist for certain isotypic genes. And these alleles encode for subtle differences in the amino acid sequences

(b) Members within the same species have different allotypic determinants

(c) Members within the same species always have the same allotypic determinants

(d) None of the statements is incorrect

51. In which scenarios anti-allotypic antibodies are not produced?

(a) Produced by mother during pregnancy in response to paternal allotypic determinants on the fetal immunoglobulins

(b) Arise from a blood transfusion

(c) When antibodies from one species say human, is injected into another species, say mouse

(d) None of the above

52. Where are idiotypic determinants located?

(a) Variable regions of heavy chain and light chain

(b) Constant regions of heavy chain

(c) Constant regions of light chain

(d) Variable regions of light chain only

53. What are blocking anti-ID antibodies?

(a) Simultaneously bind to the target idiotypic antibody without affecting the antigen's binding capability of the target antibody

(b) Compete with the antigen to bind to the target antibody

(c) Bind to the target idiotypic antibody unless the target Ab is already bound to its antigen

54. Which type of anti-ID antibodies are used to specifically detect if the antibody-drug is bound to its target antigen.

(a) Antigen blocking anti-ID antibodies

(b) Non-blocking anti-ID antibodies

(c) Complex specific anti-ID antibodies

(d) All of the above

55. Which type of anti-ID antibodies are used to examine if the antibody-drug is present in unbound form?
(a) Antigen blocking anti-ID antibodies
(b) Non blocking anti-ID antibodies
(c) Complex specific anti-ID antibodies
(d) All of the above

56. Which type of anti-ID antibodies are used to detect both the antigen-bound and unbound antibody drug in the patient?
(a) Antigen blocking anti-ID antibodies
(b) Non-blocking anti-ID antibodies
(c) Complex specific anti-ID antibodies
(d) All of the above

Answer Key

1. (d) 2. (c) 3. (c) 4. (b) 5. (d) 6. (d) 7. (c) 8. (a) 9. (c) 10. (b) 11. (b) 12. (a) 13. (b) 14. (b) 15. (c) 16. (b) 17. (d) 18. (a) 19. (c) 20. (a) 21. (b) 22. (f) 23. (d) 24. (d) 25. (a) 26. (a) 27. (d) 28. (d) 29. (e) 30. (a) 31. (c) 32. (e) 33. (c) 34. (a) 35. (b) 36. (d) 37. (a) 38. (c) 39. (b) 40. (b) 41. (a) 42. (b) 43. (d) 44. (d) 45. (a) 46. (a) 47. (a) 48. (a) 49. (b) 50. (c) 51. (c) 52. (a) 53. (b) 54. (c) 55. (a) 56. (b)

Chapter 13: Polyclonal Antibodies & Monoclonal Antibodies

13.1. Polyclonal antibodies

B lymphocytes often referred to as B cells, produce antibodies. The origin and maturation of B cells occur in the bone marrow. Then, these mature naive B cells are released into the blood, and they keep recirculating between the lymph, blood, and secondary lymphoid tissues. The B cells have specific receptors on their membrane for antigen recognition. These receptors are called B-cell receptors or BCRs, composed of membrane-bound immunoglobulins and a heterodimer Ig-α/Ig-β held together by a disulfide bond.

Every day about 1 billion cells are produced in our body. The BCRs present have pre-existing specificities, because of which B cells can recognize and react to almost any possible antigen they encounter. Each B cell has around 100,000 BCRs on its surface. The important point is that all these BCRs of one B cell are specific for only one particular epitope on an antigen.

When a mature B cell encounters an antigen, it gets activated and proliferates into a large clone of B cells (*Fig 13-1*). Some of them differentiate into antibody-producing plasma cells, and others become long-lived memory B cells. These plasma cells and memory cells are specific to the antigen, or more specifically, the antigen's epitope, which the mature B cell initially encountered. These are the sequences of events that lead to the production of antibodies.

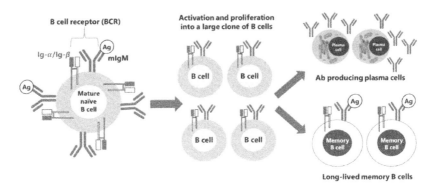

Fig 13-1: Production of antibodies by B cells

Assume a bacterial cell invaded the body. The bacterial cell membrane contains many molecules like polysaccharides, lipopolysaccharides, proteins, etc., and these molecules vary in their chemical nature. These molecules of bacteria are recognized as foreign by the B cell receptors. Or in other words, the bacterial cell is the antigen, and the bacterial cell molecules are the epitopes to which the B cells bind via their B cell receptors. B cells of diverse specificities circulating in the body recognize the different bacterial cell membrane molecules (*Fig 13-2*).

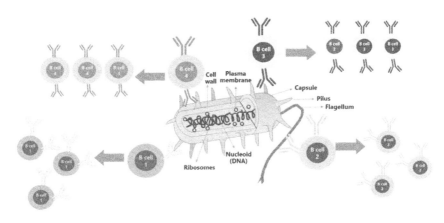

Fig 13-2: Bacterial cell is the antigen, and bacterial cell molecules are the epitopes to which different B cells bind and proliferate

For ease of understanding, suppose four types of B cells are circulating in the body, with different specificities. Each of these B cells is specific for a single epitope on an antigen; in our case, the antigen is a bacterial cell. So, when there is an invasion by the bacterial cell, these B cells recognize and bind to the specific epitopes on the antigen and get activated. Each of these B cells then proliferates and produces a large clone of cells.

Some of the activated B cells in each case get differentiated into antibody-producing plasma cells. And each of the plasma cells secretes antibodies specific to the epitope, which triggered their differentiation (*Fig 13-3*).

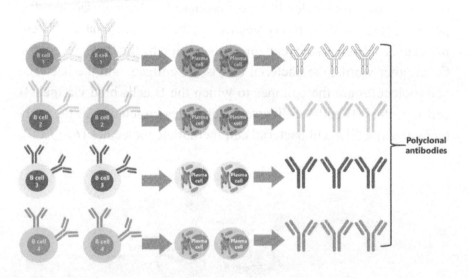

Fig 13-3: Production of polyclonal antibodies

So, as a result, our immune system produces four types of antibodies for the antigen bacterial cell, each type specific for a different epitope. **Antibodies derived from multiple B cell clones are called polyclonal antibodies.** In other words, polyclonal antibodies are the heterogeneous mixture of antibodies, each recognizing a different epitope on the same antigen.

13.2. Monoclonal antibodies

Now let's discuss monoclonal antibodies (often referred to as mAbs) that have revolutionized the treatments for several severe conditions like cancer, arthritis, autoimmune diseases, etc. (O'Mahony & Bishop, 2006). As already discussed, most antigens have multiple epitopes; therefore, they induce the proliferation and differentiation of various B cell clones. Each clone is derived from a B cell that recognizes a particular epitope (*Fig 13-4*). When an antigen binds to a specific B cell, it stimulates it to divide into a clone of cells that have the same antigen specificity as that of the parent B cell.

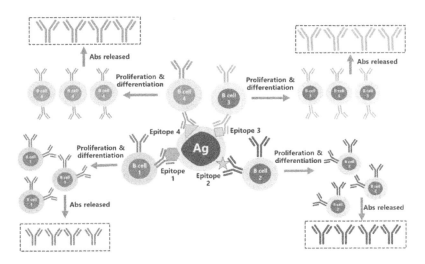

Fig 13-4: Proliferation and differentiation of various B cell clones

Like in Figure 13-4, clone 1 of B cells is derived from a B cell that can recognize epitope 1 of the Ag. And clone 2 of B cells is derived from B cell that can recognize epitope 2 of the Ag and so on.

Therefore, if the antibodies are raised against all the four epitopes of antigen, then the resulting serum antibodies are heterogeneous, comprising a mixture of antibodies, each specific for one epitope. These heterogeneous antibodies are called **polyclonal antibodies**.

On the other hand, the **monoclonal antibodies,** as the name indicates, are the antibodies that are **derived from the clones of a single activated B cell that recognizes a particular epitope** (*Fig 13-5*).

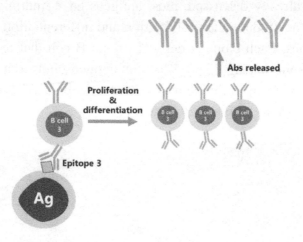

Fig 13-5: Production of monoclonal antibodies

Thus, the monoclonal antibodies recognize a single specific epitope on an antigen. In other words, monoclonal antibodies are identical antibodies with the same antigen specificity (*Fig 13-6*). Monoclonal antibodies have enormous applications for research, diagnostic and therapeutic purposes. Though polyclonal Abs facilitate phagocytosis and lysis of pathogens *in vivo*. But unfortunately, Ab heterogeneity that increases immune protection *in vivo* often reduces the efficacy of an antiserum for various *in vitro* purposes. Therefore, for research and diagnostic purposes, monoclonal antibodies that are specific for a single epitope are preferable.

Fig 13-6: Monoclonal antibodies with same antigen specificity

13.3. Hybridoma Technology

The hybridoma technology for the production of monoclonal antibodies was developed by Georges JF Koehler and Cesar Milstein in 1975.

The first step in producing monoclonal antibodies is the immunization of an animal, say mouse (*Fig 13-7*). The mouse, which is 2-4 weeks old, is immunized with the antigen against which monoclonal antibodies are to be raised (Pandey, 2010; Tomita & Tsumoto, 2011). Suppose the injected antigen has four epitopes.

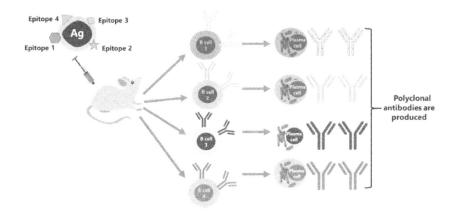

Fig 13-7: Polyclonal antibodies are produced in mice after immunization

As a result, the four types of B cells in the mouse get activated. The activated B cells then differentiate into antibodies producing plasma cells, producing polyclonal antibodies.

After several weeks, when the B cells reach the optimal amount, the mouse is sacrificed, and its spleen is removed. Spleen is then subjected to mechanical and enzymatic disruption, resulting in the release of cells. The plasma cells are separated from the other cells by density gradient centrifugation. And as a result of this step, the four types of plasma cells are isolated that can produce antibodies against the four epitopes present on the injected antigen (*Fig 13-8*). In the next step, the antibody-producing plasma cells are fused with myeloma cells to generate hybrid cells known as hybridomas. Here it is essential to understand that the antibody-producing plasma cells have a definite life span, but the myeloma cells are cancerous plasma cells, which are immortal and can divide indefinitely.

The myeloma cells used in the hybridoma technology have mutations in 2 genes.
- One in hypoxanthine-guanine phosphoribosyltransferase gene abbreviated as HGPRT. Because of the mutation, the HGPRT gene is non-functional in myeloma cells.
- And the second mutation is in immunoglobulin genes, because of which myeloma cells are unable to produce antibodies.

The fusion of plasma and myeloma cells is facilitated either with polyethylene glycol, abbreviated as PEG, or by electrofusion. As a result of fusion, three types of cells are obtained: fused hybridoma cells, unfused plasma cells, and unfused myeloma cells. The fused hybridoma cells possess the immortal growth properties of the myeloma cell and secrete the antibodies produced by the plasma cells. On the other hand, the unfused antibodies producing plasma cells have a limited life span. And unfused myeloma cells, though immortal, are unable to produce antibodies because of the mutations in the immunoglobulin genes.

Since the injected antigen has four epitopes, four types of plasma cells were produced in the mouse. Thus, when the four types of plasma cells are fused with the myeloma cells, four types of hybridoma cells are obtained. The hybridoma cells are then selected out of the mixture of fused and unfused cells.

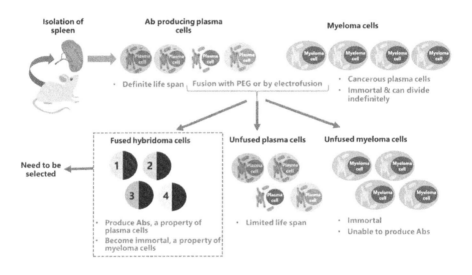

Fig 13-8: Plasma cells and myeloma cells are fused to form hybridoma cells

13.4. Selection of Hybridoma Cells on HAT Media

The selection of hybridoma cells from the mixture of fused and unfused cells is carried out on HAT media. HAT stands for Hypoxanthine Aminopterin Thymidine. The selection of the cells on the media is based on the fact that there are two pathways of nucleotide synthesis. In the media, the mother cells divide to form daughter cells for which DNA replication occurs, and DNA replication requires the synthesis of new nucleotides. Two pathways of nucleotide synthesis are the Salvage pathway and the De-novo pathway.

1. The salvage pathway is the pathway in which new nucleotides are synthesized from the parts of degraded nucleotides.

2. Whereas in the case of the de-novo pathway, completely new nucleotides are synthesized using small metabolites like sugars and amino acids present in the media.

When the cells are grown on HAT media, they are unable to operate the de-novo pathway because of the presence of Aminopterin (*Fig 13-9a*). Aminopterin blocks the critical enzyme dihydrofolate reductase involved in nucleotide synthesis. Once this enzyme is blocked, cells can not convert simple sugars into nucleotides and thus can't operate the de-novo pathway. Therefore, the cells are left with the option of using the salvage pathway to synthesize nucleotides.

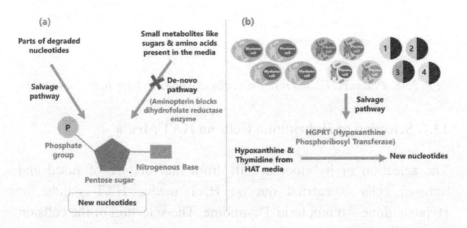

Fig 13-9: (a) Inhibition of de-novo pathway and (b) HGPRT is required for salvage pathway

But for the Salvage pathway to operate, cells must possess the enzyme Hypoxanthine guanine phosphoribosyltransferase, i.e., HGPRT. HGPRT is a key enzyme that helps cells to use hypoxanthine and thymidine from the HAT medium as precursors to synthesize nucleotides (*Fig 13-9b*).

Because of this reason, the unfused myeloma cells die on the HAT media, as they have non-functional HGPRT gene; therefore, they cannot produce nucleotides by the salvage pathways (*Fig 13-10*).

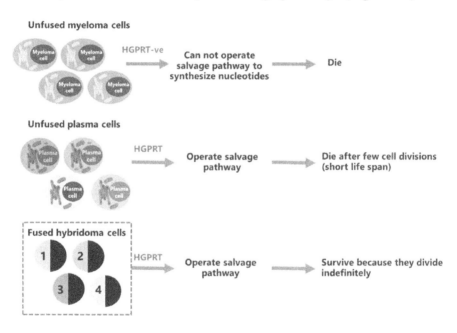

Fig 13-10: Selection of hybridoma cells on HAT media

On the contrary, unfused plasma cells and hybridoma cells can operate salvage pathways on the HAT media. The functional HGPRT gene in hybridoma cells is contributed by the plasma cells that get fused with the myeloma cells. But the unfused plasma cells die after a few cell divisions as they have a short life span. In contrast, the hybridoma cells can divide indefinitely on the HAT media, and this property is contributed by the myeloma cells. Therefore, at last, only the hybridoma cells are left in the HAT media. These hybridoma cells:

- Possess the capability to produce antibodies, a property of plasma cells
- And they also become immortal, a property of myeloma cells

The population of hybridoma cells that survive selection is heterogeneous, containing clones of 4 different types of hybridoma cells that produce antibodies with different epitope specificities. Recall that each type of hybridoma cell produces antibodies specific to an epitope on the antigen. But the aim is to select and propagate a single antibody-producing hybridoma cell. For this, these hybridomas are needed to be isolated and grown individually. The isolation of hybridomas of a single specificity is done by a method known as limiting dilution (*Fig 13-11*).

Limiting dilution is a technique that dilutes the concentrations of the heterogeneous population such that, on average, each well contains one cell. In practice, some wells may contain no cells, some may have a single cell, and others may contain multiple cells.

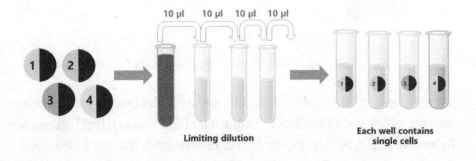

Fig 13-11: Limiting dilution technique

In the next step, each hybridoma cell is screened for the secretion of antibodies with the desired specificity. This screening is done by ELISA technique and selects only those hybridomas that produce antibodies of appropriate specificity (*Fig 13-12*).

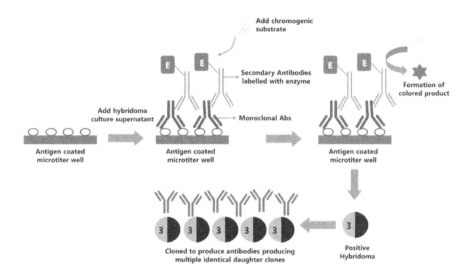

Fig 13-12: ELISA technique to select desired Ab producing hybridoma cell

For this, the hybridoma culture supernatant containing monoclonal antibodies (mAbs) is added to the antigen-coated microtiter well. The antigen-coated is the desired Ag against which mAbs are to be raised. The mAbs are then allowed to interact with Ag. After this, the mAbs bound to Ag are detected by adding secondary anti-isotype antibodies labeled with an enzyme, which binds with primary mAbs. Then the chromogenic substrate is added. And upon addition of this substrate, if a colored product is obtained, it indicates a positive hybridoma. After this, the desired antibody-producing hybridoma cell can be cloned to produce multiple identical daughter clones. These identical daughter cells produce monoclonal antibodies or, in other words, identical antibodies with the same antigen specificities.

Chapter 14: Advantages and issues of mouse monoclonal antibodies for therapeutic purposes

14.1. Advantages over conventional drugs

As already discussed, monoclonal antibodies are identical antibodies that recognize a single specific epitope on an antigen. This property of monoclonal antibodies can make them useful for therapeutic purposes and more effective than conventional drugs.

The conventional drugs not only attack the foreign pathogen or diseased cells, but they also attack the body's cells that cause serious side effects (*Fig 14-1a*). On the other hand, therapeutic monoclonal antibodies target only the foreign antigen or the specific protein markers on the target cells. For instance, in the case of cancer treatment, monoclonal antibodies are developed to bind to the proteins present specifically on the tumor cells (*Fig 14-1b*). After binding, the antibodies tag the target cancerous cells for destruction by the immune system.

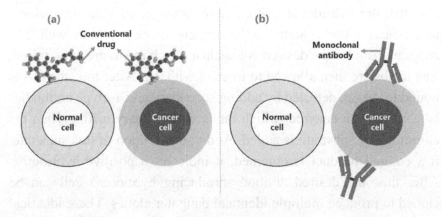

Fig 14-1: Mechanism of action of (a) conventional drug and (b) monoclonal antibody

This property of monoclonal antibodies makes them very suitable for therapeutic use in many diseases such as cancer, genetic disorders, HIV, autoimmune diseases, etc. Furthermore, since the therapeutic monoclonal antibodies bind only to the intended target cells, therefore there are very few unexpected side effects while using them.

14.2. Issues of mouse monoclonal antibodies

One major issue in generating antibodies for therapeutic purposes is that **most monoclonal antibodies are produced in mice**. There are many clinical applications in which the mouse monoclonal antibodies are useful like in diagnostic and research purposes. However, when mouse monoclonal antibodies are introduced into the patients, the isotypic determinants of mouse antibodies are recognized as foreign by the patients' bodies (*Fig 14-2*).

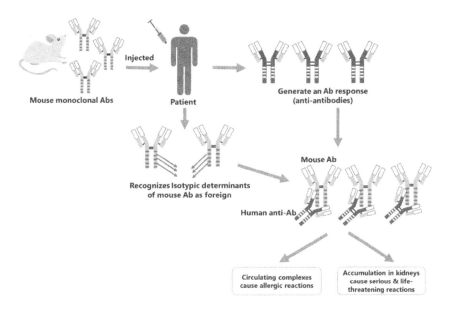

Fig 14-2: Patients recognize isotypic determinants of mouse antibodies as foreign and generate an antibody response against them

As a result, the patients generate an antibody response or anti-antibodies against the isotypic determinants on the foreign mouse antibody. Thus, clearing the mouse monoclonal antibodies from the bloodstream. In addition to this, circulating complexes of mouse and human antibodies can also cause allergic reactions. In some cases, these complexes can accumulate in organs such as the kidneys and cause severe and even life-threatening reactions (Courtenay-Luck, 1986).

To minimize the complications resulting from using mouse monoclonal antibodies in humans, scientists are undertaking a significant effort to engineer monoclonal antibodies with recombinant DNA technology.

With the knowledge of antibody structure and antibody regulation, three types of therapeutic antibodies have been engineered. These are:
- chimeric monoclonal antibodies,
- humanized monoclonal antibodies
- and fully human monoclonal antibodies.

Chapter 15: Chimeric monoclonal antibodies

As already discussed, an antibody molecule consists of two identical light (L) chain polypeptides and two identical heavy (H) chain polypeptides. And each light chain and heavy chain contains two distinct regions: Variable regions (V) and constant regions (C). It is the variable region in the light and heavy chains of an antibody molecule that together forms an antigen-binding site. Because the target recognition only happens in the antibody's variable domains, the scientists thought, why not take the mouse antibody's variable region and graft them onto the human antibody's constant region. Such generated antibodies are called **chimeric antibodies** (*Fig 15-1*). In other words, the chimeric antibodies contain variable regions from one species and the constant regions from the other species (Billetta & Lobuglio, 1993).

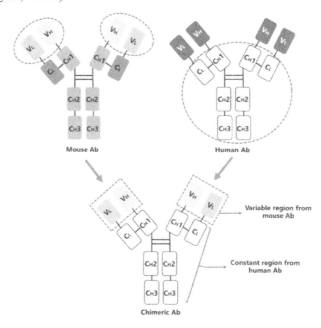

Fig 15-1: Chimeric monoclonal Ab

217

15.1. Production of chimeric monoclonal antibodies

Chimeric antibodies are generated using recombinant DNA technology. The immunoglobulin (Ig) variable regions of a selected mouse hybridoma are joined to the human Ig constant regions. For this, first, the mouse is immunized with a specific antigen against which the antibodies are to be generated. The antigen that is introduced in the mouse is called **a human therapeutic target**.

After a few days of immunizing, the mouse is sacrificed, and its spleen is isolated. Then, plasma cells are separated from the spleen and are fused with the myeloma cells to construct hybridoma cells. Hybridoma technology and its procedure have already been discussed in detail in sections 13.3 and 13.4. The hybridoma cells that produce the antibodies against the desired therapeutic target are then isolated from the mixture of fused hybridoma cells (*Fig 15-2*).

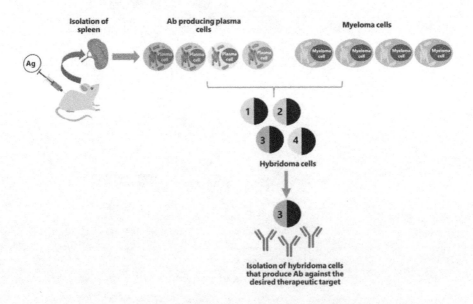

Fig 15-2: Through hybridoma technology, hybridoma cells producing antibodies against the desired therapeutic target are selected

From the selected hybridoma cell, using specific primers, Polymerase chain reaction, abbreviated as PCR, is done to amplify the DNA sequences, including promoter, leader, and V_H and V_L sequences encoding variable regions of the mouse antibody (*Fig 15-3*). In addition, the PCR primers create restriction enzyme sites in the amplified sequences to conveniently insert variable regions into the vectors.

On the other hand, a gene construct is made that contains DNA sequences including promoter and C_H and C_L sequences encoding constant regions of human antibodies. Then, the mouse/human chimeric genes are constructed by inserting human and mouse genes into a circular piece of DNA called a plasmid. The plasmid is then introduced into mammalian cells via a process called transfection.

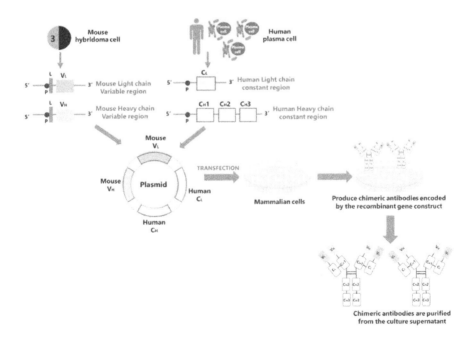

Fig 15-3: Production of chimeric monoclonal antibodies

After transfection, the mammalian cells produce the antibodies encoded by the recombinant gene construct. Finally, the antibodies are purified from the culture supernatant. The antibodies encoded by mouse/human chimeric gene construct are called **chimeric antibodies** or **mouse-human chimera**.

The antigenic specificity of this chimeric antibody is determined by the variable region derived from the mouse. But the constant region of the chimeric antibody is encoded by human genes, because of which the chimeric antibodies have fewer antigenic determinants and therefore are far less immunogenic than the mouse monoclonal antibodies when administered in humans.

Additionally, since the chimeric antibodies possess the mouse's variable regions, they have the appropriate binding sites to recognize and bind to the specific target antigen. And the constant regions are encoded by the human DNA because of which they retain the biological effector functions of a human antibody and are more likely to trigger complement system activation and Fc receptor binding.

15.2. Examples of chimeric monoclonal antibodies

Mouse-human chimeric antibodies have been developed to treat patients suffering from various diseases, including cancer. The antibodies are designed in such a way that the mouse variable region recognizes the tumor antigens. In contrast, the human constant region activates the biological effector functions like activating natural killer cells to kill the tumor cells (*Fig 15-4*).

Due to their prolonged circulating half-life and relative ease of production, **generally used therapeutic monoclonal antibodies are IgGs**.

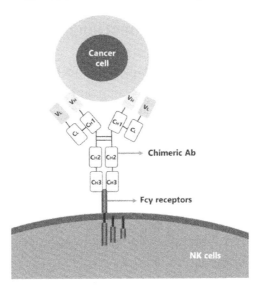

Fig 15-4: Chimeric monoclonal antibodies for cancer treatment

The IgG chimeric therapeutic antibody, "rituximab," was the first monoclonal antibody approved by the US Food and Drug Administration (FDA) in 1997 to treat non-Hodgkin's lymphoma. This medication has since been used to treat several CD20-positive B-cell malignancies and rheumatoid arthritis. The naming convention of Chimeric antibodies includes using the "**xi**" stem in their name. A few examples of chimeric antibodies that are approved for human therapy include abci**xi**mab, basili**xi**mab, cetu**xi**mab, infli**xi**mab, ritu**xi**mab, etc.

Chapter 16: Humanized monoclonal antibodies

The second type of engineered therapeutic antibody is humanized antibodies. To further improve humanization proportion and reduce the immunogenicity of the chimeric antibodies, humanized antibodies were developed (Jolliffe, 1993; Vaswani & Hamilton, 1998; Waldmann, 2019; Lu et al., 2020). A humanized antibody can be developed through grafting the complementarity determining regions abbreviated as CDRs from the mouse antibody into the corresponding region of the human antibody (*Fig 16-1*). It is achieved through recombinant DNA methods using an appropriate vector and expression in mammalian cells.

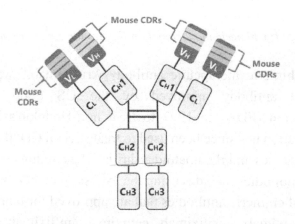

Fig 16-1: Humanized monoclonal Ab

16.1. Production of humanized monoclonal antibodies

First, the mouse is immunized with a specific antigen (therapeutic target) against which the antibodies are to be generated. After a few days of immunizing, the mouse is sacrificed. Next, its spleen is separated, from which plasma cells are isolated and are fused with the myeloma cells to generate hybridoma cells. The hybridoma cells that produce the antibodies against the desired therapeutic target are then isolated from the mixture of fused hybridoma cells.

From the selected hybridoma cell, mRNA is isolated and is reverse transcribed into cDNA. After this step, using specific primers, Polymerase chain reaction, abbreviated as PCR, amplifies the DNA sequence corresponding to the CDRs of the desired mouse antibody. Once the desired CDRs are amplified, these CDR sequences are inserted appropriately into a construct containing the DNA for a human antibody (*Fig 16-2*).

In the next step, the cloned target-specific antibody DNA sequence is expressed as a monoclonal Ab into the mammalian cells like Chinese hamster ovary cells, abbreviated as CHO cells. In this way, the humanized antibody is produced, containing the CDRs of mouse origin and antibody scaffold of human origin.

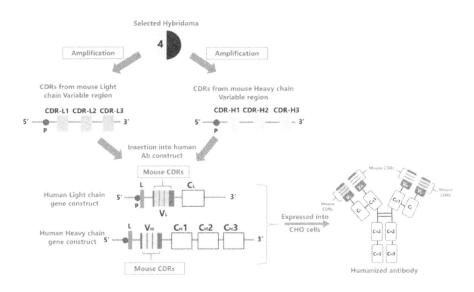

Fig 16-2: Production of humanized monoclonal antibodies

In some cases, apart from CDRs, certain other amino acids in the framework region of mouse antibodies are crucial to maintaining antibody binding activity. These amino acid residues cooperate with CDRs to directly interact with antigens. These essential framework amino acid residues can be identified by observing the structure of the antibody-antigen complex by X-ray crystallography, cryo-electron microscopy, and computer-aided protein homology modeling. Therefore, specific framework residues in humanized antibodies are replaced with the crucial amino acids present in the framework region of mouse antibodies, thereby improving the affinity and stability of the humanized monoclonal antibody.

16.2. Examples of humanized monoclonal antibodies

Humanized therapeutic antibodies have the potential to improve humanization proportion to 85%-90%. Humanized antibodies contain "**zu**" in their name. One such humanized antibody is Otelixi**zu**mab which is currently in clinical trials to treat rheumatoid arthritis and diabetes mellitus. Another humanized antibody in clinical trials is dacli**zu**mab to treat adults with relapsing forms of multiple sclerosis.

Currently, chimeric and humanized antibodies are the primary forms of human therapeutic antibodies playing an essential role in cancer therapy.

Chapter 17: Fully Human monoclonal antibodies

The third type of engineered therapeutic antibody is fully human monoclonal antibodies. Fully human monoclonal antibodies can further reduce the incidence of generating the anti-drug antibodies against them. These antibodies can be produced by two methods: Either from transgenic mice or human antibody libraries.

17.1. Transgenic mice

The transgenic mice are created by replacing the entire mouse antibody genes with human antibody genes (Longberg, 2005; Laffleur et al., 2012). For this, the human heavy chain construct is cloned, which contains human V_H, D_H, J_H, and the constant region gene segments. Also, the human light chain construct is cloned that has V_L, J_L, and the constant region gene segments.

Then these constructs are micro-injected into fertilized eggs of the mouse in which endogenous mouse Ig genes are disrupted. Microinjection allows the insertion of human heavy and light chain constructs into the mouse genome to produce the transgenic mouse that is unable to produce mouse antibodies but is capable of producing human antibodies upon immunization (*Fig 17-1*). Thus, upon immunizing the transgenic humanized mouse with a target antigen, it produces the human antibodies. No part of the antibodies produced is mouse-derived. The monoclonal antibodies are produced through hybridoma technology (discussed in section 13.3). Plasma cells are isolated from the mouse and are fused with myeloma cells to create a mouse hybridoma that secretes human monoclonal antibodies. Then the hybridoma producing the desired human monoclonal antibodies is selected and cloned to make multiple identical daughter cells that produce the desired human monoclonal antibodies.

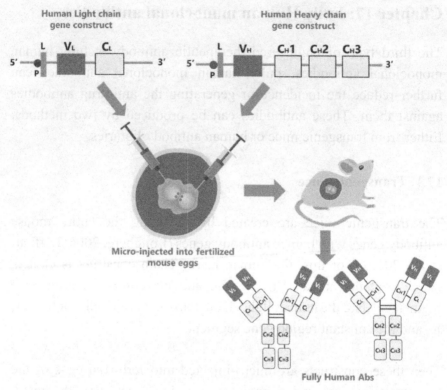

Fig 17-1: Production of fully human antibodies by transgenic mouse

17.2. Phage display method

The second method by which fully human monoclonal antibodies can be created is the phage display method. Using recombinant DNA techniques, the gene encoding a foreign protein (protein of interest) is integrated into the genome of filamentous bacteriophage M13 (McCafferty et al., 1990, Bazan et al., 2012; Ledsgaard et al., 2018). It leads to the expression of foreign peptides in conjugation with coat protein pIII, as a fusion protein, causing the bacteriophage to display the foreign peptides on its surface (*Fig 17-2*). A bacteriophage is a type of virus that infects bacteria.

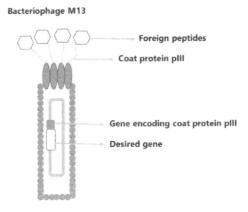

Fig 17-2: Phage display method

For the generation of humanized antibodies, the phage-display antibody library is generated. In this, mRNA from the B cells is isolated and is reverse transcribed into cDNA. After this step, Polymerase chain reaction, abbreviated as PCR, is done to amplify different V_H and V_L chain-region gene families using specific primers to amplify all the possible transcribed variable regions within the Ig repertoire (*Fig 17-3*). The amplified V_H and V_L domains are joined by a protease-resistant glycine-serine linker into a single DNA sequence. These antibody sequences are then introduced and cloned as a gene fusion with the bacteriophage pIII gene in phagemid vectors. Phagemid vector is a plasmid that carries an antibiotic resistance gene, bacterial, and phage origins of replication. Additionally, phagemid vectors can be packaged into the capsid of a bacteriophage because of the presence of a genetic sequence that signals for packaging.

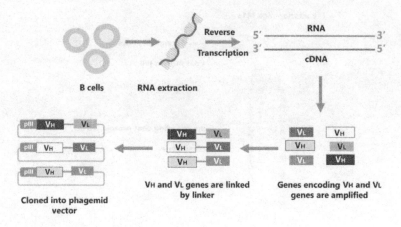

Fig 17-3: Cloning of antibody sequences in a phagemid vector

These phagemid vectors are electroporated into the *E. coli* cells. The *E. coli* cells are then infected with bacteriophages. After infection, the bacteriophages generate a phage-display library in which the Fv fragments containing V_H and V_L region are displayed on the phage coat protein (*Fig 17-4*).

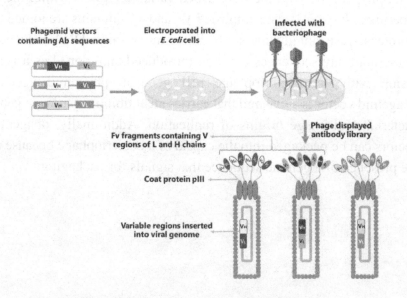

Fig 17-4: Phage-display human antibody library

After this, affinity screening of the phage-display antibody library is done by a process called **biopanning**. In this, the phages expressing the Fv region of antibodies on the surface are added to the antigens immobilized on a solid surface, for example, on ELISA plates (*Fig 17-5*). The antigen can be a protein on tumor cells or other cells against which a therapeutic antibody is required to be generated. The phages that have Fv regions specific for the antigens bind to the coated antigen. Non-specific phages are removed by stringent washing. Antigen-bound phages are then eluted and are re-infected into *E. coli* to produce a subset of phages for the next cycle of panning.

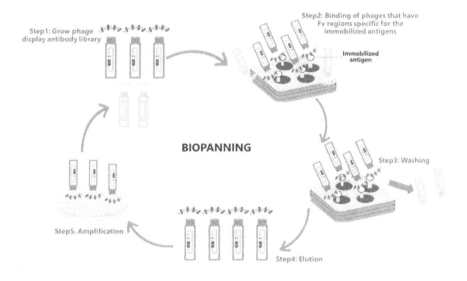

Fig 17-5: Biopanning method

After several rounds, the specific antigen-binding phages are sufficiently enriched. In other words, the antibody Fv fragments displayed on the phage coat protein that exhibits a strong affinity for the antigen are selected. These Fv fragments are then isolated from the phage coat with the help of enzymes that cleave at the protease site engineered between the antibody and pIII protein of the phage (*Fig*

17-6). The isolated Fv fragments are then converted to intact IgG antibodies without impairing their antigen-binding activity. These intact IgG antibodies are called fully humanized antibodies.

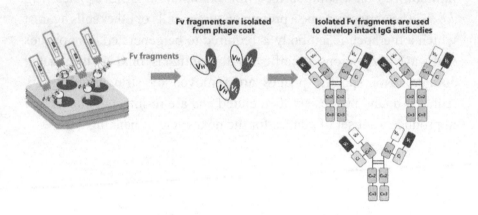

Fig 17-6: Intact IgG antibodies are developed from isolated Fv fragments

This method can also be used to generate a phage-display library of complementarity determining regions abbreviated as CDRs. The phages express the CDRs on their surface, after which the expressed CDRs are screened to identify those CDRs that exhibit the strongest affinity for the desired antigen. Once the best CDRs are identified, they are grafted onto a human antibody scaffold to form fully human monoclonal antibodies. These are the several techniques by which fully human monoclonal antibodies can be generated.

The fully human antibodies contain **-u-** in their name. For instance, the first fully human therapeutic antibody developed was adalimumab. Also, this was the first phage-display derived fully human monoclonal antibody. Adalimumab binds and suppresses Tumor necrosis factor-alpha, abbreviated as TNFα, and is approved to treat inflammatory diseases, like rheumatoid arthritis, Crohn's disease, and psoriasis. Other fully human monoclonal antibodies derived from phage display method are belimumab, necitumumab, avelumab, etc.

17.3. Isolation of monoclonal antibodies directly from humans

The biopanning approach can also be used to isolate and identify specific antibodies against novel or gene-mutated pathogens in an outbreak of emerging infectious diseases. The antigens on pathogens usually induce an immune response in patients; thus, the patients naturally produce high-affinity antibodies against the pathogens. Therefore, isolating mAbs directly from patients who were infected and cleared infections could be essential tools to neutralize the infectious agent. To obtain these antibodies, mRNA from the peripheral blood mononuclear cells (PBMCs) of pathogen-recovered people is collected. Then V_H and V_L chain-region gene families are amplified using specific primers to amplify all the possible transcribed variable regions within the immunoglobulin repertoire.

After this, these cloned fragments are cloned into phagemid vectors. Phagemid vectors are then electroporated into the *E. coli* cells. The *E. coli* cells are then infected with bacteriophages. After infection, the bacteriophages generate a phage-displayed library in which the Fv fragments containing V_H and V_L regions are displayed on the phage coat protein. After this, the phages expressing the Fv region of antibodies are added to the antigens immobilized on a solid surface. By the process of biopanning, the library can allow for the rapid identification of high-affinity antibodies, i.e., the Fv regions that strongly bind to the antigen.

These Fv fragments are then isolated from the phage coat and are used to develop intact antibodies or therapeutic drugs against the pathogens that infected the patients. Even these antibodies can be used as diagnostic reagents to diagnose if the person is infected with that pathogen.

Let's take the example of isolating antibodies against pandemic influenza A virus H7N9, which broke out in 2013. For this, the researchers generated the phage-displayed antibody library from the human peripheral blood mononuclear cells of recovered patients that were infected with a novel influenza A virus H7N9. Using this library, antibodies targeting purified H7N9 virions were isolated. Two human antibodies were found to exhibit high neutralizing activity against live H7N9 virus due to their interactions with the receptor-binding site of viral hemagglutinin antigens. Thus, the isolation of the human antibodies can be used to develop human antibody-based drugs for the prevention and early treatment of influenza A or related viral pathogens.

18. Immunogenicity of engineered mAbs

18.1. Anti-drug antibodies (ADA)

Immunogenicity is the ability of engineered monoclonal antibodies to provoke the immune system to generate antibodies against them. Since the therapeutic mAbs, also called antibody drugs are glycoproteins; thus, they have specific regions on them called antigenic determinants. These antigenic determinants can induce the immune system to produce antibodies against the antibody drugs or therapeutic mAbs. The antibodies generated against the antibody drugs are referred to as anti-drug-antibodies, abbreviated as ADAs (*Fig 18-1*).

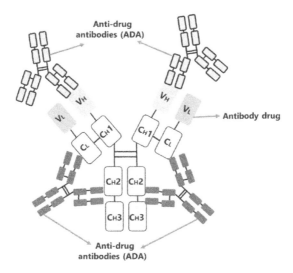

Fig 18-1: Anti-drug antibodies (ADAs) generated against antibody drugs

Anti-drug antibodies can lead to the negation of all antibody drug-related effects, thus completely inhibiting the therapeutic aspect of the drug. Importantly, anti-drug antibodies may further cause adverse effects ranging from skin rashes to systemic inflammatory responses in the patients, impacting both the safety and efficacy of the antibody drugs in clinical use (Warnke et al., 2012). Therefore, it is essential to humanize antibodies as much as possible to lower the generation of anti-drug-antibodies in the patients.

18.2. Comparison of immunogenicity of engineered mAbs

 Humanized antibodies harbor human sequences in constant regions and also exhibit nearly all human sequences in the variable region, except the CDRs, which are mouse-derived. On the other hand, chimeric antibodies contain variable regions from mouse antibodies and the constant regions from human antibodies. Since the humanized antibodies are more human-like, thus compared to chimeric monoclonal antibodies, the ADAs generated against the humanized monoclonal antibodies are reduced (*Fig 18-2*). However, the incidence of ADAs is not eliminated because the humanized antibodies still retain mouse CDRs, which could be regarded as foreign antigens by host immune systems and eventually arise **ADAs** against them.

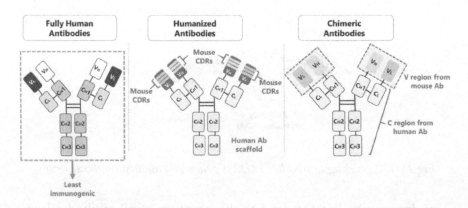

Fig 18-2: Fully human, humanized, and chimeric monoclonal antibodies

On the other hand, since in the case of fully human monoclonal antibodies, CDRs and frameworks of fully human antibodies are derived from human immunoglobulin gene repertoires; therefore, they generally show a lower incidence of ADAs than the humanized antibodies or chimeric antibodies.

However, immune responses to several fully human monoclonal antibodies have been reported when administered in patients. For instance, **Adalimumab**, a human IgG1 monoclonal antibody, has been reported to generate significant immune responses through eliciting anti-idiotypic antibodies in some patients (van Schouwenburg et al., 2013).

The research is going on to reduce the immunogenicity of the engineered therapeutic monoclonal antibodies in order to negate their adverse effects.

Chapter 19: Drug Conjugates

Drug conjugates such as antibody-drug conjugates (ADCs) and immunotoxins are designed to combine the specific targeting moiety of an antibody with the efficacy of a toxic drug.

19.1. Antibody-drug conjugate (ADC)

Antibody-drug conjugates (ADCs) are highly potent biological drugs where a monoclonal antibody is linked to a biologically active drug (a small molecule) forming a conjugate (Chari et al., 2014; Hoffmann et al., 2018; Dan et al., 2018; Ponziani et al., 2020).

Components of ADC: There are three components of ADCs: a monoclonal antibody, a cytotoxic drug (also known as payload), and a chemical linker that connects the monoclonal antibody with the drug (*Fig 19-1*).

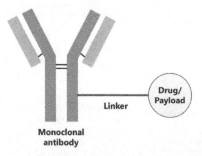

Fig 19-1: Components of Antibody-drug conjugate (ADC)

(i) Monoclonal Antibody: The monoclonal antibody targets a specific antigen found or overexpressed only on target diseased/cancer cells, but not on the normal healthy cells (Weidle et al., 2011; Khongorzul et al., 2020). For example, the HER2 receptor is almost 100-fold highly expressed in the tumor cell than the healthy one. In addition, the target antigen should also possess internalization properties as it facilitates the ADC to transport into the cell, which enhances the cytotoxic agent's efficacy.

Furthermore, the monoclonal antibody should bear good retention, low immunogenicity, and low cross-reactivity properties.

(ii) Linker: The linkers are critical components in ADC design as linkers link the cytotoxic drug/payload to the monoclonal Ab. When the ADC complex circulates in the blood, the linker must be stable enough to keep the antibody-drug conjugate intact and avoid the release of the cytotoxic drug in the off-target tissue. Also, the linker must maintain the drug in an inactive, nontoxic state while bound to the antibody. At the same time, the linker should possess the property of releasing the cytotoxic drug once the ADC binds to the target cell and is internalized. Upon internalization, the drug induces target cell death by causing irreversible DNA damage or interfering with the mechanism of cell division (*Fig 19-2*).

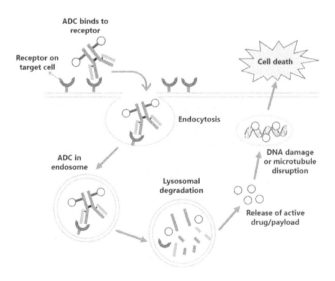

Fig 19-2: Mechanism of the release of drug from the ADC

To achieve this, various linkers have been developed that are divided into two types: cleavable linkers and non-cleavable linkers (Nolting, 2013; Bargh et al., 2019).

Cleavable linkers: Cleavable linker consists of a chemical trigger in its structure that can be efficiently cleaved to release the cytotoxic drug in the target cell (*Fig 19-3*). Cleavage of the chemical trigger depends on environmental differences (such as pH, redox potential) and specific lysosomal proteases, etc.

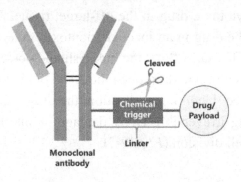

Fig 19-3: Chemical trigger in the cleavable linker

(a) pH-sensitive linkers: This group of cleavable linkers are sensitive to the acidic environment (pH 4.0-6.0) but are stable in the alkaline environment (pH 7.4) of the systemic circulation. Upon internalization into the targeted cells, the acid-sensitive hydrazone group in acid-labile linkers gets hydrolyzed in the lysosomal (pH<5) and endosomal (pH 5–6) acidic environment, leading to the release of cytotoxic drug (*Fig 19-4*).

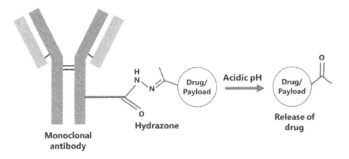

Fig 19-4: Cleavage of the pH-sensitive linker

(b) Lysosomal protease-sensitive linkers: Lysosomal protease-sensitive linkers are the most common linkers used in ADC designed for targeting tumor cells. For instance, the β-glucuronide linker is recognized and hydrolyzed by the β-glucuronidase enzyme, which is present abundantly in lysosomes (*Fig 19-5*). The cleavage of the β-glucuronide linker with the β-glucuronidase enzyme enables the release of cytotoxic drugs. The enzyme is inactive at physiologic pH (pH 7.4) and active at lysosomal pH (pH<5). Therefore, an ADC with a glucuronide linker may improve the stability of the ADC in blood circulation.

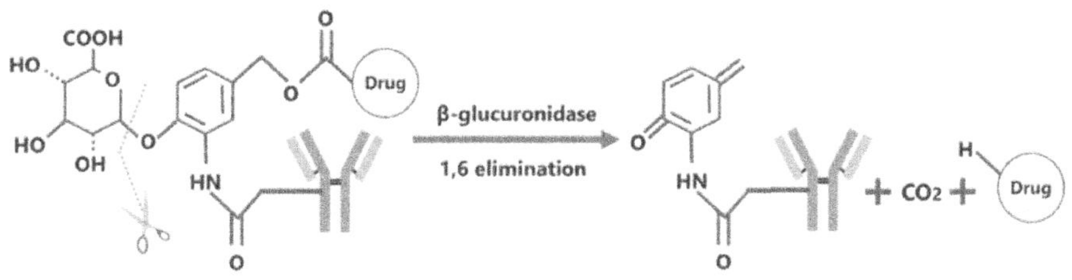

Fig 19-5: Cleavage of the lysosomal-protease sensitive linker

(c) Disulfide linker: Other cleavable linkers used in ADCs are the disulfide linkers, which are stable at physiological pH in the systemic circulation but are vulnerable to nucleophilic attacks by the thiols such as reduced glutathione (GSH). GSH reduces the disulfide bond of the

239

linker, eventually releasing the cytotoxic drug that leads to the killing of target cells (*Fig 19-6*).

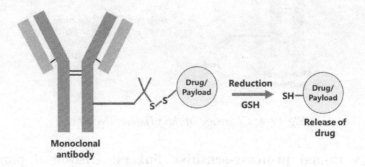

Fig 19-6: Cleavage of disulfide linker

In addition, disulfide-linked drugs resist reductive cleavage in the circulation because the glutathione (GSH) concentration in the blood (5 μmol/L) is lower than in the cytoplasm (1–10 mmol/L), allowing GSH thiol groups to be very effective in the cell cytoplasm. In addition, glutathione is highly released during tumor growth and cell stress conditions such as hypoxia; thus, a higher concentration of glutathione can be found in cancer cells than in normal cells. Low glutathione levels in normal healthy tissues discriminate release of the payload, allowing the selective release of payload in the tumor cell.

Compared with pH-sensitive (acid-labile) linkers such as hydrazones, disulfide linkers exert enhanced ADC stability in circulation, reduce off-target drug release/toxicity, and selective drug release in the cytosol.

Non-cleavable linkers: Unlike cleavable linkers, non-cleavable linkers consist of stable bonds that are resistant to proteolytic degradation. These linkers require degradation of the monoclonal antibody component within the lysosome after ADC internalization to release the cytotoxic drug.

(iii) Cytotoxic drug/payload: The third essential component of ADCs is a cytotoxic drug, also called payload, that kills the target cell once released from the ADC. The payload used should have certain properties like (a) stable and soluble in the systemic circulation, (b) low immunogenicity, small molecular weight, and a long half-life (c) possess an appropriate functional group to facilitate conjugation to the monoclonal antibody through the linker.

Currently, most ADCs are constructed with two main classes of toxic compounds, acting either on microtubule (Klute et al., 2014; Chen et al., 2017) or DNA structure (Fu and Ho, 2018). Both molecules are potently cytotoxic against rapidly dividing cancer cells and have reduced toxicity to normal cells.

Microtubule-disrupting agents

As the name indicates, microtubule-disrupting agents disrupt microtubules that then inhibit mitosis, which is essential for cell division.

Microtubules are components of the cytoskeleton that give each cell its shape and are involved in various eukaryotic cellular processes like intracellular transport, cell movement, and mitosis. Microtubules are polymers of a dimer of two protein units called α-tubulin and β-tubulin, which form long protein fibers called protofilaments. About 13 protofilaments arrange themselves in parallel to form a hollow, cylindrical microtubule (*Fig 19-7*).

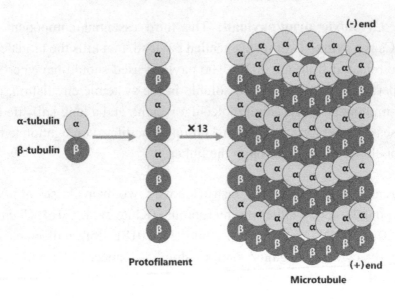

Fig 19-7: Structure of a microtubule

The protofilaments are arranged such that one end of the microtubule has α-tubulin subunits, and the opposite end has β-tubulin subunits. The end where α-tubulins are exposed is known as the minus (–) end. In contrast, the end where β-tubulins are exposed is known as the positive (+) end. Microtubules can grow by adding more tubulin dimers, and also, at the same time, they can depolymerize by losing tubulin dimers. Thus, the ends of microtubules can grow (polymerize) and shrink (depolymerize). The addition and release of tubulin dimers at the plus end are much higher than the minus end.

The microtubule grows out from a specific intracellular location called Microtubule organizing centers (MTOCs). In the cell, the MTOC is centrosome, which comprises two centrioles (*Fig 19-8*). Additionally, each centriole is made up of 9 sets of triplet microtubules arranged in a ring. From the centrosome, microtubules grow out during cell division. The minus ends of microtubules are embedded in the centrosome. In contrast, the plus ends of microtubules are free in the cell's cytoplasm. When the cell enters mitosis for cell division, the centrosome duplicates.

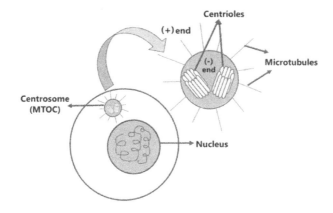

Fig 19-8: MTOC is centrosome from which microtubules grow

Mitosis can be divided into four subphases: prophase, metaphase, anaphase, and telophase.

Prophase: During prophase, the membrane around the nucleus disintegrates, and chromosomes condense (*Fig 19-9*).

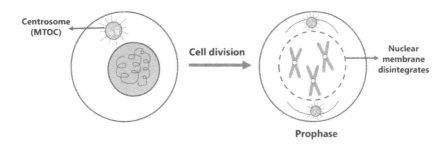

Fig 19-9: Prophase stage of mitosis

Metaphase: During metaphase, the chromosomes move towards the middle of the cell on a line called metaphasic plate (*Fig 19-10a*). Each chromosome is made up of a pair of sister chromatids which are joined

243

together in the centromere where there is a specific protein complex called kinetochore (*Fig 19-10b*). During this phase, each centrosome sends out thread-like projections called spindle fibers that attach to the kinetochore of each sister chromatid. Spindle fibers consist of microtubules that originate from the centrioles and polymerize in the direction of kinetochores.

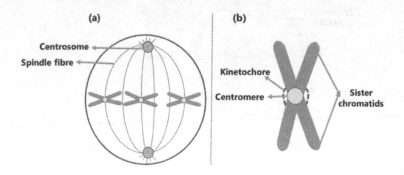

Fig 19-10: (a) Metaphase stage of mitosis and (b) structure of chromosome

Anaphase: During anaphase, the centrosomes start pulling the spindle fibers to pull the sister chromatids apart from their partner sister chromatids (*Fig 19-11*). It occurs because of the depolymerization and shortening of the microtubules.

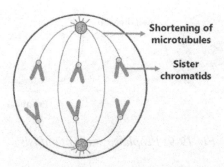

Fig 19-11: Anaphase stage of mitosis

Telophase: Finally, in telophase, a nuclear membrane forms around each new set of daughter single chromatid c hromosomes (*Fig 19-12*). After that, during cytokinesis, the cell membrane pinches in until the two daughter cells separate.

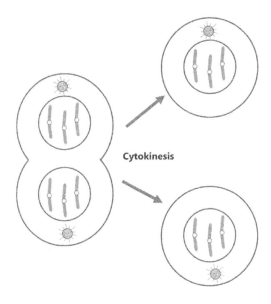

Fig 19-12: Telophase stage of mitosis

Since cancer cells replicate rapidly, they are constantly undergoing mitosis, and microtubules are always at work. It means that microtubule inhibitors will affect the rapidly dividing cancer cells more than the normal healthy cells, most of which only divide occasionally. Interfering with the formation of microtubules causes mitosis to fail; therefore, the cell eventually dies without replicating.

Microtubule inhibitors thus act by **interfering with the dynamics of the microtubule**, i.e., growing (polymerization) and shortening (depolymerization) (Jordan, 2002; Li and Sham, 2002). These molecules can be grouped into two main categories depending on their mechanism of action:

- tubulin polymerization inhibitors (microtubule destabilizers)
- and tubulin polymerization promoters (microtubule stabilizers).

Microtubule destabilizers bind to β-tubulin and block the polymerization of tubulin dimers to form protofilaments. Thus, preventing the mitotic spindle formation, and the cells can not enter metaphase; because of which cells can no longer divide (*Fig 19-13*).

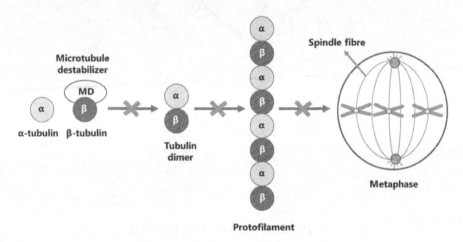

Fig 19-13: Mechanism of action of microtubule destabilizer

Examples include analogs of Auristatin (derived from the natural product dolastatin): Monomethyl auristatin E (MMAE) and Monomethyl auristatin E (MMAF). One of the auristatin-based ADC is the Brentuximab vedotin, composed of anti-CD30 chimeric IgG1 mAb, conjugated to MMAE drug by a cathepsin-cleavable linker. It is used to treat anaplastic large-cell lymphoma (ALCL) and Hodgkin lymphoma. The second class of microtubule destabilizers is Maytansinoids. Its derivatives, DM1, and DM4, have been used in designing ADC, such as Trastuzumab emtansine. It is composed of an anti-HER2 receptor mAb conjugated to the drug DM1 using a non-cleavable thioether linker. It is used to treat patients with HER2-positive metastatic breast cancer that are resistant to other treatments.

Microtubule stabilizers act differently from microtubule destabilizers. Microtubule stabilizers bind to spindle fibers and stabilize them, preventing them from depolymerization. Depolymerization of spindle fibers is essential for pulling the sister chromatids apart from their partner sister chromatids. Thus, the microtubule stabilizers block the cell cycle at metaphase, and the cell cannot enter anaphase, arresting its growth (*Fig 19-14*). Examples include Paclitaxel and Docetaxel.

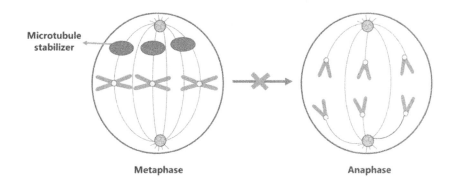

Fig 19-14: Mechanism of action of the microtubule stabilizer

DNA-damaging agents

The second category of payload used for ADC design is DNA-damaging drugs. There are at least four mechanisms of the action exerted by DNA-damaging agents, which are as follows: (a) DNA cross-linking, (b) DNA alkylation, (c) DNA double-strand breakage, and (d) DNA intercalation (*Fig 19-15*). The most used DNA-damaging payloads are pyrrolobenzodiazepines, duocarmycins, doxorubicins, and calicheamicins.

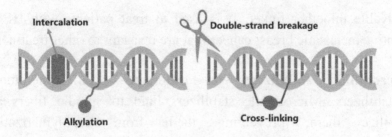

Fig 19-15: Mechanism of DNA-damaging agents

(i) Pyrrolobenzodiazepines (PBDs): PBD molecules are a class of DNA-crosslinking agents that bind to the C2-amino groups of guanine residues in the minor groove of double-stranded DNAs (*Fig 19-16*). PBD-dimer is conjugated to the monoclonal antibody through a linker. PBD dimers bind to guanidine residues on different positions of the dsDNA helix of the targeted cell and cause the crosslinking of DNA strands (Cooper et al., 2002; Hartley. 2011).

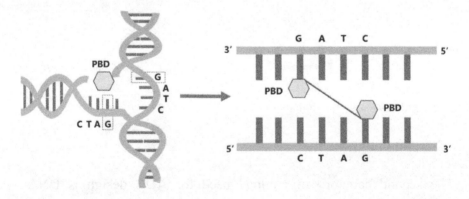

Fig 19-16: Interstrand crosslinks by pyrrolobenzodiazepines (PBDs) dimer

The crosslinking leads to decreased DNA repair and disrupted replication; thus, the cell cannot divide and undergo apoptosis, resulting in its death. One of the FDA-approved PBD dimer-based ADC is the Zynlonta (Loncastuximab tesirine) for treating adult patients with relapsed or refractory diffuse large B-cell lymphoma

(DLBCL). It comprises an anti-CD19 humanized monoclonal antibody conjugated through a linker to a PBD dimer cytotoxin. Upon binding to CD19, ADC is internalized, and lysosomal enzymes release the cytotoxic PBD-based dimer, which binds to DNA to create interstrand cross-links (Kahl et al., 2019; Jain et al., 2020).

(ii) **Duocarmycins:** Duocarmycins are alkylating agents that bind at the AT-rich region in the minor groove of dsDNA and alkylate adenine residues at the N3 position. The irreversible DNA alkylation eventually leads to DNA cleavage and, subsequently, tumor cell death via apoptosis (Asai et al., 1994). There are two duocarmycin-based ADCs: SYD985 and BMS-936561, which are being tested in clinical trials.

(iii) **Calicheamicins:**   Calicheamicins are a class of DNA-cleaving agents that bind in the DNA minor groove, within which they undergo a cyclization reaction and generate 1,4-didehydrobenzene diradicals. 1,4-didehydrobenzene then extracts hydrogen atoms from the DNA deoxyribose (sugar) backbone, resulting in DNA double-strand cleavage, followed by cell death. One of the FDA-approved calicheamicin-based ADC is Gemtuzumab ozogamicin for the treatment of CD33-expressing acute myeloid leukemia. It consists of humanized anti-CD33 monoclonal antibody conjugated to calicheamicin, which once released binds to the minor groove of DNA and induces double-stranded breaks, resulting in cell apoptosis (Naito et al., 2000; Walter et al., 2003).

(iv) **Camptothecin (CPT)** and analogs are also a class of DNA-cleaving agents and are inhibitors of the enzyme topoisomerase I. During DNA replication, the topoisomerase I (TopI) enzyme is responsible for relaxing supercoiled DNA. TopI first introduces a single-strand break or nick in the supercoiled DNA, then covalently binds to the nicked 3'-end DNA and allows the nicked strand to rotate around the intact strand in a controlled manner to relieve tension. After rotation, TopI re-ligates the nicked strand. CPT binds to the ToPI and the intact DNA strand through H bonding resulting in a ternary complex and thus stabilizing it. It prevents re-ligation of the nicked DNA. Additionally, the ternary complex acts as a roadblock for the replication fork and causes shear stress upon the intact DNA strand. Thus, causing ds breaks in the target DNA, ultimately leading to cell death via apoptosis. One camptothecin-based ADC is Sacituzumab govitecan, which received approval to treat patients with triple-negative breast cancer (Bardia et al., 2019; Seligson et al., 2021).

(v) **Doxorubicin:** The mechanisms of action of doxorubicin involves the drug's ability to damage DNA mainly through DNA intercalation and generation of free radicals. Because of which DNA and RNA synthesis is inhibited, resulting in apoptosis-mediated cell death. One doxorubicin-based ADC Milatuzumab doxorubicin is being tested in clinical trials to treat chronic lymphocytic leukemia, multiple myeloma, and Non-Hodgkin's lymphoma (Govindan et al., 2013; Lambert. 2013).

19.2. Immunotoxins

Immunotoxins are composed of monoclonal antibodies coupled to protein toxins and are potentially valuable therapeutic agents. The toxins used in preparing immunotoxins are of bacterial or plant origin. Examples of bacterial toxins used are Shigella toxin, diphtheria toxin, etc. And examples of plant toxins used in the construction of immunotoxins are ricin, saporin, etc. These toxins inhibit the protein synthesis of mammalian cells, thus killing the target cells. For instance, bacterial toxins are ADP-ribosylating toxins that transfer ADP ribose from nicotinamide adenine dinucleotide (NAD) to diphthamide (modified histidine) in the translation elongation factor-2 (EF-2) protein. The ADP-ribosylated EF-2 is inactive in catalyzing the translocation of peptidyl-tRNA from the A site to the P site of the ribosome, thus inhibiting the protein synthesis (Middlebrook and Dorland, 1984; Lubran, 1988). On the other hand, plant toxins are ribosome-inactivating proteins that hydrolyze the 28S-rRNA (a component of the 60S subunit of the ribosome) and prevent recruitment of translation EF-2, thus inhibiting protein synthesis (Lord et al., 1994; Bergamaschi et al., 1996).

Each of these toxins consists of two polypeptides: inhibitory polypeptide and binding polypeptide (*Fig 19-17*). The inhibitory polypeptide kills the target cells, and the binding polypeptide interacts with the receptors on the cell surface. Without the binding polypeptide, the toxin cannot go into cells and is harmless (Kreitman, 1999; Antignani and FitzGerald, 2013).

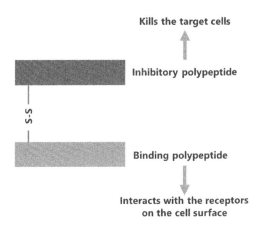

Fig 19-17: Bacterial/Plant toxin

An immunotoxin is prepared by replacing the binding polypeptide of toxin with a monoclonal antibody that is specific to a target cell, say

251

tumor cell or HIV infected cell (*Fig 19-18*). Thus, the immunotoxin interacts with the receptors or specific proteins on the target cell.

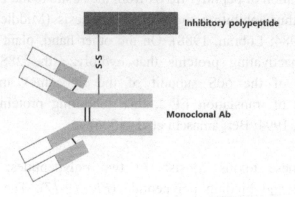

Fig 19-18: Immunotoxin

Let's assume **AIDS therapy** as an example. An immunotoxin to kill HIV-infected cells is developed by raising monoclonal antibodies that bind to GP120. GP120 is an envelope glycoprotein of HIV that is also expressed on the surface of HIV-infected cells. When an immunotoxin is injected into the AIDS patient, the immunotoxin passes through the bloodstream and binds only to the GP120 molecule present on an HIV-infected cell.

Once the immunotoxin gets bound to GP120, the GP-120 immunotoxin complex gets internalized by endocytosis (*Fig 19-19*). In the endosome, the linker holding the toxin to the antibody is cleaved, thus releasing the toxin into the cytoplasm. Usually, the linker is made with an internal disulfide bond. It is stable in the oxidizing environment outside the cell but is cleaved by GSH reduction in the reducing environment inside the cell, eventually releasing the toxin. Say the toxin used is diphtheria toxin. Therefore, once freed from the antibody, the diphtheria toxin inhibits the cell's protein synthesis machinery by inactivating the Elongation Factor-2 (EF-2). Since the EF-2 protein is an essential factor for protein synthesis thus, inactivation of the protein synthesis leads to the death of the HIV-infected cell.

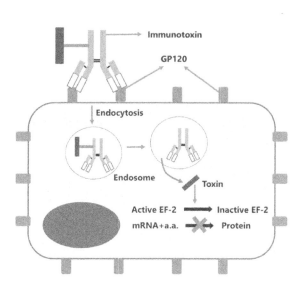

Fig 19-19: Immunotoxin to kill HIV infected cells

Another example can be **acute myelogenous leukemia therapy**. For this therapy, the immunotoxin is developed as a conjugate of a monoclonal antibody that binds to CD33, a cell-surface molecule expressed by the cancerous cells in acute myelogenous leukemia.

Since CD33 is not found on normal stem cells, the immunotoxin binds to the specific proteins present on the tumor cells, thus causing their death.

Limitations of Immunotoxins: Although immunotoxins are specific for the target cells, there are certain problems in using them like: (a) they have a large molecular size and (b) have certain side effects such as:

- The bacterial or plant toxins used for generating immunotoxin are highly immunogenic as they are considered foreign particles by the body. Because of which when immunotoxin is injected into the patient's body, his immune system starts recognizing the toxin as foreign and generates antibodies against the toxin moiety of the immunotoxin (*Fig 19-20*). These neutralizing anti-drug antibodies (ADAs) raised against the immunotoxin inactivate the immunotoxin (Madhumathi and Verma, 2012; Akbari et al., 2017).

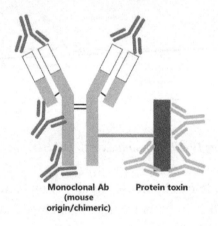

Fig 19-20: Antibodies produced against the toxin moiety and monoclonal antibody, inactivate the immunotoxin

- Apart from the toxin, the monoclonal antibodies used in immunotoxin can also be immunogenic. Especially if the monoclonal antibodies used for developing the immunotoxin are of mouse origin or are chimeric monoclonal antibodies, then the patient's immune system may generate antibodies against the antibody moiety of the immunotoxin. To overcome these limitations, the immunogenicity of immunotoxin is required to be reduced as much as possible.

19.3. Recombinant immunotoxins

Recombinant immunotoxins have the potential to overcome the immunogenicity issues of immunotoxins. Recombinant immunotoxins are made of the variable regions of heavy and light chains of the antibodies (Fv) combined with the functional components of toxins that lack cell-binding domains (*Fig 19-21*). Thus, the toxin contains only the inhibitory polypeptide component of the toxin. And the Fv region of the antibody molecule replaces the binding component of the toxin to generate recombinant immunotoxin (Kreitman and Pastan, 2011; Kreitman et al., 2012).

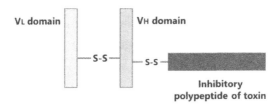

Fig 19-21: Recombinant immunotoxin

The Fv region binds to the receptors or specific proteins on a target cell, and then the toxin is delivered to the cell, thus leading to the killing of the target cell.

Since bacterial and plant toxins used in developing immunotoxins are proteins, thus recombinant immunotoxins can also generate antibody formation against them. Therefore, to overcome this problem, mutations in such toxins are done to create less immunogenic toxins. For instance, modification in the B cell and T cell epitopes of the toxin can reduce the immunogenicity of immunotoxin without impacting its cytotoxic activities.

19.4. Humanized and Fully Human immunotoxins

Another category of immunotoxins that can overcome the immunogenicity issues of immunotoxins and recombinant immunotoxins is humanized immunotoxins. In the case of humanized immunotoxins, the cytotoxic toxin is replaced with an endogenous cytotoxic protein of human origin like proapoptotic protein or RNase (Mathew and Verma, 2009; Mathew et al., 2013). One such proapoptotic protein used is human granzyme B, which is fused to the monoclonal antibody to generate immunotoxin (*Fig 19-22*). Granzyme B is a serine protease most commonly found in the granules of cytotoxic lymphocytes (CTLs), natural killer cells (NK cells), and cytotoxic T cells. When immunotoxin containing granzyme B interacts with the target cell, the granzyme B kills the target cell by mediating apoptosis.

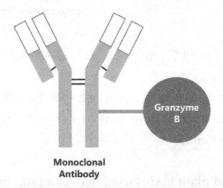

Fig 19-22: Humanized immunotoxin

Since the monoclonal antibody of immunotoxin can also be immunogenic, therefore, any other human ligand like cytokine or growth factor receptor can be used instead of the monoclonal antibody. The cytokine or growth factor receptor can be fused with an endogenous cytotoxic protein of human origin to form fully human immunotoxin (*Fig 19-23*). For instance, IL-2 cytokine can be fused with RNAse enzyme to form fully human immunotoxin.

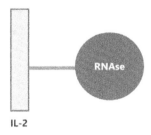

Fig 19-23: Fully human immunotoxin

This immunotoxin targets the malignant T-cells, which produce increased levels of high-affinity IL-2 receptors, and the RNAse enzyme inhibits protein synthesis by degrading the mRNA. Thus, killing the malignant T cells.

19.5. Antibody-directed Enzyme Prodrug Therapy (ADEPT)

The basic principle of Antibody-directed enzyme prodrug therapy (ADEPT) is to activate the prodrug selectively at the target site by an enzyme, which has been targeted to the target site by an antibody (antibody-enzyme conjugate). For instance, in the case of cancer, a monoclonal antibody designed against a tumor antigen is linked to an enzyme. When the Ab-enzyme complex is injected into the blood, it selectively binds to the tumor cell. After the Ab-enzyme complex is bound on the tumor cell and the excess conjugate is removed from the blood and normal tissues, the prodrug is administered into the blood circulation (*Fig 19-24*). Once the non-toxic prodrug reaches the Ab-enzyme complex, the enzyme converts the prodrug into a potent cell-killing agent, which causes target/cancer cell death (Bagshawe et al., 2004; Tietze and Krewer, 2009; Amly and Karaman, 2014).

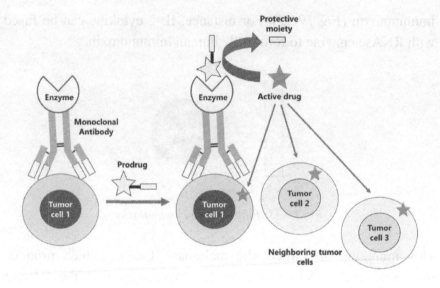

Fig 19-24: Antibody-directed Enzyme Prodrug Therapy (ADEPT)

For instance, the prodrug used for designing ADEPT can be Methotrexate (MTX) peptide/alanine, and the enzyme can be carboxypeptidase A. The prodrug methotrexate peptide/alanine can be activated by carboxypeptidase A hydrolysis, yielding the active drug methotrexate. Methotrexate can competitively and irreversibly inhibit dihydrofolate reductase enzyme. The dihydrofolate reductase enzyme catalyzes the conversion of dihydrofolate into the active tetrahydrofolate (folic acid), which is essential for DNA synthesis. Therefore, methotrexate can inhibit DNA synthesis and ultimately cell growth arrest.

Another advantage of ADEPT is that the small cytotoxic agents produced within a tumor site show a bystander effect. It means the active cytotoxic agents generated at the target tumor cell also enable the vast killing of neighboring tumor cells with low target antigen expression.

Chapter 20: Therapeutic Applications of mAbs

20.1. Monoclonal Antibodies for cancer treatment

For many years, the mainstay of cancer therapy was the chemotherapeutic cytotoxic drugs used together with radiation therapy. However, this approach has certain limitations since the strategy of killing rapidly dividing cancer cells also adversely affects some other normal, healthy cells such as mucosal lining cells, blood cells, and hair follicles, resulting in mouth sores, nausea, low blood counts, hair loss, etc. The consequences of nonspecific therapeutic approaches producing an array of toxic effects for patients lead to poor tolerance of chemo and radiation therapies and ultimately poor survival outcomes. Additionally, tumors can become resistant to chemotherapy and radiation therapy treatments, and these resistances may extend to drugs not yet administered to the patient.

Effective targeted therapies for cancers without causing adverse effects to normal healthy cells have always been desired by oncologists. Thanks to the advent of hybridoma technology, and subsequent advances in genetic engineering, mAb-based therapy has revolutionized the treatment of several cancers when used alone or in combination with chemotherapy or radiotherapy (Stern and Herrmann, 2005; Weiner et al., 2009).

Monoclonal antibodies that can target antigens, either unique or overexpressed by the cancer cells, can be used to cause cancer cell death by several mechanisms. The monoclonal antibodies used in cancer treatment can be divided into two types.

- Naked monoclonal Antibodies
- Conjugated monoclonal antibodies

Naked monoclonal antibodies: Naked mAbs are those antibodies that work by themselves, and there is no drug or radioactive material attached to them. Naked mAbs can work in different ways.

1. Blocking growth factor receptor signaling: The main targets of therapeutic mAbs are growth factor receptors that are overexpressed in cancer cells, such as members of the epidermal growth factor receptor (EGFR), Human epidermal growth factor receptor 2 (HER2), etc. The receptors are more than 100 times overexpressed in cancer cells in comparison to the normal non-cancerous cells. These receptors are responsible for the proliferation and invasion of cancer cells upon binding to the respective growth factor ligand. mAbs target these receptors and block the ligand binding, which in turn blocks the signals that tell cancer cells to divide, proliferate and invade (Leonard et al., 2002; Capdevila et al., 2009; Martinelli et al., 2009). Thus, induce apoptosis in the cancer cells.

For example, **Cetuximab** is a chimeric monoclonal antibody that targets the EGFR overexpressed in many human cancers, including head and neck and colorectal (Blick and Scott, 2007; Jonker et al., 2007). When activated by its ligand epidermal growth factor (EGF), EGFR undergoes dimerization, followed by activation of the intracellular tyrosine kinase (TR) region of EGFR and promoting autophosphorylation, which then initiates a series of downstream signaling cascades, including proliferation, cell differentiation, invasion, and angiogenesis.

Targeting EGFR with the monoclonal Ab Cetuximab competitively inhibits the binding of epidermal growth factor (EGF), thus preventing the dimerization of EGFR and autophosphorylation of tyrosine kinase (*Fig 20-1*). Inhibiting the EGFR signaling pathway ultimately induces apoptosis in cancer cells by blocking cancer cell proliferation and invasion.

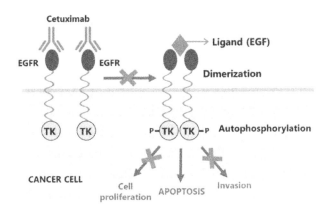

Fig 20-1: Mechanism of action of Cetuximab

Another growth factor that is overexpressed in many cancers, including ovarian and breast carcinomas, is the Human epidermal growth factor receptor 2 (HER2), a tyrosine kinase receptor (*Fig 20-2*). Trastuzumab was the first FDA-approved anti-HER2 humanized monoclonal antibody, which, when binds to HER2, blocks it from sending signals the cancer cells need to grow (Hudis, 2007; Garnock-Jones et al., 2010).

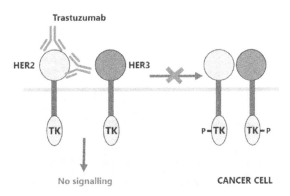

Fig 20-2: Mechanism of action of Trastuzumab

The third example of growth factor overexpressed in certain cancer cells (colorectal cancer, lung cancer, breast cancer, renal cancers, brain cancers, and ovarian cancer) is vascular endothelial growth factor A (VEGF-A). When VEGF-A binds to its receptor (VEGFR-1 and VEGFR2), it activates a signaling cascade that results in the development of angiogenesis and increased vascular permeability. Thus promoting the growth of blood vessels that cancer cells need to survive (McCormack and Keam, 2008; Mukherji, 2010). A recombinant humanized monoclonal antibody called Bevacizumab blocks the growth of new blood vessels by inhibiting the binding of VEGF-A to its receptors, thus hampering the growth of cancer cells (*Fig 20-3*).

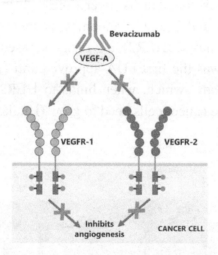

Fig 20-3: Mechanism of action of Bevacizumab

2. Flagging cancer cells: Monoclonal antibodies can also kill cancer cells by flagging them for destruction by the individual's immune system. For example, Rituximab, a chimeric monoclonal antibody, attaches to a molecule called CD20 on cancer cells. CD20 antigen is expressed on the surface of more than 90% of B cell non-Hodgkin's lymphomas.

Another anti-CD20 mAb is Ofatumumab which is a fully human mAb.

The third example of a monoclonal antibody is Alemtuzumab, a humanized mAB directed against the CD52 molecule on cancer cells.

Once attached, the monoclonal antibodies attract immune cells to destroy the cancer cells by inducing ADCC, antibody-dependent phagocytosis (opsonization), complement activation, and apoptosis (*Fig 20-4*). Such monoclonal antibodies that trigger the immune system to attack and kill cancer cells are also called immunotherapy (Cerny et al., 2002; Lin, 2010; Ruck et al., 2015).

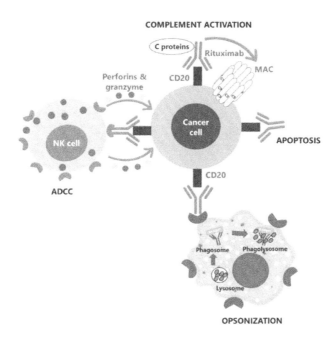

Fig 20-4: Mechanism of action of Rituximab

3. Targeting immune system checkpoints: The third way monoclonal antibodies work is by blocking the checkpoints on the immune cells (Lee et al., 2016; Gravbrot et al., 2019). Immune checkpoints are regulators of the immune system that are essential for self-tolerance and prevent the immune system from attacking the cells indiscriminately. However, cancer cells find ways to protect themselves from being attacked by immune cells (T cells) by stimulating immune checkpoints. When the checkpoint on the cancer cells and partner proteins on T cells bind together, they send an "off" signal to the T cells and prevent them from destroying the cancer cells. Monoclonal antibodies have the potential to block the immune checkpoints and help the immune cells kill cancer cells. Such monoclonal antibodies are also called immune-checkpoint inhibitors (*Fig 20-5*). The immune-checkpoint inhibitors generally target the checkpoints cytotoxic T-lymphocyte associated antigen 4 (CTLA-4) and programmed cell death protein 1 (PD-1)/PD1 ligand 1 (PD-L1).

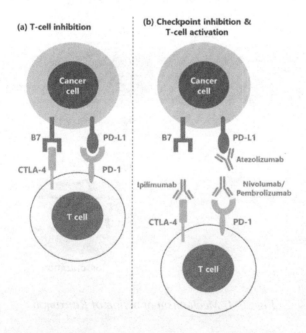

Fig 20-5: (a) T-cell inhibition after binding of immune checkpoints on the cancer cells and partner proteins on T cells; and (b) T-cell activation after checkpoint inhibitors target the checkpoints

(i) Monoclonal Abs that target CTLA-4: CTLA-4 expressed by activated T cells, after binding to B7 molecule present on antigen-presenting/cancer cells, mediates immunosuppression by transmitting inhibitory signals to T-cell. CTLA-4 blockade restores T-cell function to kill malignant cells. Ipilimumab, an anti-CTLA4 mAb, was approved for advanced melanoma in 2011 (Sondak et al., 2011).

(ii) Monoclonal Abs that target PD1-PDL1: Like CTLA-4, PD-1 is another checkpoint protein present on T cells that usually acts as an "off switch" by attaching to a protein PD-L1, present on the other cells. The PD1-PDL1 interaction signals the activated T cells from not attacking those cells in the body and leaving them. Some cancer cells stimulate the expression of large amounts of PD-L1, which helps them evade immune attacks. Monoclonal antibodies that target either PD-1 or PD-L1 can activate the immune response against cancer cells and have shown to be effective in treating several types of cancer, including melanoma of the skin, kidney cancer, lung cancer, Hodgkin lymphoma, and head and neck cancers.

Nivolumab and Pembrolizumab are PD-1 inhibitors, and Atezolizumab, a PD-L1 inhibitor, are certain examples of mAbs approved to treat various cancers (Gunturi and McDermott, 2015; McDermott and Jimeno, 2015).

Conjugated monoclonal antibodies

Some monoclonal antibodies fight cancer by delivering drugs, toxins, or radioactive particles to cancer cells.

1. Antibody-drug-conjugate (ADC): Antibody-Drug Conjugates are highly potent biological drugs built by attaching an anticancer drug to a monoclonal antibody with a linker. The monoclonal antibody targets a unique antigen found only on the cancer cells but not on the normal healthy cells. Or the antibody recognizes an overexpressed protein only at the tumor site to avoid delivering the drug inappropriately to non-target sites. Once the monoclonal antibody binds to the target cell, it triggers the internalization of the antibody, together with the drug. Upon internalization, the drug is released and induces cancer cell death (*Fig 20-6*). Thus, the antibody-drug conjugate delivers drugs with very high specificity to the diseased cells, maximizing their efficacy and minimizing the associated risk of side effects (Hafeez et al., 2020).

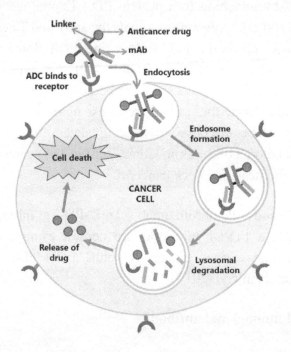

Fig 20-6: Mechanism of action of ADC conjugated with anticancer drug

Examples include Gemtuzumab ozogamicin, an anti-CD33 targeting ADC, which received approval by the U.S. Food and Drug Administration (FDA) in 2000 to treat CD33-expressing acute myeloid leukemia. It consists of humanized anti-CD33 monoclonal antibody conjugated to calicheamicin, which, once released, binds to the minor groove of DNA and induces double-stranded breaks, resulting in cell apoptosis (Giles et al., 2003).

The second example of ADC is Brentuximab vedotin, an anti-CD30 targeting ADC that received FDA approval in 2011 to treat Hodgkin lymphoma (HL) and systemic anaplastic large cell lymphoma (ALCL). The ADC consists of a chimeric anti-CD30 monoclonal antibody linked to tubulin inhibitor monomethyl auristatin E (MMAE). MMAE disrupts the microtubule network within the target cancer cell, leading to induction of cell cycle arrest in the G2/M-phase, ultimately resulting in cell death by apoptosis (Bradley et al., 2013).

Other FDA approved ADCs for treatment of several types of cancers include Trastuzumab Emtansine (for ErbB2-positive advanced breast cancer treatment), Inotuzumab ozogamicin (for treatment of relapsed or refractory CD22+ acute lymphoblastic leukemia), Polatuzumab Vedotin (for relapsed or refractory diffuse large B cell lymphoma treatment), Trastuzumab deruxtecan (for treatment of ErbB2+ advanced breast cancer patients), Enfortumab vedotin (treatment of patients with relapsed or refractory locally advanced or metastatic urothelial cancer), Sacituzumab govitecan (for the treatment of metastatic triple-negative breast cancer) and Belantamab mafodotin (for the treatment for patients with relapsed or refractory multiple myeloma).

2. Antibody-radioimmunoconjugate or Radioimmunotherapy (RIT): Unlike radiotherapy, the radiation is not administered from outside the body. But instead, it is delivered systemically and is directed to the target cancer cells. For this, mAbs are conjugated to the radioisotopes that mediate the selective delivery of radioisotopes to the cancer cells (*Fig 20-7*). Examples include Ibritumab tiuxetan, FDA approved mouse anti-CD20 mAb and is conjugated to yttrium-

90 (^{90}Y) radioisotope. Radioimmunotherapy aims to deliver cytotoxic radiation from therapeutic radioisotopes to tumors using the monoclonal antibody molecule as a 'guided missile' (Davies, 2007).

The targeted cells absorb high amounts of radiation, which promotes cell damage. Also, the reactive oxygen and/or nitrogen species is generated, which damages DNA strands. The damage then induces apoptosis or programmed necrosis in the target cell.

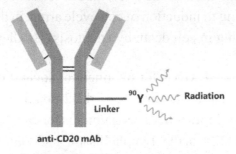

Fig 20-7: Antibody radioimmunoconjugate Ibritumab tiuxetan

RIT has therapeutic potential for various types of cancer including prostate cancer, metastatic melanoma, ovarian cancer, neoplastic meningitis, leukemia, high-grade brain glioma, and metastatic colorectal cancer.

20.2. Monoclonal antibodies for the treatment of bacterial infections

Antibiotics are highly efficacious, cost-effective, and have been the only weapon against bacterial infections. Unfortunately, for the last few years, antibiotics have become less and less effective, and the problem of antibiotic resistance is increasing in the bacteria. Additionally, existing antibiotics act against a broad spectrum of disease-causing and beneficial bacteria. In such cases, antibacterial monoclonal antibodies offer more targeted treatment; in other words, mAbs can be used as treatment against one desired bacterial species responsible for infection without disrupting normal bacterial flora in the body (Motley et al., 2019; Zurawski and McLendon, 2020). The specificity of antibacterial monoclonal antibodies can also slow the development of antibiotic resistance by targeting conserved pathways of bacteria and activating the body's immune system. In addition, mAbs could also extend and save the lives of patients infected with drug-resistant/multidrug-resistant/extensively drug-resistant strains of bacteria. Finally, these antibodies can also improve the patient's quality of life by reducing toxicity associated with antibiotic treatment.

Antibacterial monoclonal antibodies are divided into three categories based on their targets (*Fig 20-8*):

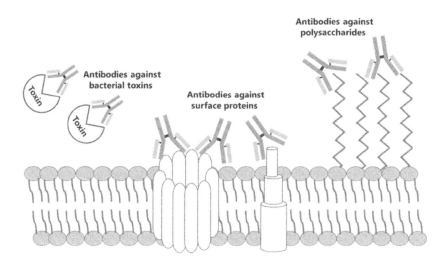

Fig 20-8: Targets of antibacterial monoclonal antibodies

1. Antibodies against bacterial toxins: Anti-toxin mAb therapies bind to the toxins secreted by the bacteria. Bacterial toxins are virulence factors that act by manipulating host cell functions and controlling vital processes of living organisms to favor microbial infection. For instance, the toxin B secreted by *Clostridium difficile* after binding to the host cell disturbs the signal transduction mechanisms, disrupts the cytoskeletal structure, and ultimately causes its death via apoptosis. Thus, the anti-toxin mAb, after binding to the toxin, inhibits its virulence by limiting its binding to the host cell. In past years attempts have been undertaken to generate mAbs against toxins of various bacteria like *Staphylococcus aureus*, *Streptococcus pyogenes*, Clostridia species, and *Escherichia coli*.

2. Antibodies against Surface Proteins: The second category of antibacterial monoclonal antibodies targets surface proteins present on bacteria's cell walls. The surface proteins are embedded in or span the layer of the cell wall. These proteins are essential for bacteria to interact with their environment, in particular the tissues of the infected host.

3. Antibodies against polysaccharides: The third category of antibacterial monoclonal antibodies targets polysaccharides of bacteria, including lipopolysaccharides (LPS) and capsular polysaccharides (CPS).

Examples of antibacterial monoclonal antibodies include:

Bezlotoxumab: The FDA-approved bezlotoxumab is a fully-humanized IgG1 mAb that targets *Clostridium difficile* and is currently approved to prevent the recurrence of *C. difficile* infection but has not been shown to cure the active infection.

It is an anti-toxin mAb that binds to *C. difficile* toxin B and neutralizes its effects. The two Fab regions of a single molecule of bezlotoxumab bind specifically to two epitopes within the N-terminal half of the combined repetitive oligopeptides (CROPs) domain of the Toxin B

(*Fig 20-9*). The binding results in blocking the carbohydrate-binding pockets of the toxin and thus preventing its attachment to the host cells, resulting in its complete neutralization (Wilcox et al., 2017; Gerding et al., 2018).

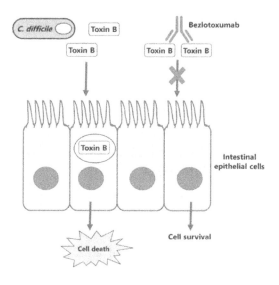

Fig 20-9: Mechanism of action of Bezlotoxumab

Raxibacumab and Obiltoxaximab: The FDA-approved monoclonal antibodies Raxibacumab (human IgG1) and Obiltoxaximab (chimeric IgG1) are used to treat inhalational anthrax caused by *Bacillus anthracis* in combination with appropriate antibiotics (often ciprofloxacin). The mAbs bind to the protective antigen component of anthrax toxin and thus inhibit its binding to the host cells, resulting in its neutralization (Kummerfeldt, 2014; Yamamoto et al., 2016).

MEDI3902: MEDI3902 is a bispecific antibody against *Pseudomonas aeruginosa* fimbrial protein PcrV and exopolysaccharide Psl, both of which were found to be conserved across Pseudomonas clinical isolates (Tabor et al., 2018). MEDI3902 binding to *P. aeruginosa*, inhibits its attachment to the host cell and promotes its opsonization by the phagocytic cells, resulting in its killing. The antibody is under clinical studies.

Suvratoxumab: Suvratoxumab is a human monoclonal antibody designed to prevent nosocomial pneumonia caused by *Staphylococcus aureus* (François et al., 2019). The antibody targets the alpha-toxin secreted by *S. aureus*, a pore-forming virulence factor resulting in cell damage and eventually its death by apoptosis. The antibody is currently in clinical development.

20.3. Antibody-antibiotic conjugate (AAC) for the treatment of intracellular bacterial infections

Recent studies suggest that pathogens can subvert the antimicrobial immune mechanisms by escaping into the intracellular environment of phagocytic cells. Most conventional antibiotics are ineffective at killing intracellular bacteria, owing to poor intracellular penetration. However, arming antibodies against a particular pathogen with potent antibiotics in the form of Antibody-antibiotic conjugates (AACs) has the potential to overcome these challenges (Lehar et al., 2015; Mariathasan and Tan, 2017). Such type of targeted delivery of antibiotics to the targeted bacteria at the site of infection allows most of the drug to reach the bacteria while minimizing collateral damage exerted on the rest of the patient body.

Like antibody-drug conjugate (ADC), an AAC contains three components: a monoclonal antibody specific to an antigen present on a bacterial cell, an antibiotic for killing bacteria, and a linker that connects the two (*Fig 20-10*). To work effectively against bacteria, the AAC must meet specific requirements, including safety, efficacy, and stability, to precisely kill the target bacteria without causing damages to other healthy cells and tissues.

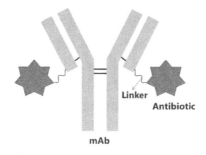

Fig 20-10: Antibody-antibiotic conjugate (AAC)

A THIOMAB antibody-antibiotic conjugate (TAC) was developed to kill intracellular *Staphylococcus aureus* (*S. aureus*) bacteria and is currently under clinical trials (Zhou et al., 2019; Cai et al., 2020). *S. aureus* infection is the leading cause of human bacterial infections, with infected patients exhibiting severe complications including pyelonephritis, endocarditis, necrotizing pneumonia, osteomyelitis, and sepsis. It is also one of the leading contributors of hospital-acquired infections, including post-surgical wound infections. Reduced susceptibility to standard therapy such as vancomycin and nafcillin and the adverse events caused by existing standard therapy raises the need to develop novel antibacterial agents. In addition, survival within the host phagocytic cells is one of the proposed mechanisms by which *S. aureus* escapes standard antibiotic treatment. Therefore, a therapeutic agent that targets the persistent intracellular *S. aureus* bacteria may show improved clinical outcomes, and keeping this in mind, THIOMAB antibody-antibiotic conjugate (TAC) was developed.

The TAC molecule consists of an IgG1 antibody that binds explicitly to teichoic acids, a major cell wall component of *S. aureus*. The mAb is conjugated to a novel antibiotic 4-dimethylamino piperidino-hydroxybenzoxazino rifamycin (dmDNA31) via a protease cleavable valine-citrulline linker (*Fig 20-11*). The dmDNA31 is a rifamycin-class antibiotic that inhibits bacterial DNA-dependent RNA polymerase with potent bactericidal activity even against methicillin-resistant *S. aureus*. When monoclonal Ab of TAC molecule binds to *S. aureus* in circulation, it facilitates its uptake into phagocytes through opsonization. In the phagolysosome, the TAC linker is cleaved by proteases such as cathepsins, and the antibiotic is released in its active form that kills the bacteria bound to TAC as well as pre-existing intracellular bacteria in the same phagocytes (Pec et al., 2019).

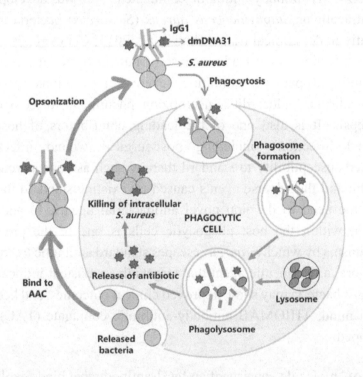

Fig 20-11: Mechanism of action of AAC

In addition, TAC exhibits a longer systemic half-life compared to small-molecule antibiotics. Therefore, when bacteria are released from pre-existing intracellular reservoirs into the extracellular space, the sustained concentrations of TAC in the circulation can capture the released bacteria and ensure their immediate "tagging" for phagocytic uptake, thereby mitigating the further spread of the infection.

20.4. Monoclonal Antibodies for COVID-19 treatment

The clinical condition caused by the novel coronavirus Severe Acute Respiratory Syndrome CoronaVirus-2, abbreviated as SARS-CoV-2, is referred to as COVID-19. SARS-CoV-2 is an enveloped virus containing single-stranded RNA as its genetic material. The RNA of the coronavirus is enclosed in the capsid, which is surrounded by the envelope. On the envelope, there are protein spikes, and these protein spikes give the appearance of crown-like projections when seen under an electron microscope. Corona in Latin means crown. Thus, when viewed under an electron microscope, the crown-like appearance led the virus to be named coronavirus.

The major structural proteins of SARS-CoV-2 include the envelope (E), nucleic capsid (N), and spike (S) proteins (*Fig 20-12*).

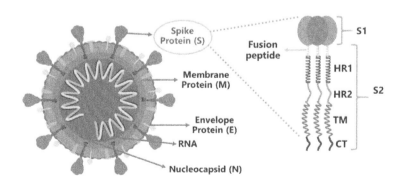

Fig 20-12: Structure of SARS-CoV-2

Coronavirus infection begins via attachment of the spike protein (S) with the receptor on the host cell surface, which gives them a way to make entry into the host cell. The spike protein, designated as S, comprises two units S1 and S2. The receptor-binding domain, abbreviated as RBD within the S1 unit, directly interacts with the host cell receptors (*Fig 20-13*). And the S2 unit mediates the fusion of viral and host cell membrane, which gives the virus a way to make entry into the host cell.

Structural and functional analysis of the SARS-CoV-2 shows that the SARS-CoV-2 spike protein binds the Angiotensin-converting enzyme 2 abbreviated as ACE2 receptor, on the host cells (Peng, 2020).

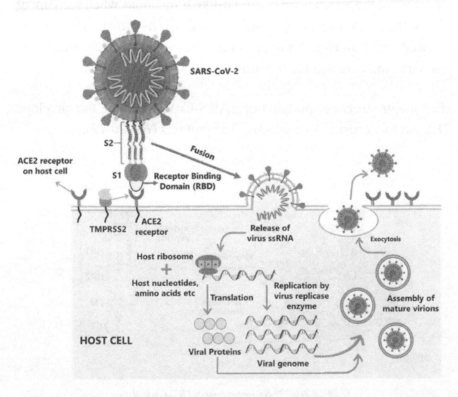

Fig 20-13: Entry of SARS-CoV-2 into the host cells

Coronavirus can't reproduce like any other virus without getting inside the living host cells and hijacking their machinery. Outside the host cell, the virus is metabolically inert. But inside the host cell, the virus becomes metabolically active. For instance, viruses cannot synthesize proteins on their own because they lack ribosomes; therefore, they use the ribosomes of the host cells to synthesize viral proteins. Viruses also use enzymes and building blocks of the host cell, such as amino acids, nucleotides, lipids, etc. Thus to reproduce, the virus needs to infect the host cells.

The monoclonal antibodies that target the spike protein of SARS-CoV-2 are of significant interest for researchers (Hansen et al., 2020; Marovich et al., 2020; Jahanshahlu and Rezaei, 2020) because spike protein allows the virus to bind to the ACE2 receptors and facilitates its entry into the human cells.

1. The first type of monoclonal antibodies in focus targets the receptor-binding domain of the S1 unit of spike protein because it docks into the ACE2 receptor on human cells *(Fig 20-14a)*. After binding to the S1 unit, these types of monoclonal antibodies can neutralize the virus by blocking its interaction with the ACE2 receptor present on the human cells, which in turn can prevent the entry of coronavirus into the human cells.

2. The second type of monoclonal antibodies recognizes the epitopes in the S2 unit of the spike protein of SARS-CoV-2, thus preventing the viral and human cell fusion, eventually preventing the virus's entry into the human cells *(Fig 20-14b)*.

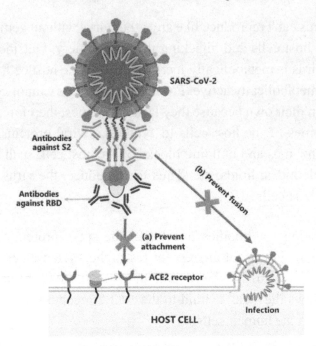

Fig 20-14: Monoclonal antibodies against (a) RBD of S1 and (b) S2 proteins

Researchers have also found that using only one type of monoclonal antibody is not very effective. Whereas the combination of two types of monoclonal antibodies, targeting different epitopes of spike proteins of SARS- CoV-2, is found to be potentially effective against the virus. These antibodies can be isolated from recovered patients or genetically engineered in the laboratory using hybridoma technology.

Monoclonal Antibodies for COVID-19 treatment

1. Casirivimab and Imdevimab monoclonal antibodies: American Biotechnology company, Regeneron Pharmaceuticals, generated Casirivimab and Imdevimab monoclonal antibody cocktail for COVID-19 treatment. A combination of these two monoclonal antibodies binds to non-overlapping epitopes of the spike protein receptor-binding domain (RBD) of SARS-CoV-2, thus blocking the binding of the RBD to the host cell receptor ACE2 (Suvvari, 2020; Kaplon and Reichert, 2021).

On November 21, 2020, the antibody therapy received the Emergency Use Authorization (EUA) from the Food and Drug Administration (FDA). In this therapy casirivimab and imdevimab are to be administered together to treat patients with mild to moderate COVID-19 who are at high risk for progressing to severe disease. A cocktail of two antibodies is used because it diminishes the ability of mutant viruses to escape treatment and protects against spike variants that have arisen in the human population. Since the mutations in the spike protein are frequent, making possible the evolution of mutants resistant to a single antibody. Therefore, the scientists generated a cocktail of two antibodies that bind to different epitopes of the RBD of the SARS-CoV2 spike protein (Elliott and Chan, 2020). In this way, the chances of emerging mutated viruses becoming resistant to treatment decreases.

Casirivimab and imdevimab are fully human monoclonal antibodies that have been produced by two strategies:
- One from transgenic humanized mice by immunizing it with different epitopes of the spike protein receptor-binding domain (RBD) of SARS-CoV-2.
- Second, the fully human monoclonal antibodies were directly isolated from the COVID-19 recovered patients.

2. Bamlanivimab (LY-CoV555) monoclonal antibodies: Bamlanivimab (LY-CoV555) monoclonal antibody developed by Eli Lilly and Company is a neutralizing monoclonal antibody intended to treat mild to moderate COVID-19 (Lundgren et al., 2020; Chen et al., 2020). It had secured emergency use authorization (EUA) from the US Food and Drug Administration (FDA) on November 9, 2020.

Bamlanivimab is a recombinant neutralizing human IgG1κ (IgG1 antibody-containing κ light chain) monoclonal antibody that binds to the receptor-binding domain (RBD) of the spike protein of SARS-CoV-2, thus preventing the attachment of spike protein with the human ACE2 receptor.

COVID-19 test-positive patients aged 12 years and older, who are at high risk of progression to severe COVID-19 and hospitalization, are eligible to receive the drug. Bamlanivimab should be administered to the patients following a positive COVID-19 test and within ten days of onset of symptoms.

3. Sotrovimab (VIR-7831) monoclonal antibody: Sotrovimab monoclonal antibody developed by GlaxoSmithKline and Vir Biotechnology had been granted emergency use authorization from the US FDA on May 27, 2021, for the treatment of confirmed mild-to-moderate COVID-19 in high-risk adults and pediatric patients (12 years of age and older weighing at least 40 kg) and who are at high risk for progression to severe COVID-19, including hospitalization or death.

Sotrovimab is a recombinant fully human IgG1κ monoclonal antibody that binds to the RBD of the S1 unit of SARS-CoV-2 and prevents its entry into human cells. In addition, the antibody binds to an epitope on SARS-CoV-2 that is shared with SARS-CoV and does not overlap with mutations observed in SARS-Cov-2 variants of concern, indicating that the epitope is highly conserved, which makes it more difficult for mutants to develop. Thus, it discourages the virus from developing resistance to the antibody.

Additionally, the Fc domain of sotrovimab contains M428L and N434S amino acid substitutions that extend its half-life and potentially enhance its distribution to the lung.

4. Tocilizumab monoclonal antibody: The normal antiviral immune system requires the activation of inflammatory pathways but exacerbated inflammatory response can cause severe disease. Cytokines produced by the macrophages, NK cells, dendritic cells, B and T lymphocytes are an essential part of the inflammatory process. They result in the recruitment of leukocytes like macrophages, neutrophils, and T cells to the site of infection to combat the infection. Three of the most critical pro-inflammatory cytokines released are IL-1, TNF-α, and IL-6. If the activation of the immune system leads to a sudden acute increase in circulating levels of pro-inflammatory cytokines, it is called "cytokine storm." This increase in cytokines results in an influx of various immune cells such as macrophages, neutrophils, and T cells from the circulation into the site of infection with destructive effects on human tissue leading to Acute Respiratory Distress Syndrome (ARSD) and multiorgan failure (Henderson et al., 2020).

Studies have suggested that COVID-19 disease is accompanied by the condition "cytokine storm." Higher levels of interleukin-6 (IL-6) have been positively correlated with cases of critical and severe COVID-19, whereas lower levels of interleukin-6 have been associated with mild disease (Chen et al., 2020). Tocilizumab is an anti–IL-6 receptor monoclonal antibody that interferes with IL-6 binding to its receptor and blocks signaling for the recruitment of leukocytes from the circulation into the site of infection. It has been approved to treat multiple inflammatory diseases and has now appeared to have a significant effect on the treatment of COVID-19 induced cytokine storm; thus, tocilizumab might be effective in treating critical patients with COVID-19 (Keske et al., 2020).

20.5. Administration of Monoclonal Antibodies

Therapeutic drugs are administered to patients through parenteral routes: intravenous (IV) infusion, subcutaneous injection (SC), intramuscular (IM), and intravitreal injection.

Intravenous (IV) infusion: The most common route by which mAbs are administered to patients is through intravenous (IV) infusion. The term "intravenous" means "into the vein." During IV infusion, the diluted mAb proteins are continuously introduced through the vein into a patient's bloodstream, where they directly interact with blood components. Since the mAbs drugs are usually prescribed in relatively high doses, a large volume of drugs can be administered safely with IV fusion.

Subcutaneous (SC) administration: Another route that can also be used for administering mAbs into patients is subcutaneous administration (Shpilberg and Jackisch, 2013). During SC administration, a needle is inserted through the epidermal and dermal layers of the skin, into the fatty subcutaneous tissue. After injecting, the drug reaches the bloodstream via the capillaries or the lymphatic system.

Advantages of SC administration over IV infusion: SC administration represents several advantages compared with IV infusion. Unlike IV fusion which requires skilled personal and hospital visits, SC injections can be administered by the patient himself, thus making it convenient and cost-effective to patients. Additionally, IV infusion usually takes several hours for administration, but administration time in the case of SC injection is less, resulting in a reduced treatment burden for patients. Although administration-associated reactions like rash, erythema, and mild discomfort may also occur with SC administration, they are likely to be less severe than IV infusion-associated reactions.

Therefore, research is being done to develop mAbs that can be delivered subcutaneously.

Limitations of SC administration: The biggest challenge with SC formulations is the ability to deliver the required volume of drug to patients. The glycosaminoglycan hyaluronan, together with collagen in the extracellular matrix, maintains tissue architecture but limits the flow of drug volumes to 1–2 ml. Since the mAbs are usually prescribed in relatively high doses, administering high doses is possible with IV fusion but not with SC injection. This obstacle can be overcome by:

- concentrating mAbs dose by almost 12-fold and then administering it subcutaneously.
- Or by adding recombinant hyaluronidase enzyme along with the mAb drug that degrades the hyaluronan and opens the interstitial space in SC tissue, allowing the delivery of >2–3 ml of the drug.

In the case of IV infusion, the bioavailability of drugs is almost 100%. Bioavailability is defined as the fraction of an administered dose of a drug that reaches the systemic circulation. mAbs given subcutaneously have a 50-80% bioavailability because, at the SC injection site, the drugs may get locally degraded prior to arrival in the systemic circulation, leading to lower bioavailability.

Other routes of mAbs administration: Efforts are also going for certain mAbs approved for treating respiratory diseases to deliver them through aerosol.

21. Bispecific antibodies or herteroconjugates

21.1. What are bispecific antibodies?

Bispecific antibodies are the hybrids of two different antibody molecules and can simultaneously bind to two different types of antigens (Kontermann, R. E., & Brinkmann, 2015). They can be constructed by chemically cross-linking two different antibodies or synthesized by the hybridomas formed by fusing two different monoclonal-antibody-producing cell lines. These methods generate mixtures of monospecific and bispecific antibodies from which the desired bispecific molecule is purified. Bispecific antibodies can also be generated using genetic engineering techniques to construct genes that encode molecules only with the two desired specificities.

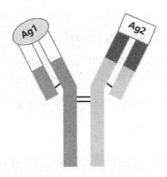

Fig 21-1: Bispecific Ab with two different types of antigens

Therefore, when bispecific antibodies are injected into the body, they can simultaneously bind to two different types of cells (*Fig 21-1*). For instance, in a bispecific antibody used in cancer treatment, one-half of the antibody has specificity for a cancer cell. The other half of Ab has specificity for the CD3 present on cytotoxic T cells (Tc cells). Additionally, the Fc region of bispecific antibodies can bind to the immune effector cells that express Fc receptors, such as an NK cell, an activated macrophage, a dendritic cell, etc. (*Fig 21-2*). The net

284

effect is that the bispecific antibody links Tc cells and Fc receptor-expressing effector cells like macrophages, NK cells, dendritic cells to the cancer cells (Krah et al., 2018). Activated Tc cells kill the cancer cells by producing proteins like perforin and granzyme that enter the cancer cell and initiate the cell's apoptosis. On the other hand, the effector cells mediate the destruction of the cancer cell through the Antibody-dependent cellular toxicity or ADCC process (discussed in section 5.3).

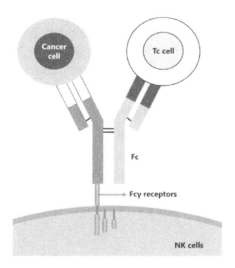

Fig 21-2: Bispecific Ab in cancer treatment

Bispecific antibodies are more potent (more than 1,000-fold) in eliminating and killing tumor cells than conventional antibodies because of their ability to recruit both cytotoxic T cells and effector cells simultaneously to the tumor cells to enhance their killing. On the other hand, the conventional antibodies don't activate T cells because their Fab regions are already used for binding the tumor cells. Thus, the bispecific antibodies might outshine the conventional mAbs as cancer therapeutics.

Types of bispecific antibodies:

There are two common formats of bispecific antibodies available: the single-chain variable fragment (scFv)-based antibody (no Fc fragment) and the full length IgG-based antibody (Wang et al., 2019).

21.1. Single-chain variable fragment (scFv)-based antibodies

The scFv based antibody is produced by fusing variable domains of the IgG heavy chain (V_H) and the light chain (V_L) through a short flexible peptide linker of about 10-25 amino acids (Ahmad et al., 2012; Monnier et al., 2013). For the generation of the scFv construct, mRNA is isolated from the hybridoma cell that produces mAbs against the desired antigen. mRNA is then reverse transcribed into cDNA. After this step, using specific primers, Polymerase chain reaction, abbreviated as PCR, amplifies the DNA sequence corresponding to the antibody V_H and V_L genes.

The scFv gene construct is designed in the orientation, V_L-linker-V_H (*Fig 21-3*).

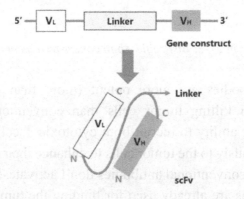

Fig 21-3: scFv is produced by fusing V$_H$ and V$_L$ through a linker

It is then either expressed in microbial systems like *E. coli* or in mammalian systems such as HEK293 cells. In the expressed scFv, the C-terminus of the V_H is linked to the N-terminus of the V_L through the peptide linker.

In short, scFv is the smallest unit of the immunoglobulin molecule with a molecular weight in the range of 25kDa and functions in antigen-binding activities. Since an scFv molecule contains one V_H and V_L domain, it has a single antigen-binding site. Additionally, each V_H and V_L domain of scFv contains three complementarity-determining regions (CDRs). The combination of the CDRs of the V_H and the CDRs of the V_L determines the binding specificity of the scFv molecule.

Also, the scFv-based antibodies are the smallest recombinant antibodies (rAb) that retain the antigen-binding activity and are popularly used for therapeutic and analytical applications because of their small size and the possibility of genetic engineering.

In addition, **glycine, serine, and threonine** are preferred amino acids for designing peptide linkers because their short side chains grant conformational flexibility and minimal immunogenicity to the scFv molecules. Also, serine and threonine amino acids improve the solubility of scFv molecules.

Types of scFv-based bispecific antibodies

There are three types of scFv-based antibodies:

- bispecific T-cell engager (BiTE)
- dual-affinity re-targeting proteins (DARTs)
- and Tandem diabodies (TandAbs)

21.2. Bispecific T-cell engager (BiTE)

This type of bispecific antibody is a fusion protein containing two scFv fragments from two different monoclonal antibodies, which are connected by a peptide linker (*Fig 21-4*). The resulting ~ 55-kDa molecule is a single polypeptide with N- and C-terminus. The two scFv fragments (Fv-A and Fv-B) retain each antibody's binding activity when assembled (Slaney et al., 2018; Tian et al., 2021).

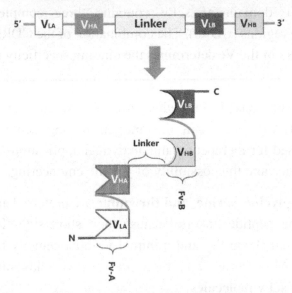

Fig 21-4: Bispecific T-cell engager (BiTE) with specificity for antigen A (Fv-A) and antigen B (Fv-B)

The linker connecting the two scFvs enables their free rotation, vital for flexible interaction with targeted receptors on two target cells. For instance, one scFv fragment binds to cytotoxic T-cell, and another scFv fragment binds to the cancer cell (*Fig 21-5*). Simultaneously binding to both T cell and cancer cell induces T-cell activation and subsequently targets the T-cell's cytotoxicity activity against the cancer cell, ultimately killing it by producing proteins like perforin and granzyme that enter the cancer cell and initiate the cell's apoptosis.

One example of BiTE drugs is blinatumomab, which has been approved by the FDA for the treatment of relapsed or refractory acute lymphoblastic leukemia (ALL) in adult patients. Blinatumomab consists of one anti-CD19 scFv connected through a short glycine–serine linker to the second anti-CD3 scFv. Thus, the drug links CD-3 containing T cells with CD-19 receptors found on the surface of B cell lymphoma (Wu et al., 2015; Goebeler et al., 2016).

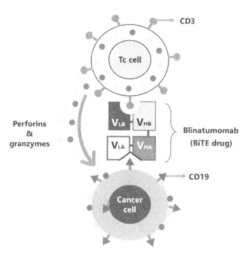

Fig 21-5: One scFv binds to cytotoxic T-cell, and the other scFv binds to cancer cell

Another BiTE drug is Solitomab which is under clinical trials. This drug also consists of two scFv fragments, in which one of the scFvs binds to T cells via the CD3 receptor and the other to EpCAM antigen, which is expressed by gastrointestinal, lung, prostate, ovarian, and other cancer cells (Bellone et al., 2016; Kebenko et al., 2018).

21.3. Dual-affinity re-targeting proteins (DARTs)

The linker sequences that connect the V regions in the BiTE structure constrain the necessary conformational flexibility required during antibody-antigen recognition, reducing the binding efficiency. To address this issue, DART proteins were developed.

A DART molecule consists of two engineered scFv fragments which have their V_H and V_L domains exchanged. Precisely, the scFv1 consists of a V_H from antibody B and a V_L from antibody A, while the scFv2 consists of V_H from Ab-A and V_L from Ab-B (*Fig 21-6*). Thus, when scFv1 and scFv2 heterodimerize, they form a bispecific DART molecule with two unique antigen-binding sites (Wang et al., 2019).

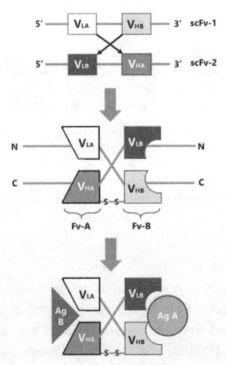

Fig 21-6: Dual-affinity re-targeting protein (DART) with specificity for antigen A (Fv-A) and antigen B (Fv-B)

This configuration of DART molecules lacks the constraint of an intervening peptide linker, allowing DART to mimic the natural interaction within an IgG molecule. In addition, adding a cysteine residue to the end of each heavy chain improves the stability of the bispecific DART molecule by forming a C-terminal disulfide bridge.

A study by Moore et al. on comparing in vitro ability of CD19xCD3 DART and BiTE molecules showed that DART molecules were better at redirecting CD3 expressing T cells to kill CD19 expressing B-cell lymphoma. In this study, both DART and BiTE molecules were derived from the same parental antibodies (mouse anti-human CD3 and CD19 mAbs).

21.4. Tandem diabodies (TandAbs)

The small size of scFvs BiTE and DART contributes to a high renal clearance rate in comparison to natural IgG antibodies. The size issue can be resolved by generating Tandem diabodies (TandAbs). A tandem diabody is formed by non-covalent association of tandem two-hybrid scFv fragments consisting of V_H and V_L domains of different specificities (say antigen A and B) (*Fig 21-7*).

In addition, the tandem diabodies have tetravalent properties, which means they provide two binding sites for each antigen. Thus, they are also called tetravalent bispecific antibodies (Kipriyanov, 2009; Azhar et al., 2017).

Moreover, TandAbs have a molecular weight of approximately 105 kDa that exceeds the renal clearance threshold (60-70kDa), thus offering a longer half-life than smaller antibody constructs. Two TandAb bispecific drugs are in clinical trials—AFM13 (CD30xCD16) and AFM11 (CD19xCD3).

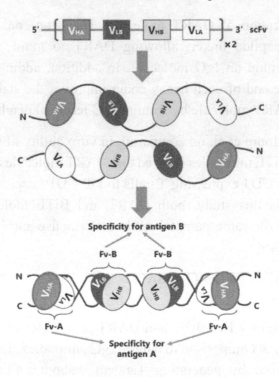

Fig 21-7: Tandem diabodies (TandAbs) with tetravalent specificity: two
binding sites for each antigen A and B

21.5. Role of the linker in designing scFv-based antibodies

Two essential features to be considered while designing the linker are
amino acid composition and sequence length (Gu et al., 2010;
Stamova et al., 2012; Yusakul et al., 2016).

(i) **Amino acid composition** is critical in designing a flexible linker
peptide. The most commonly used amino acid sequence motif in
designing linker is (G4S)n (G: glycine, S: serine; G4S means four
glycine residues and one serine residue) (*Fig 21-8*). Glycine and serine
are preferred amino acids because their short side chains grant
conformational flexibility and minimal immunogenicity, while serine
improves solubility. Besides the Gly-Ser linker, other charged amino

acid residues such as glutamic acid and lysine can also be used to enhance solubility.

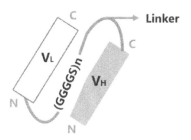

Fig 21-8: Amino acid sequence (G4S)n is used in the linker of scFv

(ii) **Length of the linker between variable domains of the heavy and light chain** is also critical in designing scFv-based antibodies. The success of scFv-based antibodies construction largely depends on the peptide linker between the V_H and V_L domains. The linker should neither interfere with the folding and association of the V_H and V_L domains nor reduce stability and binding activity.

The length of the linker has a significant impact on the monomer or multimer formation of the antibodies. For instance, a linker length longer than 12 amino acid residues allows sufficient distance between heavy and light-chain domains to associate and form monomers. On the other hand, shorter linkers connecting V_H and V_L domains prevent the direct association of the two domains to create functional Fv domain, rather result in an increased possibility for pairings between V_H and V_L of different scFv molecules, forming dimers, trimers, or multimers. Therefore, for the successful construction of bispecific scFv, it is important to optimize linker length.

For instance, in the case of BiTE scFv-based antibody, long linkers are placed between the homologous light chain and heavy chain variable domains to ensure association to form a functional Fv. On the other hand, short linkers are placed between heterologous heavy-chain fragments to create the connection between the two Fvs (*Fig 21-9a*).

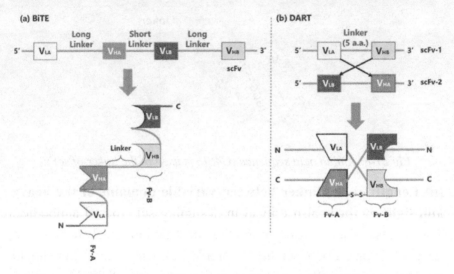

Fig 21-9: Linker length of (a) BiTE and (b) DART

In the case of the DART molecules that bind to each other to form functional dimers, the linkers between V_HA and V_LB or V_HB and V_LA need to be as short as five amino acids to prevent their association from creating an undesired Fv (*Fig 21-9b*). Instead, because of a short linker, one scFv1 molecule associates with another scFv2 molecule (heterodimerization) to form a bivalent scFv-based antibody. Moreover, the positioning of the disulfide bond is another critical feature of DART molecules, which holds the molecule together in the correct orientation.

And in the case of TandAb, the linkers between adjacent domains are too short (three amino acids) for the two variable regions to fold together, forcing scFvs to dimerize and form diabodies (*Fig 21-10*). Conversely, the linker length of less than three amino acids (one or two amino acids) favors the formation of trimers or tetramers, so-called triabodies or tetrabodies.

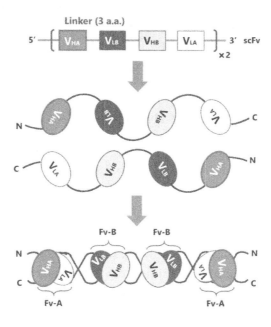

Fig 21-10: Linker length of TandAb

21.6. Full-length IgG-based antibody

Although IgG-like asymmetric bispecific antibodies have certain properties similar to natural monoclonal IgG antibodies, they are engineered molecules that have not been generated by typical plasma cells. As a result, these differences lead to significant production challenges. One of the greatest challenges for generating asymmetric IgG-like bispecific antibodies is ensuring the correct assembly of antibody fragments (Grote et al., 2012; Fan et al., 2015). A random assembly of four distinctive polypeptide chains (two different heavy and two different light chains) results in 16 combinations, among which only two represent the desirable asymmetric heterodimeric bispecific antibody. The remaining pairings result in non-functional or monospecific molecules. Therefore, two key things are required to be considered while producing the desired IgG-like bispecific antibody—the heterodimerization of two different heavy chains and the discrimination between the two light-chain/heavy-chain interactions. Full-length IgG-based antibodies can be generated by different strategies. For instance,

21.7. Quadroma (or Hybrid-Hybridoma) Technology

Bispecific antibodies can be generated by the hybridomas that are formed by the somatic fusion of two different hybridoma cells (*Fig 21-11*). Each hybridoma cell expresses a unique monoclonal antibody with predefined specificity. So, when the two different antibody-expressing hybridoma cells are fused, the resulting hybrid-hybridoma cell produces the immunoglobulin heavy and light chains from both parent hybridoma cells, and their assembly allows the formation of bispecific antibodies.

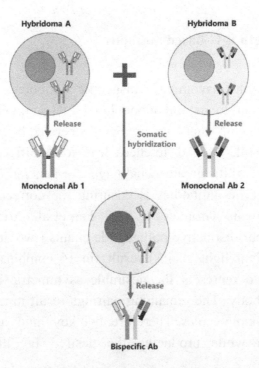

Fig 21-11: Quadroma technology

Suppose 2 H chains from both parent hybridoma cells (aAAa and aBBb) are represented as A and B, and light chains are represented as a and b. The random assembly of two different heavy and two different light chains can theoretically result in (2^4) 16 combinations, and only one of those is a functional bispecific antibody (*Fig 21-12*).

Six of these combinations occur twice due to symmetry and produce similar antibodies (aABb, aBBb, aABa, bABb, aAAb, and bABa). The remaining four combinations (aAAa, bAAb, bBBb and aBBa), occur only once.

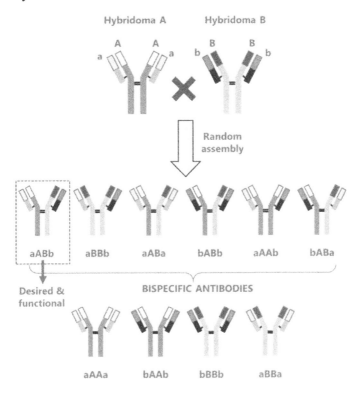

Fig 21-12: Theoretical combinations of antibodies from both parent hybridoma cells

Thus, ten types of antibodies are produced. Six of them are bispecific antibodies, out of which only one is a functional bispecific antibody and the resulting combinations result in non-functional antibodies.

Catumaxomab (anti-EpCAM x anti-CD3) is the first approved IgG-like bispecific antibody generated via quadroma technology by the fusion mouse IgG2a producing hybridoma cell and rat IgG2b producing hybridoma cell.

In Catumaxomab antibody, one Fab antigen-binding site binds T-cells via the CD3 receptor, and the other site binds tumor cells via the tumor antigen epithelial cell adhesion molecule (EpCAM). On the other hand, the Fc region of the antibody recruits and activate immune effector cells via binding to FcγR receptors present on NK cells, dendritic cells, activated macrophages, etc. (Seimetz et al., 2010; Heiss et al., 2010).

However, immunogenicity remains the concern with Catumaxomab antibody, a chimeric mouse/rat bispecific Ab. Because when injected in patients, they may generate human anti-mouse or anti-rat antibody responses, which can lead to the negation of Catumaxomab's drug-related effects, thus completely inhibiting the therapeutic aspect of the drug. The anti-drug antibodies may also cause allergic and several other adverse effects in the patients. Therefore, it is essential to humanize antibodies as much as possible to lower the generation of anti-drug-antibodies in the patients.

21.8. Knobs-into-holes (KIH) technology

The second method of generating bispecific antibodies is Knobs-into-holes technology (KIH), which refers to producing either a "knob" or a "hole" in the C_H3 domain of the Fc region of each heavy chain to promote heterodimerization. The knobs and holes are engineered in the C_H3 domain because H chains of an IgG antibody directly interact at their Cн3 domains (*Fig 21-13*). However, at Cн2 domains, they interact through the carbohydrate bound to the asparagine (Asn). Therefore, several amino acid changes must be done to make a knob on the Cн3 domain of the heavy chain of mAb1 and a hole on the Cн3 of the heavy chain of mAb2 (Xu et al., 2015).

To generate a knob, smaller amino acid in the Cн3 domain of the H chain of mAb1 is replaced with a larger amino acid; for instance, threonine (T) at position 366 is replaced with larger amino acid tyrosine (Y). On the other hand, to generate a hole, the larger amino acid in the Cн3 domain of the H chain of another mAb2 is replaced with a smaller amino; for instance, tyrosine at position 407 is replaced with a smaller amino acid threonine (Wang et al., 2019).

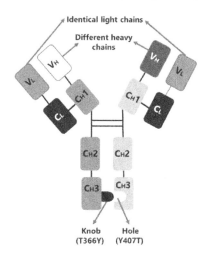

Fig 21-13: Knobs into holes technology

The engineered Cн3 domains containing knob and hole fit into each other, favoring the heterodimerization. The heteromeric heavy chains have the ability to produce functional bispecific antibodies and also retain Fc-mediated effector functions, such as ADCC and complement activation. An identical light chain is used for each arm of the IgG-based bispecific antibody. Therefore, coexpression of engineered heavy chains with the light chains either in *E. coli* or mammalian cells, e.g., human embryonic kidney (HEK) cells, produce the IgG-based bispecific heterodimer with two antigen-binding sites (Rouet and Christ, 2014).

21.9. CrossMab technology

The Knobs-into-holes technology enables correct heavy-chain heterodimerization and generates desired bispecific antibodies when identical light chains are used. However, it is not always possible to use a common light chain because, in many cases, antigen recognition critically relies on the partner light chain. By using two different light chains, their random assembly with the heterodimer heavy chain (obtained by KIH technology) results in the generation of four different combinations of antibodies, with only one being the desired bispecific antibody (*Fig 21-14*).

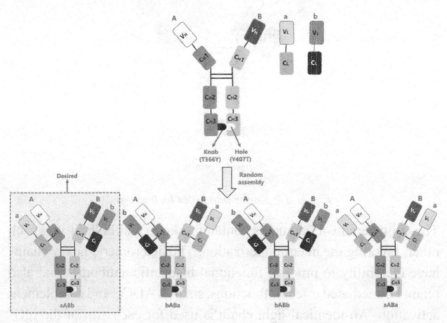

Fig 21-14: Random assembly of heterodimer heavy chain with different light chains

To solve the problem of light chain mispairing, CrossMab technology has been developed that allows the correct pairing of the light chain and heavy chain to minimize the generation of non-functional and undesired bispecific antibodies (Liu et al., 2017).

The basis of the CrossMab technology is the crossover of domains of the light and heavy chains within one arm of a bispecific IgG antibody enabling correct light chain association. In contrast, correct heterodimerization of the heavy chains is achieved by the knob-into-hole technology (KIH). CrossMab is achieved in three ways (Schaefer et al., 2011; Klein et al., 2019):

1. In the first method, the entire heavy chain of the Fab region of one-half of the bispecific antibody is interchanged with a cognate light chain to generate CrossMab Fab bispecific Ab (*Fig 21-15*). The "crossover" obtained retains the binding affinity while favoring the assembly of the engineered Fab fragment.

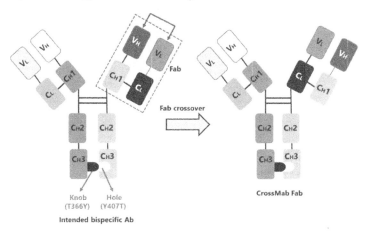

Fig 21-15: CrossMab Fab bispecific Ab

2. The second method involves swapping the V_H of a Fab region with its corresponding V_L domain to generate CrossMab V_H-V_L bispecific Ab (*Fig 21-16*).

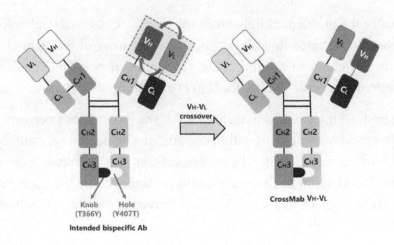

Fig 21-16: CrossMab VH-VL bispecific Ab

3. In the third method, CH1 and CL of one Fab region are interchanged to generate CrossMab CH1-CL bispecific Ab (*Fig 21-17*).

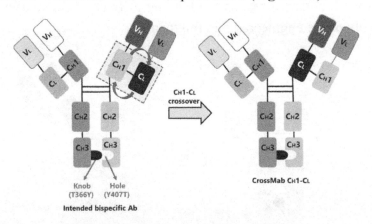

Fig 21-17: CrossMab CH1-CL bispecific Ab

Such crossover designs reduce the heavy–light chain mispairing to yield functional bispecific antibodies with the potential to recognize two antigens simultaneously. Additionally, the cross-over bispecific antibodies retain the affinity and stability of the parent antibodies.

For instance, **Vanucizumab** (CrossMabCH1-CL) bispecific antibody exhibits antitumor activity by targeting vascular endothelial growth factor (VEGF-A) and angiopoietin-2 (Ang-2) simultaneously (*Fig 21-18*). As a result, VEGF-A and Ang-2 are unable to bind to their receptors VEGFR and Tie-2, respectively, because of which angiogenesis in tumor cells is hampered (Hidalgo et al., 2018; Heil et al., 2021).

Angiogenesis is a highly regulated process by which tumors develop new vasculature because for cancer cells to proliferate, a continuous supply of oxygen is needed. But without the formation of new tumor vasculature in the presence of Vanucizumab, tumor growth is arrested.

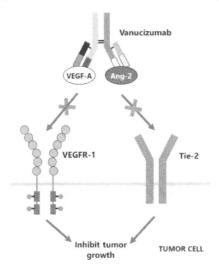

Fig 21-18: Mechanism of action of Vanucizumab (CrossMab C$_{H}$1-C$_{L}$)

Chapter 22: Abzyme or Catalytic antibody

22.1. What are abzymes?

Another type of therapeutic antibody is abzymes. As the name suggests, abzyme means **antibody behaving like an enzyme**. It is also called **catmab** or **catalytic monoclonal antibody**. We know that antibody binds to the target antigen or pathogens and then activates the complement system, phagocytosis, and other processes to eliminate the pathogen. In contrast, the enzymes are the catalysts that drive a reaction by stabilizing its transition state, decreasing the activation energy, and allowing for more rapid conversion of substrate to product. (*Fig 22-1*).

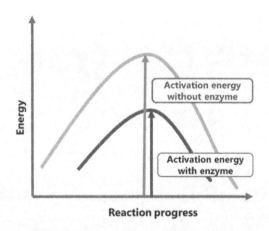

Fig 22-1: Enzymes lower the energy barrier of the reaction

So, scientists thought, why not combine the actions of an antibody and an enzyme and make a substance that catches hold of the antigen, analogous to the function of an antibody and neutralizes antigen on its own, similar to the function of enzymes. So this is how the idea of combining the functions of antibodies and enzymes to create abzymes was born.

22.2. Production of abzymes

Suppose an antibody is developed to bind to a molecule that is structurally similar to the transition state of a given chemical reaction. In that case, the developed antibody will bind to and stabilize the transition state, just like a natural enzyme, by lowering the activation energy of the reaction, thus catalyzing the reaction. Therefore, raising an antibody to bind to a stable transition-state analog can produce a new and unique type of antibody behaving like an enzyme.

Let's take an example of generating abzymes that can undergo ester hydrolysis. For this, the hapten-carrier complex is synthesized in which hapten structurally resembles the transition state of an ester undergoing hydrolysis (*Fig 22-2*). Then the mice are immunized with this hapten-carrier complex, generating antibody-producing plasma cells, which are then fused with myeloma cells to yield hybridoma cells. These hybridoma cells can produce anti-hapten monoclonal antibodies.

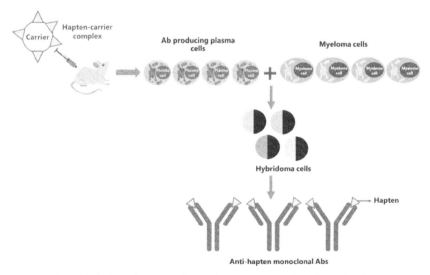

Fig 22-2: Production of anti-hapten monoclonal antibodies

When these anti-hapten monoclonal antibodies are incubated with an ester substrate, they can accelerate the hydrolysis of the ester substrate, thus behaving like enzymes (*Fig 22-3*).

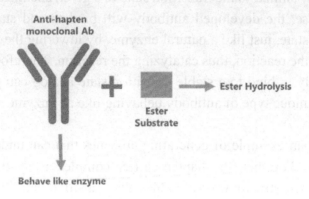

Fig 22-3: Ester hydrolysis by anti-hapten monoclonal Ab

The catalytic activity of abzymes is highly specific as they hydrolyze only those esters whose transition state structure resembles that of the transition state analog used as a hapten. Thus, the abzymes can be generated that cut peptide bonds at specific amino acid residues like the restriction enzymes that cut DNA at specific nucleotides. Antibodies have exceptional specificity and high affinity, so combining this with catalytic activity seems like a perfect combination.

22.3. Applications of abzymes

There are potential clinical applications of abzymes like:

1. Abzymes can prevent cells from getting infected by HIV. They have been developed to hydrolyze the antigenic region of protein gp102 of HIV, which is the CD4 binding site of the HIV (*Fig 22-4*). The hydrolysis of gp102 prevents the virus from binding to the CD4

protein present on the target cells like T helper cells. Thus the virus becomes inert and is unable to infect its target cells.

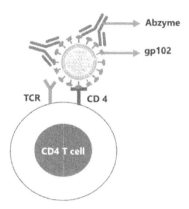

Fig 22-4: Abzyme hydrolyzes gp102 protein, preventing the virus from binding to the CD4-T cell

2. In cancer treatment, one of the major obstacles is that the cytotoxic drugs destroy both the normal and cancer cells. Hence there is a need for specific targeting of cancer cells and subsequent prodrug activation, which then destroys the oncogenic cells. Abzymes can be used in the treatment of cancer. They are the therapeutic agents that function as homing devices for the site-specific delivery of the prodrug and then activating the prodrug into the active anti-cancer drug (*Fig 22-5*).

One out of the two sites of a monoclonal antibody acts as an antigen-binding site on the cancer cell, while the other site serves as an abzyme to activate the anti-cancer drug.

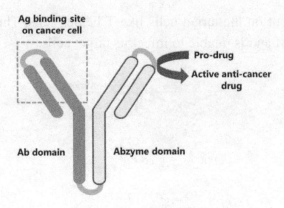

Fig 22-5: Abzyme in activating anti-cancer drug at the target site

The prodrug is a pharmacologically inactive compound converted into an active form by endogenous enzymes or metabolism (*Fig 22-6*). Here, the abzyme can activate the prodrug into the active cytotoxic form of the drug, which in turn can potentially kill the target cancer cells.

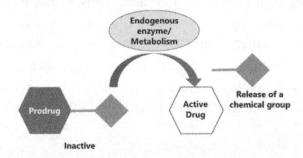

Fig 22-6: Inactive prodrug is converted into the active form by endogenous enzymes or metabolism

Chapter 23: Fc fusion proteins

Many biologically active proteins are attractive drug candidates. However, their clinical potential is limited because of their short serum half-lives due to renal clearance that limits their exposure to the target tissue. Renal clearance plays a vital role for products with a molecular weight of less than 60 kDa. As a result of the limited target tissue exposure, many therapeutic proteins require more frequent administration to maintain their circulating concentrations within the effective range.

Two strategies are commonly used to reduce the impact of the renal clearance of the biologically active protein of interest:

1. First is continuous administration of the therapeutic protein or drug into the systemic circulation for extended periods of time at sufficiently high concentrations to exert pharmacological activity.

2. The second strategy involves reducing renal filtration and elimination by increasing the size of the therapeutic protein. It can be achieved:

- Either by increasing the hydrodynamic radius of the therapeutic protein by chemical conjugation with a large polymer like polyethylene glycol (PEG)
- or by increasing the molecular weight of the therapeutic protein to approximately 60-70 kDa, the renal threshold for renal filtration. It can be achieved by either non-covalent association of the therapeutic protein to a larger carrier serum protein, such as albumin, or by covalent fusion of a therapeutic protein to a carrier protein, e.g., Fc domain via genetic recombination. Therefore, increasing the size of the active

protein by coupling to an Fc-domain can increase the half-life of the biologically active proteins and increase their circulation time.

23.1. Generation of Fc fusion proteins

Fc-fusion proteins are produced by the fusion of the C-terminus of a biologically active protein, domain, or peptide to the N-terminus of the Fc fragment of IgG antibody either through a covalent bond or with a spacer peptide to generate a molecule with significant therapeutic potential and extended half-life (Czajkowsky et al., 2012; Pechtner et al., 2017). Each antibody molecule contains a Fab fragment and an Fc fragment. Fab fragment contains V_H, V_L, C_H1, and C_L. The Fc fragment is dimeric, which includes two C_H2 domains and two C_H3 domains. The biologically active protein of interest replaces the Fab region and is fused with the hinge forming the connection to the Fc region of human IgG (*Fig 23-1*). The hinge serves as a flexible spacer between the two parts of the fusion protein, allowing each part of the molecule to function independently.

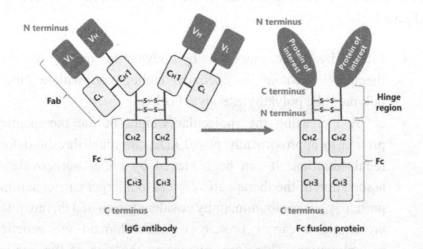

Fig 23-1: Fc fusion protein produced by fusing of protein of interest with the Fc region of IgG through a covalent bond

If a spacer peptide linker is used to fuse the protein of interest and Fc region, in that case, its sequence and length must be optimal because it can significantly influence the stability of the fusion protein (*Fig 23-2*).

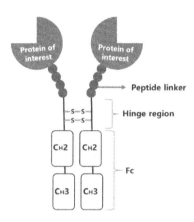

Fig 23-2: Fusion of protein of interest with Fc region by a peptide linker

The protein of interest is fused to the Fc region using recombinant DNA technology. For this, the DNA sequences that code the protein of interest and the Fc region of IgG are isolated. Both the DNA sequences are then fused either through overlap PCR or ligation. The fused DNA sequence encoding protein of interest and Fc region is inserted into the expression vector, which is then transfected into mammalian cells (e.g., CHO cell lines), where the fused gene is expressed as a single Fc fusion protein (*Fig 23-3*).

Mammalian expression systems are used because they enable the expression of human or other mammalian proteins which require posttranslational modifications, e.g., glycosylation, γ-carboxylation, sulfation, and intra- and interchain disulfide-bonded domains to maintain their structure and function.

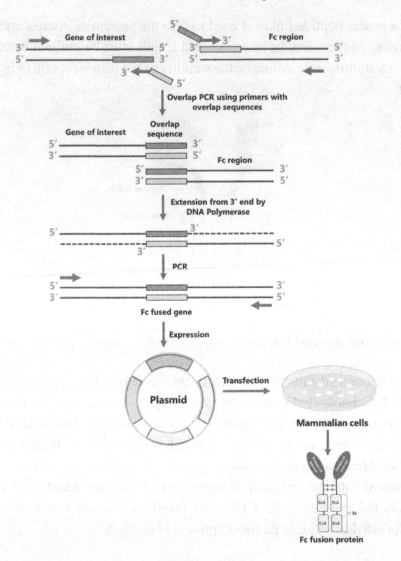

Fig 23-3: Production of Fc fusion protein using recombinant DNA technology

23.2. Advantages of Fc-fusion proteins

Fc-fusion proteins are produced by fusing the C-terminus of a biologically active protein domain or peptide to the N-terminus of the Fc crystallizable fragment (Fc) domain of IgG antibody to generate a

312

molecule with significant therapeutic potential and extended half-life. Among the five classes of antibodies, IgG is the preferred one for producing Fc-fusion proteins because it has the longest half-life among plasma proteins. Therefore, beyond renal elimination due to large size, the presence of the IgG Fc domain markedly increases the plasma half-life of biologically active proteins, which prolongs their therapeutic activity.

IgG Fc domain prolongs the circulation time of Fc fusion proteins via interaction with neonatal Fc-receptor designated as FcRn in a pH-mediated recycling procedure (Rath et al., 2015; Deissler et al., 2017). Expression of FcRn is limited on the cell surface of vascular endothelial cells, but the majority are present in intracellular compartment endosomes. In the endothelial cells, the Fc-fusion proteins are taken up into the endosomes by pinocytosis.

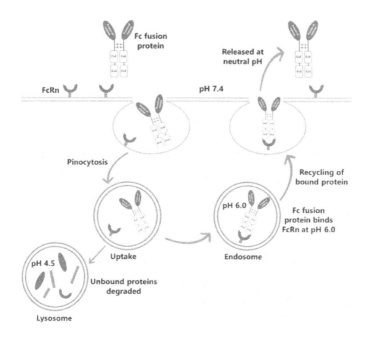

Fig 23-4: FcRn-mediated recycling of Fc fusion protein

Once inside the cell, the interaction of FcRn with the Fc domain only occurs at acidic pH (<6.5), which is characteristic of early and late endosomes but not neutral pH (7.0). Unbound Fc-fusion proteins are transported to the lysosome for degradation (*Fig 23-4*). After associating with the FcRn receptors, Fc fusion proteins are transported back to the cell membrane, where they dissociate from the receptor and are released back into the bloodstream. Thus, both IgG and ligands are protected from proteolytic degradation and are recycled.

In addition, IgG plays an essential role in the protective immunity against pathogens and toxins by interacting with the Fcγ receptor (FcγR) present on the cell surface of macrophages, neutrophils, and natural killer cells, which mediate effector mechanisms like opsonization, antibody-dependent cellular cytotoxicity (ADCC) and complement-dependent cytotoxicity (CDC). Therefore, the choice of the IgG subclass is critical in therapeutics: IgG1, IgG2, and IgG4 are often preferred to IgG3 due to their longer half-lives. Also, IgG subclasses differ in the binding affinity to FcγRs: IgG1 and IgG3 have the highest binding affinity to FcγRs and, therefore, are more efficient in mediating effector functions.

Most of the approved therapeutic antibodies for the treatment of cancer and autoimmune diseases belong to the IgG1 subclass because of its potent ability to exert effector functions through high-affinity binding to the Fc receptors, which is an essential advantage for the treatment of these diseases.

On the other hand, IgG2 and IgG4 subclasses are the preferred backbones of a therapeutic candidate where effector functions ADCC and CDC are not desired; instead, the goal is to activate or repress the desired receptors.

Types of Fc fusion proteins

Fc-fusion proteins can be categorized into different types based on therapeutic proteins like extracellular domains (ECD) of cell surface receptors, functionally active peptides, and recombinant enzymes fused to the Fc region.

23.3. Receptor ECD-based Fc-fusion proteins

Etanercept: Etanercept is a human tumor necrosis factor (TNF) receptor-Fc fusion protein that the FDA approved in 1998 for the treatment of various autoimmune disorders like rheumatoid arthritis, psoriatic arthritis, ankylosing spondylitis, juvenile idiopathic arthritis, and plaque psoriasis (Nanda and Bathon, 2004; Gottlieb, 2004).

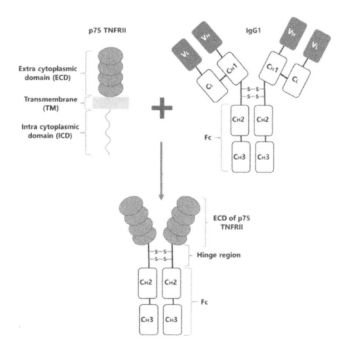

Fig 23-5: Fc-fusion protein Etanercept

Etanercept is a dimeric fusion protein composed of ECDs of two p75 TNF receptors II (TNFRII) covalently linked with the Fc region of human IgG1 (*Fig 23-5*). The mechanism of action of the drug involves binding to pro-inflammatory cytokine TNF (TNF-α or TNF-β) and inhibits its binding to the TNF receptor I (TNFRI) or TNF receptor II (TNFRII) (*Fig 23-6*). TNF, upon binding to TNFRI and TNFRII, activates inflammatory pathways such as NFkB and MAPK, responsible for causing the aforementioned autoimmune disorders. But etanercept blocks the effect of TNF and thus, treats autoimmune diseases.

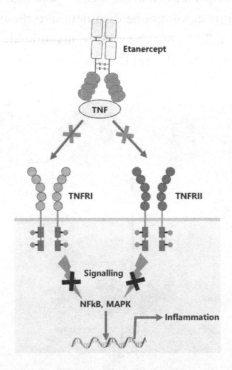

Fig 23-6: Mechanism of action of Etanercept

Aflibercept: Another ECD-based Fc-fusion protein is aflibercept, approved to treat age-related macular degeneration abbreviated as AMD (Trichonas and Kaiser, 2013; de Oliveira Dias et al., 2016).

AMD is characterized by the growth of abnormal blood vessels in the eye and is stimulated by angiogenic factors like vascular endothelial growth factor (VEGF) and placental growth factor (PlGF). Aflibercept is a recombinant fusion protein composed of portions of extracellular domains of human VEGF receptors (domain 2 of VEGRI and domain 3 of VEGFRII, covalently linked with the Fc region of human IgG1 (*Fig 23-7a*). Aflibercept binds to the circulating VEGFs and blocks their binding to VEGF receptors VEGFRI and VEGFRII, thus inhibiting the growth of new blood vessels in the affected eye (*Fig 23-7b*).

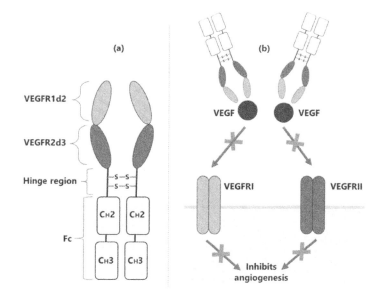

Fig 23-7: (a) Structure and (b) mechanism of action of Aflibercept

23.4. Peptide-Fc fusion proteins

Dulaglutide: Dulaglutide is a human glucagon-like peptide-1 receptor agonist (GLP-1 agonist), approved for the treatment of Type-II diabetes (Thompson and Trujillo, 2015; Smith et al., 2016). GLP-1, upon binding to the GLP-1 receptor, improves insulin resistance and stimulates glucose-dependent insulin release from the pancreatic cells that normalizes glucose levels in the blood. But the secretion of GLP-1 is decreased in type 2 diabetes, thus making it a target for novel treatments of type 2 diabetes. Dulaglutide is a recombinant fusion protein composed of glucagon-like peptide-1 (GLP-1) analog fused to the heavy chain-Fc region of IgG4 antibody, with a small peptide linker (*Fig 23-8a*). The drug dulaglutide binds and activates the GLP-1 receptor found in pancreatic beta cells, leading to increased insulin secretion by pancreatic beta cells and reducing the elevated glucagon secretion by inhibiting alpha cells of the pancreas (*Fig 23-8b*). The secreted insulin binds to the insulin receptors on target cells like adipose tissues, liver skeletal muscles, etc., and induces glucose intake and subsequently reduces the blood glucose concentrations in patients with Type-II diabetes.

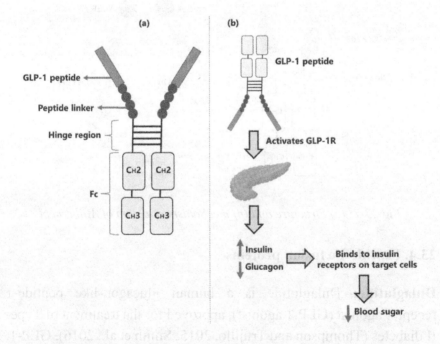

Fig 23-8: (a) Structure and (b) mechanism of action of Dulaglutide

Romiplostim: Romiplostim is a thrombopoietin receptor agonist, approved to treat autoimmune disease thrombocytopenia, caused by increased platelet destruction and suboptimal platelet production (Jamali et al., 2009; Schifferli et al., 2019). Romiplostim is a recombinant peptide-Fc fusion protein, where thrombopoiesis stimulating dimers, i.e., four 14-amino acid thrombopoietin receptor-binding peptides, are chemically coupled by glycine spacer domains to the carboxy terminus of the Fc domain of IgG1 antibody (*Fig 23-9a*). Upon interacting with the thrombopoietin receptor present on the hematopoietic cells in bone marrow, the drug activates a range of signaling pathways that promote platelet production (*Fig 23-9b*).

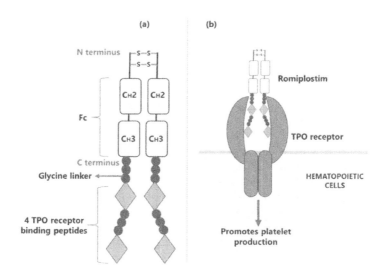

Fig 23-9: (a) Structure and (b) mechanism of action of Romiplostim

23.5. Recombinant enzymes-Fc fusion proteins

Asfotase alfa: Asfotase alpha is a human tissue-nonspecific alkaline phosphatase (TNSALP) recombinant enzyme-Fc fusion protein, approved for the treatment of hypophosphatasia abbreviated as HPP (Magdaleno et al., 2019; Kalinchenko et al., 2019). Hypophosphatasia is the rare metabolic disease caused by the loss of function of the gene ALPL that encodes the tissue-nonspecific isoenzyme of alkaline phosphatase (TNSALP). Low TNSALP activity leads to extracellular accumulation of the TNSALP substrates: pyridoxal 5'-phosphate (PLP), inorganic pyrophosphate (PPi), and phosphoethanolamine. PPi is an inhibitor of bone mineralization, and its elevated levels can cause rickets in children or osteomalacia in adults. Asfotase alfa is a dimeric human recombinant enzyme-Fc fusion protein composed of the catalytic domain of recombinant enzyme TNSALP fused to the Fc region of the IgG1 antibody. The Fc fusion protein also contains a deca-aspartate peptide domain D_{10} intended to target bone (*Fig 23-10*). Upon administering the drug, the fused TNSALP enzyme reduces the PPi levels in the body and ultimately treats HPP; thus, the drug is a form of enzyme replacement therapy.

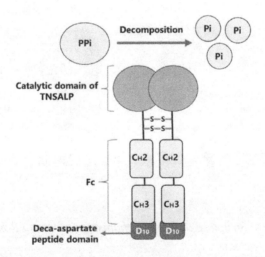

Fig 23-10: Structure and mechanism of action of Asfotase alpha

Efmoroctocog alpha: Another recombinant enzyme-Fc fusion protein is Efmoroctocog alpha, used for replacement therapy for patients with haemophilia A (Chowdary et al., 2016; Pitance et al., 2021). Haemophilia A is a rare bleeding disorder associated with a slow clotting process and is caused by the deficiency of blood coagulant factor VIII. Patients with this disorder are more susceptible to recurrent bleeding episodes and excessive bleeding following minor injuries. Efmoroctocog alfa is the first commercially available recombinant factor VIII-Fc fusion protein (rFVIIIFc) where the B-domain deleted recombinant factor VIII is fused to the Fc domain of human IgG1 (*Fig 23-11*). Upon administration, the Fc fusion protein initiates the coagulation cascade, which activates factor VIII. Factor VIII upon activation, converts prothrombin into thrombin, and sequentially, thrombin converts fibrinogen to fibrin which polymerizes and crosslinks into a blood clot.

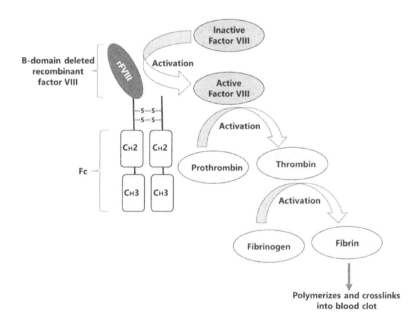

Fig 23-11: Structure and mechanism of action of Efmoroctocog alpha

Currently, 11 Fc fusion proteins have been approved by the FDA, and there are several other Fc fusion proteins in the pre-clinical and clinical development stage.

Chapter 24: Single-domain antibodies or nanobodies

The discovery of light-chains lacking functional antibodies produced by camelids (llamas, camels, dromedaries, and alpacas) and cartilaginous fishes (sharks) formed a further breakthrough in therapeutic antibodies (Saerens et al., 2008; Khodabakhsh et al., 2018). The antibodies derived from the single variable domain of these antibodies are called single-domain antibodies, abbreviated as sdADs or nanobodies. They are of 2 types: V_HH and IgNAR.

24.1. V_HH single-domain antibody

The conventional structure of antibodies is tetramers of two heavy chains and two light chains (*Fig 24-1a*). The variable domains of each light and heavy chain together form the antigen-binding site, and there are two antigen-binding sites in an antibody molecule. In 1993, Hamers-Casterman et al. discovered that in addition to the conventional tetrameric antibodies, camelids (llamas, camels, dromedaries, and alpacas) produce functional homodimeric heavy-chain only antibodies, devoid of light chains. Apart from the light chains, these heavy chain antibodies also lack C_H1 domains (*Fig 24-1b*). Thus, the heavy chain antibodies are composed of two identical heavy chains, each comprising two constant domains (C_H2 and C_H3), a hinge region, and a variable domain responsible for antigen recognition.

So, in contrast to the paired variable domains of light (V_L) and heavy (V_H) chains that form an antigen-binding site, the single variable domain of camelid antibodies can bind to the antigen without domain pairing (Hamers-Casterman et al., 1993; Muyldermans, 2013). The variable domains of camelid antibodies are often referred to as V_HH domains, meaning V_H domain obtained from heavy-chain antibodies (*Fig 24-1c*). The single V_HH domain size is 15 kDa in contrast to the

150 kDa size of a conventional antibody. Because of the smaller size, single-domain antibody fragments can recognize targets and active sites that are not accessible by traditional antibodies. Therefore, the V$_H$H domain can be developed as a **single-domain antibody** with appropriate modification (Hoey et al., 2019).

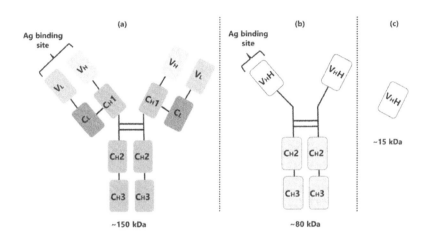

Fig 24-1: Structure of (a) conventional Ab, (b) camelid heavy chain Ab and (c) V$_H$H single-domain Ab

We have already discussed the antibody fragments Fab or single-chain Fv (scFv) contains V$_H$ and V$_L$ domains joined either by a disulfide bond (Fab) or by a polypeptide linker (scFv). V$_H$ and V$_L$ domains together form the antigen-binding site (*Fig 24-2*).

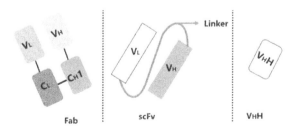

Fig 24-2: Antibody fragments Fab, scFv and V$_H$H

But the single-domain antibody fragment contains the single variable domain VₕH of the heavy chain antibodies. The single VₕH recognizes and binds to the antigen, thus representing the functional equivalent of a Fab fragment of conventional antibodies.

Properties of VₕH domains: Like the V domain of conventional antibodies, the VₕH domain of a camelid antibody contains three complementarity determining regions (CDRs) and framework regions (FRs). The CDRs mediate interaction with the antigen. On the other hand, FRs support the binding of CDRs to the antigen.

Antigen binding by VₕH domains is mediated by only three CDRs rather than the six CDRs of conventional antibodies (*Fig 24-3*).

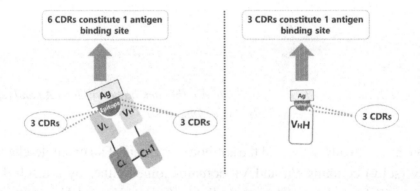

Fig 24-3: 3 CDRs constitute the antigen-binding site in the VₕH domain

To make up for the reduced CDRs, the CDRs of VₕH domains have certain characteristic features: Firstly, the N-terminal part of CDR1 is more variable. Secondly, VₕHs have a long and extended CDR3 that is often stabilized by an additional disulfide bond with a cysteine in CDR1, resulting in the folding of the CDR3 loop to form finger-like projections (*Fig 24-4b*). The long and extended CDR3 is responsible for the binding of the VₕH to the concave epitopes, such as protein clefts/pockets, including active sites of the enzymes (Iezzi et al., 2018; Soetens et al., 2020).

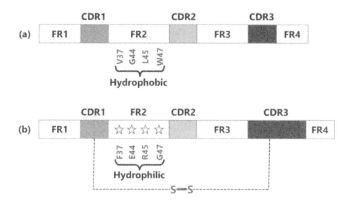

Fig 24-4: Representation of (a) VH domain and (b) VHH domain

The framework region (FR) of VHH also exhibits certain differences from the VH domain of conventional antibodies. In the case of conventional antibodies, the amino acid residues in the framework region 2 (FR2) of the VH domain contain hydrophobic residues that are responsible for interaction with the light chains (*Fig 24-4a*). But in the case of the VHH domain of heavy-chain antibodies, hydrophobic residues in the FR2 are replaced by more hydrophilic residues (*Fig 24-4b*). Thus, it increases the solubility of heavy-chain antibodies.

24.2. IgNAR single domain antibody

Two years after the discovery of camelid heavy-chain antibodies, it was reported that sharks and other cartilaginous fish also produce homodimeric heavy chain antibodies called Ig new antigen receptors or IgNARs. IgNARs are composed of two identical heavy chains, each comprising one variable VNAR domain and five constant domains (*Fig 24-5a*). Like camelid antibodies, IgNAR targets antigen through a single variable domain VNAR, of size 13 kDa (*Fig 24-5b*). The VNAR domain contains 2 CDRs: CDR1 and CDR3, in contrast to 3 CDRs in the V$_H$H domain (Cheong et al., 2020). The CDR3 loop of V$_{NAR}$ is long and extended, which allows it to reach and bind the buried epitopes.

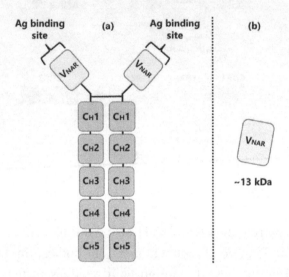

Fig 24-5: Structure of (a) IgNAR Ab and (b) V$_{NAR}$ single-domain Ab

The ability to recognize and bind hidden functional sites of a target antigen makes novel single-domain antibodies attractive as novel therapeutics for human diseases.

24.3. Advantages over conventional antibodies

High stability: Contrary to conventional antibodies, which lose their antigen-binding ability upon heat denaturation, sdABs have been shown to remain functional up to 60-80°C (Dumoulin et al., 2002). Also, the sdABs are resistant to high pH. Therefore, they are also suitable for oral immunotherapy.

Recognize inaccessible antigenic targets: Another advantage of sdABs over conventional antibodies is that the V$_H$Hs and V$_{NAR}$S are adept at recognizing the antigenic sites that are otherwise inaccessible to conventional antibodies, such as enzyme active sites and conserved cryptic epitopes. The ability to recognize these inaccessible antigenic sites has been attributed to the V$_H$Hs or V$_{NARS}$ smaller size and the ability of the extended CDR3 loop to penetrate such sites.

Easy production in the microbial system: The antibody fragments produced from the conventional antibodies are monovalent antibody fragments (Fab) or single-chain Fv (scFv), where a flexible peptide linker joins the V$_H$ and V$_L$ domains. The main advantage single-domain antibodies hold over Fab or scFv is that V$_H$Hs and V$_{NARS}$ contain only one domain, making them more convenient for cloning and genetic engineering. Also, the production of Fabs or scFvs in microbial cells is often cumbersome because of the requirement for correct V$_H$ and V$_L$ domains association. But the sdAbs or nanobodies contain only the V$_H$H domain or V$_{NAR}$; thus, they do not need domain pairing; therefore, they are easily produced and expressed in microbial systems.

Multivalent antibody fragments: In some cases, like virus neutralization, it is advantageous to engineer monovalent antibody fragments into multivalent formats because they are more effective in virus neutralization. Multivalent formats using conventional recombinant antibodies like scFvs are generated using linkers between the V$_H$ and V$_L$ domains of a specific length. But the problem of mispairing of V$_H$ and V$_L$ domains arises, which reduces their affinity for antigen binding (*Fig 24-6*). On the other hand, there is no problem with domain mispairing in the case of V$_H$H or V$_{NARS}$ domains; therefore, they are more suitable for producing multivalent formats. Furthermore, V$_H$H or V$_{NARS}$ domains with the same antigen specificity can be fused with flexible linkers to recognize the same repeating antigen to increase the functional affinity of the V$_H$H or

V<small>NAR</small> single-domain antibodies. For instance, it was observed that a bivalent V<small>H</small>H sdAB targeting H5N1 hemagglutinin was at least 60-fold more effective than the monovalent one in controlling influenza virus replication.

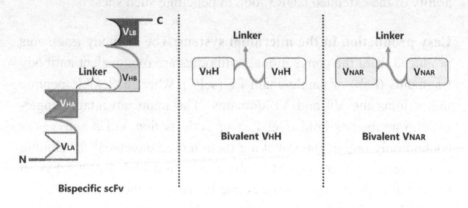

Fig 24-6: Multivalent antibody fragments

Rapid tissue penetration: In addition, the small size of sdAbs results in their fast tissue penetration. It is advantageous for targeting V<small>H</small>Hs coupled to toxins or drugs to tumors and *in vivo* diagnosis using imaging.

Cross blood-brain barrier: Because of the small size, sdAbs can cross the blood-brain barrier (BBB), thus making them excellent candidates for treating neurological disorders and neurotropic virus infections like rabies virus.

Clearance from the body: Because of their small size of about 15 kDa, sdAbs can rapidly pass the renal filter, which has a cutoff of approximately 60 kDa, resulting in their rapid blood clearance. It is advantageous when using the single-domain antibody coupled to a toxic substance.

Limitations

sdAbs have a short serum half-life of about 2 hours, which limits their applications in many therapeutic applications. It can be extended by the chemical addition of polyethylene glycol (PEG), by Fc-fusion, or by binding to long-lived serum components, for example, albumin.

24.4. Production of single-domain antibodies

To develop a VнH single-domain antibody, firstly, it is required to immunize alpaca or llama with an antigen against which single-domain antibodies are needed to be generated (*Fig 24-7*). Over the course of a few weeks, the animal generates antibodies. Then, the antisera are collected, and peripheral blood mononuclear cells (PBMCs) are isolated. From PBMCs, total RNA is isolated, and cDNA is prepared by the process of reverse transcription. The VнH genes are then amplified from cDNA by the PCR process using the primers specific to the variable regions of the heavy chain antibodies.

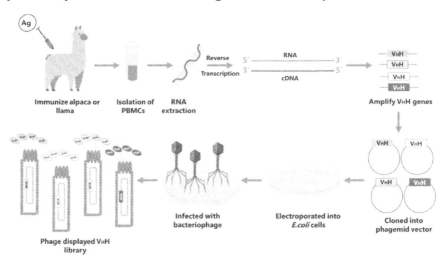

Fig 24-7: Phage displayed VнH library

The PCR products are then cloned into phagemid vectors which are electroporated into the *E. coli* cells. The *E. coli* cells are then infected with bacteriophages. After infection, the bacteriophages generate a phage-display library in which the $V_H H$ regions are displayed on the phage coat protein.

After this, affinity screening of the phage-display antibody library is done by a process called biopanning. In this, the phages expressing the $V_H H$ region of antibodies on the surface are added to the antigens immobilized on a solid surface, for example, on ELISA plates (*Fig 24-8*). The antigen can be a protein on cancer cells or other cells against which single-domain antibodies are required to be generated. The phages that have $V_H H$ regions specific for the antigens bind to the coated antigen. Non-specific phages are removed by stringent washing. Antigen-bound phages are then eluted and are re-infected into *E. coli* to produce a subset of phages for the next cycle of panning.

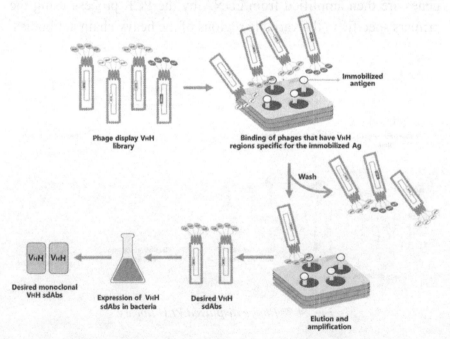

Fig 24-8: Biopanning process to obtain desired monoclonal sdAbs

After the multiple rounds of affinity panning (phage display method), we can retrieve those phage particles that express single-domain antibodies of interest, specific for the desired antigen. Finally, the positive clones are then expressed in bacterial cells to produce a high yield of llama monoclonal single-domain antibodies.

Similarly, the shark monoclonal single-domain antibodies V_{NAR} can be generated.

The conventional functional antibodies can only be efficiently produced using mammalian cells, especially when appropriate glycosylation and other post-translational modifications are required for therapeutic applications. However, antibody fragments like V_HH and V_{NAR} lack the Fc region with N-linked oligosaccharides. Thus they can be efficiently produced in microbial systems like *E. coli*, yeasts, or filamentous fungi.

24.5. Immunogenicity and humanization of sdAbs

Immunogenicity of sdAbs: Certain features of sdAbs, such as small size which decreases the number of potentially immunogenic epitopes, high solubility which reduces the formation of immunogenic aggregates, and rapid clearance of the sdAb favors low immunogenicity in humans. But still, the nonhuman origin of V_HHs and V_{NARs} may increase the chance of triggering unwanted immune responses when administered as therapeutic agents. For example, we have already discussed that the transition from fully murine to chimeric, humanized, or fully antibody therapy significantly reduced the frequency of anti-drug antibody (ADA) development and thus immunogenicity. Similar is the case with single-domain antibodies. Since the interface between the V_H and V_L domains of conventional antibodies is exposed in sdAbs, which have just one domain and no pairing partner; therefore, ADAs may be generated against them. In addition, while the CDR1 and CDR2 loops of V_HHs adopt similar canonical structures as human antibodies, their long and extended CDR3 loops may adopt conformations absent in the human repertoire, thus raising the possibility of generating ADAs against the CDR3 loop. Therefore, it becomes imperative to humanize sdAds as much as possible.

Humanization of sdAbs: Humanization is defined as replacing xenogeneic sequences with human sequences in the antibody variable domain.

The first approach of humanization of sdAbs is CDR grafting (*Fig 24-9a*). It is a process by which CDRs from xenogeneic antibodies (e.g., CDRs from mouse Abs) are grafted into the human framework regions (FRs) of the V_H domains of human antibodies. Also, the mutations in the FR residues of the V_H domain must be done to restore the properties of non-human sdAbs (Ju et al., 2017; Rossotti et al., 2021). A conventional antibody consists of two domains (V_H and V_L), which tend to dimerize or aggregate because of their lipophilicity. Therefore, hydrophobic amino acid residues of the FR region are replaced by hydrophilic amino acids to mimic the V_HH domain and inhibit its interaction with the V_L domain (*Fig 24-9b*).

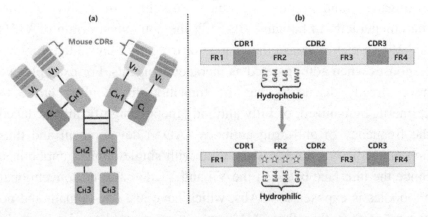

Fig 24-9: (a) CDR grafting and (b) mutations in the FR residues of V_H domains of human Ab

Thus, the single-domain V_H antibodies generated are similar to the sdAbs or nanobodies.

The second approach of humanization of sdAbs is resurfacing of xenogenic sdAb (camelid sdAbs) sequence to mimic V_H domains of human antibodies (*Fig 24-10*). For this, amino acids in framework regions (FRs) of sdAbs are modified at fixed positions to mimic the V_H of human Abs. Also, the mutations should not affect the properties of sdAbs. For this, two of the FR2 hydrophilic amino acids at positions 49 and 50 responsible for the solubility of VHHs are substituted without compromising the solubility, monomeric behavior, and function of the nonhuman sdAbs. The remaining two FR2 amino acids at positions 42 and 52 cannot be humanized as they are crucial in maintaining the structural integrity of the VHH domain and are essential for the proper conformation of the CDR3 loop.

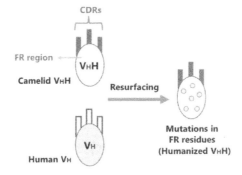

Fig 24-10: Resurfacing of VHH sdAbs to generate humanized sdAb

24.6. Therapeutic applications of sdAbs

VHHs have a wide range of therapeutic applications. For instance,

Therapeutic potential for cancer treatment: VHHs may outperform mAbs in treating solid tumors as their small size allows tumor penetration. The epidermal growth factor receptor (EGFR) is overexpressed in many cancer cell types, leading to increased cell proliferation, migration, and angiogenesis. V$_H$Hs binding to EGFR can block epidermal growth factor (EGF) binding to its receptor, inhibiting the EGFR signaling pathway that ultimately induces apoptosis in tumor cells by blocking tumor cell proliferation and survival invasion. Thus, V$_H$Hs can be used to treat solid tumors.

Even the sdAbs can be conjugated to the tumor penetrating peptides (TPPs) to enhance their antitumor activity by penetrating the tumor cells.

Additionally, sdAbs can be used to generate immunotoxins. For instance, anti-CEA V$_H$H sdAb directed against tumor antigen CEA is fused with the β-lactamase enzyme. When sdAb binds to the CEA antigen on the tumor cell, the fused enzyme converts an injected non-toxic prodrug into a toxic drug in the vicinity of the targeted tumor cells, leading to their killing.

Therapeutics against human viral diseases: Currently, sdAbs are being developed against several viruses, including human immunodeficiency virus-1 (HIV-1), respiratory syncytial virus (RSV), influenza viruses, hepatitis C virus (HCV), etc.

Therapeutics against arthritis and sepsis: V$_H$Hs binding to TNF-α can be used to treat rheumatoid arthritis. Studies have shown that the potency of bivalent formats was 500 times more as compared to monovalent V$_H$Hs and even exceeded the potency of clinically used conventional antibodies both *in vitro* and in a murine arthritis model.

Similarly, lipopolysaccharide (LPS)-binding V$_H$Hs work by blocking LPS binding and signaling to host cells to treat sepsis.

sdAbs as intrabodies: sdAbs can also be used as "intrabodies." The term intrabodies is derived from intracellular antibodies and refers to antibodies that are expressed intracellularly. In contrast to naturally expressed antibodies or administered antibodies, which target

334

extracellular proteins, intrabodies target proteins inside the cell. Originally, intrabodies mainly existed as single-chain variable fragments (scFvs) that could be used to treat diseases. The inherent stability of single-domain antibodies makes them much more suitable for intracellular expression compared to the scFvs. But the reducing environment of the cytoplasm, in which the intra-domain cysteine bridges fail to form, often inhibits their proper folding. For designing intrabodies, the cysteine residues V_HHs are replaced by serine residues, without affecting their ability to bind their cytosolic targets. Additionally, the sdABs are easier to engineer and allow targeting of epitopes that would not be available to scFvs. The propensity of V_HHs to bind cleft-like structures makes them ideal for binding to the active sites of enzymes inside the cells. Intracellular expression of these V_HHs opens up a whole new range of potential therapeutic targets, which were previously inaccessible using traditional monoclonal antibody (mAb) therapy. For instance, intrabodies have the potential to treat diseases caused by protein misfolding.

Misfolding and aggregation of intracellular proteins like α-synuclein in the brain is a hallmark of many neurodegenerative diseases like Parkinson's disease. In addition, aggregation of proteins leads to neuron toxicity. The two V_HH intrabodies NbSyn2 and NbSyn87 can bind distinct epitopes in the C-terminus of α-synuclein. V_HH binding leads to a destabilization of α-synuclein fibrils and reduced cellular toxicity (Soetens et al., 2020). To increase the efficacy of the α-synuclein-specific V_HHs, a proteasomal targeting PEST motif can be added to the V_HH C-terminus, which allows the V_HHs to target monomeric as well as oligomeric α-synuclein for proteasomal degradation and effectively preventing fibril formation; thus leading to the treatment of neurodegenerative disease.

24.7. FDA approved single domain antibody

Currently, more than 30 sdAbs are being in preclinical to clinical development. In February 2019, the FDA approved the first VнH-based therapy, Cablivi, to treat acquired thrombotic thrombocytopenic purpura, abbreviated as aTTP (Duggan, 2018). It was developed by Belgian biotech company Ablynx (now acquired by Sanofi).

aTTP is a rare life-threatening autoimmune blood-clotting disorder. During the normal blood clotting process, the plasma protein von Willibrand factor (vWF) is essential in recruiting blood-clotting cells called platelets to the damaged vessels and stopping blood loss at the sites of blood vessel injury. In healthy individuals, the von Willibrand factor is immediately cut up into smaller pieces by an enzyme called ADAMTS13 to prevent the spontaneous recruitment of platelets when blood vessels are not damaged. However, in aTTP patients, anti-ADAMTS13 autoantibodies are present that block ADAMTS13 from working correctly (*Fig 24-11*). It results in an accumulation of ultra-large von Willibrand factor molecules in the blood, which bind to the platelets and cause the excessive formation of blood clots.

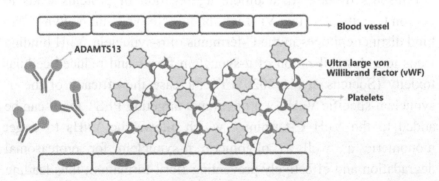

Fig 24-11: vWF-platelet aggregation due to the presence of anti-ADAMTS13 autoantibodies in aTTP condition

The formation of blood clots in small blood vessels throughout the body leads to a severe reduction in platelets that circulate in the blood (thrombocytopenia), breakdown of red blood cells (hemolytic anemia), and an insufficient blood supply to tissue (tissue ischemia). In addition, it results in organ dysfunction, especially brain, heart, and kidneys. There is currently no authorized treatment for aTTP. Patients often receive immunosuppressants and plasma exchange but remain at risk of significant morbidity and mortality.

Cablivi (Caplacizumab) is a bivalent single-domain humanized anti-vWF antibody in which two anti-vWF sdAbs are linked by a tri-alanine (AAA) linker (*Fig 24-12a*).

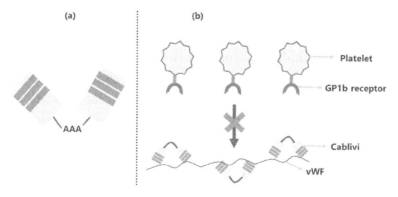

Fig 24-12: (a) Structure and (b) mechanism of action of Cablivi

The drug binds to the von Willibrand factor and blocks its interactions with the GP1b receptors on platelets (*Fig 24-12b*). Thus, it results in the reduction of platelet aggregation, and ultimately formation and accumulation of blood clots in the blood vessels are reduced (Elliott and Chan, 2019). The drug is used in combination with plasma exchange and immunosuppressive therapy.

Chapter 25: Side effects of monoclonal antibody therapy

Although the therapeutic monoclonal antibodies hold great promise for treating various diseases, they have certain side effects.

25.1. Infusion-related reactions

One of the complications of monoclonal antibody therapy is the occurrence of infusion-related reactions (IRRs) experienced by patients after the intravenous (IV) administration of monoclonal antibodies. Mild to moderate infusion reactions are associated with chills, fever, mild hypotension, dyspnea, and rash. Severe reactions are less common and are associated with severe hypotension, anaphylaxis, and cardiac dysfunction. IRRs usually start within 30 to 120 min after the start of administration of monoclonal antibodies. But in some cases, delayed infusion reactions can occur up to 24 hours (and even a week like in the case of trastuzumab) after infusion of the drug.

Anaphylaxis: Anaphylaxis is an acute, life-threatening hypersensitivity reaction caused by releasing mediators from mast cells, basophils, and recruited inflammatory cells. It can occur within minutes or up to a few hours after exposure to a provoking agent. The infused monoclonal Abs may be recognized as allergens by the patient, against which IgE antibodies are raised (Doessegger and Banholzer, 2015; Isabwe et al., 2018; Pintea et al., 2021). During the sensitization phase, the patient's first exposure to allergens (i.e., infused mAb drug) drug-specific B cells are activated that differentiate into plasma cells which produce antidrug IgE antibodies. The antidrug IgE antibodies then bind to a specific high-affinity Fcε receptor (FcεRI) on the membrane of mast cells and basophils by their Fc regions (*Fig 25-1*). Thus, the first exposure to the mAb drug never triggers symptoms, whereas every subsequent exposure initiates a hypersensitivity reaction. When the pre-sensitized individual is given a second dose of the mAb drug, the infused drug binds to the IgE antibodies attached to Fc receptors of mast cells and basophils. This binding of the mAb drug to IgE antibodies results in crosslinking of IgE antibodies. The crosslinking sends the signal to the basophils and mast cells to translocate their granules to the plasma membrane and release the granule contents to the extracellular environment by a process known as degranulation. As a result of degranulation, there is a rapid release of immune mediators from the granules, such as histamines, leukotrienes, and prostaglandins.

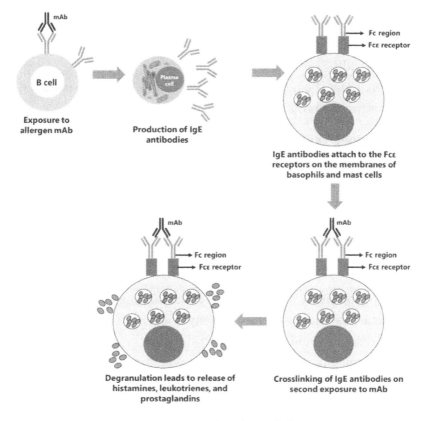

Fig 25-1: IgE-mediated anaphylaxis

The total amount of mediators released is a function of the concentration of IgE antibodies bound to the mast cells and basophils and also on the serum concentration of the antigen (mAb drug). These mediators then act on a person's cutaneous, respiratory, gastrointestinal, and cardiovascular organ systems, causing allergy symptoms like skin rash, nausea, vomiting, difficulty breathing, shock, abnormal heart rate, etc.

In most of the infused mAbs, the first exposure to antigen drug is required for IgE sensitization; hypersensitivity reactions do not occur during the first infusion of a mAb. However, in some instances, the pre-existing IgE antibodies cross-react with the infused mAbs and induce hypersensitivity reactions on the first exposure. For example, the pre-existing IgE antibodies in humans recognize an oligosaccharide (galactose-α-1,3-galactose), which is a post-translational modification on the cetuximab molecule and is shared by some mammalian proteins.

Anaphylactoid reactions: Anaphylactoid reactions are immediate systemic reactions that mimic anaphylaxis but are caused by the non-IgE-mediated release of mediators from mast cells and basophils. These reactions may occur with the first exposure to the administered mAb drug and are clinically indistinguishable from anaphylaxis. Unlike anaphylaxis, anaphylactoid reactions are milder upon repeated administration.

Monoclonal antibodies contain sequences that may be recognized by the patients as the antigens against which the patients stimulate immune response and generate anti-drug antibodies. For instance, chimeric monoclonal antibodies where V region is of mouse origin, or humanized monoclonal antibodies where CDRs are of mouse origin. The patient's body recognizes murine regions of mAbs as antigens and induces synthesis of anti-drug antibodies IgG or IgM. IgG or IgM antibodies, after binding to the murine regions of infused mAbs activate complement cascade activation (*Fig 25-2*). During complement activation, the complement proteins C3a, C4a, and C5a are produced, which bind to the receptors on mast cells and basophils and then induce degranulation. As a result, histamine and other pharmacological active mediators are released, mediating inflammation reactions (Hansel et al., 2010; Asselin, 2016).

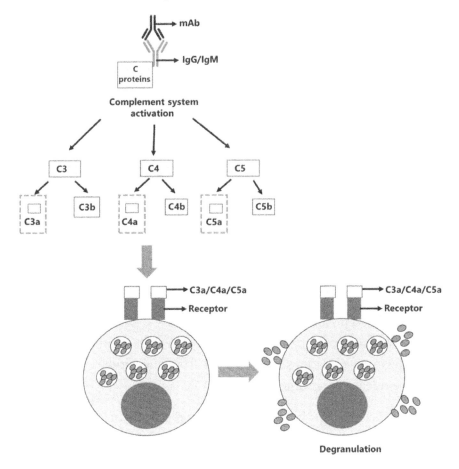

Fig 25-2: IgG/IgM-mediated anaphylactoid reactions

The risk of IgE-mediated anaphylaxis and non-IgE-mediated anaphylactoid reactions can be reduced by pre-treating the patients with antihistamines, acetaminophen, and corticosteroids before infusing the mAb drugs.

Cytokine release syndrome: Infused monoclonal antibodies can also cause a condition known as cytokine release syndrome or a cytokine storm (Bugelski et al., 2009; Shimabukuro-Vornhagen et al., 2018). It occurs due to the activation of various immune cells, including monocytes, macrophages, natural killer cells, T cells, and B cells. The activation of the immune system leads to a sudden acute increase in circulating levels of pro-inflammatory cytokines. The cytokines released include IL-1, IL-2, TNF-α, IL-6, IL-8 and IL-10. The increased cytokine levels also called "cytokine storm" can activate the inflammatory cascade and present with various symptoms ranging from mild symptoms like fever, fatigue, headache, rash to severe life-threatening conditions like acute respiratory distress syndrome (ARSD) and multiorgan failure.

The infused mAbs can cause the release of cytokine storm in 3 ways (Wing, 2008):

(a) The infused mAbs bind directly through the CDRs to their cognate receptors on the target cells. The binding causes the stimulation of the cells; thus, the cytokines are released from the target cells causing cytokine release syndrome (*Fig 25-3a*).

(b) The infused mAbs bind to the cognate receptors on the target cells and are then crosslinked by the pre-existing IgG. This cross-linking activates and releases cytokines from the target cells (*Fig 25-3b*).

(c) The infused mAbs, after binding to their cognate receptors on the target cells, bind to the Fcγ receptors bearing non-target cells such as macrophages through its Fc region. The interaction of the Fc of the infused mAb with the FcγR on macrophages contributes to cytokine release from both target cells and macrophages (*Fig 25-3c*).

Premedication with corticosteroids has been reported to be effective in reducing the severity of symptoms caused by cytokine release.

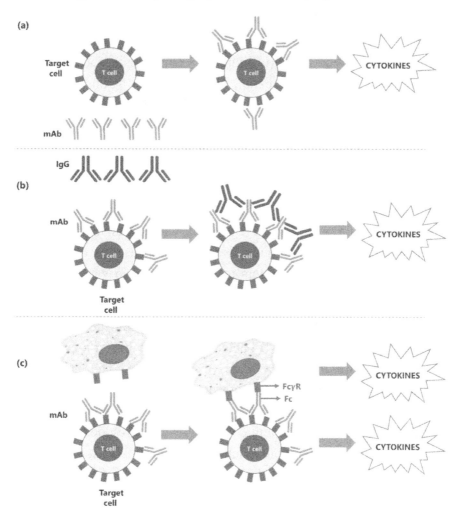

Fig 25-3: Mechanism of cytokine storm release by infused mAbs through (a) binding to cognate receptors on target cells, (b) cross-linking by IgG, and (c) binding to FcγR on macrophages

343

To summarize, Infusion-related reactions, non-IgE mediated anaphylactoid reactions, and cytokine storm reactions may occur from the first infusion of mAbs. In contrast, IgE-mediated reactions must have previous exposures to allow sensitization.

25.2. Reactivation of tuberculosis

Monoclonal antibodies (infliximab, etanercept, adalimumab, golimumab, certolizumab pegol, etc.) directed against the pro-inflammatory cytokine TNF-α have contributed significantly to the treatment and management of rheumatoid arthritis, psoriasis, inflammatory bowel disease, and other inflammation-related diseases. However, the tendency to reactivate latent tuberculosis (caused by *Mycobacterium tuberculosis* abbreviated as Mtb) is a serious and limiting side effect. Latent tuberculosis or latent TB refers to the condition when a person has TB bacteria within their body, but the bacteria remain inactive in the body and do not cause any disease. On the other hand, active TB refers to the condition in which bacteria become active if the immune system can't stop them from growing.

In Latent TB infection, the immune system of the host develops granuloma to wall off the TB bacteria where the bacteria are viable and possibly are in a slow state of replication. The granuloma formation prevents the TB bacteria from disseminating into the blood and causing disease. TNF-α is a proinflammatory cytokine that plays a significant role in granuloma formation and provides protective mechanism against infections, including tuberculosis. It, along with interferon (IFN)-γ, increases the phagocytic capacity of macrophages and enhances intracellular killing of Mtb via the generation of reactive nitrogen and oxygen intermediates. In some individuals, inside granuloma structure, sometimes all Mtb are not dead; there might be some living Mtb remaining which remain dormant or inactive for the rest of their lives. In this scenario, tuberculosis infection is referred to as a latent state which means that the TB bacteria are kept under control by the body's immune system, because of which TB bacteria remain inactive in the body for the person's entire life without causing any disease.

However, latent TB infections can progress to active disease in certain circumstances when the immune system of a person is compromised, for instance, if a person gets coinfected with HIV infection or suffers from diabetes.

Additionally, the use of corticosteroids and immunosuppressive agents such as TNF-α blockers also lead to reactivation of latent TB infection to active TB disease in the patient by inhibiting the granuloma formation (Keane and Bresnihan, 2008; Harris and Keane, 2010; Kelsey et al., 2018). Therefore, the administration of anti-TNF-α monoclonal antibodies that target TNF-α increases the risk of TB reactivation (*Fig 25-4*).

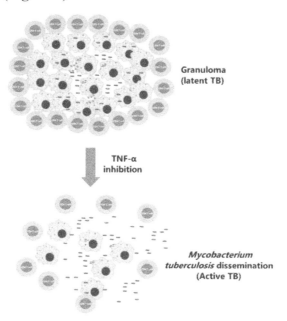

Fig 25-4: Reactivation of TB with TNF-α inhibition

Thus, during the anti-TNF monoclonal antibody therapy, the patients should be closely monitored to identify the reactivation of latent TB. In addition, the patients' adherence to isoniazid (INH) treatment is essential for preventing the reactivation of latent TB.

26.3. Reactivation of viral infections

Like reactivating tuberculosis, monoclonal antibodies directed against the immune cells or pro-inflammatory cytokine TNF-α make the patients more susceptible to viral infections and infections by opportunistic pathogens. Monoclonal antibodies such as Rituximab that target the CD20 antigen on the surface of normal and malignant B-lymphocytes are effective in treating a variety of haematological malignancies but also result in a depletion of normal B-cells, which are crucial for T-cell-activation. And activated T cells keep Hepatitis B viral (HBV) infection in check. But the shortage of B cells cannot activate T cells, thus causing the reactivation of HBV infections (Mastroianni et al., 2011).

TNF-α cytokine is essential for controlling the replication of viruses like herpes simplex virus (HSV)-1, cytomegalovirus (CMV), EBV, etc. But with the use of anti-TNFα antibodies, reactivation of latent HSV-1, CMV, and EBV infections can occur (Kim et al., 2010; Gentile and Foa, 2011; Bohra et al., 2017).

Therefore, the patients who are at risk of viral infections must be given antiviral treatment before starting with monoclonal antibody therapy.

Practice Test 3

1. Each B cell has around 100,000 B cells receptors on its surface. All of these B cell receptors of one B cell are
(a) Specific for only one particular epitope on an antigen
(b) Specific for different epitopes

2. Polyclonal antibodies mean
(a) Antibodies derived from multiple B cell clones
(b) Antibodies derived from the clones of a single activated B cell that recognizes a particular epitope

3. Which of the following statements is/are correct about monoclonal antibodies?
(a) Monoclonal antibodies are derived from the clones of a single activated B cell that recognizes a particular epitope
(b) Monoclonal antibodies recognize a single specific epitope on an antigen
(c) Monoclonal antibodies are identical antibodies with the same antigen specificity
(d) All of the above

4. Technology used for the production of monoclonal antibodies is:
(a) Mass Culture technology
(b) Hybridoma Technology
(c) Suspension culture
(d) None of the above

5. Hybridoma technology was developed by
(a) Kohler and Milstein
(b) Khorana and Nirenberg
(c) Khorana and Korenberg
(d) Beadle and Tatum

6. The hybridomas are made by

(a) fusing T cells with myeloma cells
(b) fusing plasma cells with myeloma cells
(c) fusing T helper cells with myeloma cells
(d) fusing B memory cells with myeloma cells

7. Myeloma cells used in the hybridoma technology have mutations in which genes?
(a) HGPRT gene and immunoglobulin genes
(b) RAG and BCR
(c) Thymidine Kinase and AID
(d) Dihydrofolate reductase and Thymidine Kinase

8. In hybridoma technology, hybrid cells are selected in
a) MS medium
b) HAT medium
c) x-gal medium
d) YT medium

9. Which of the following statements is incorrect regarding HAT medium?
a) HAT medium is a selective medium
b) Aminiopterin in the HAT medium blocks de novo pathway of nucleotide synthesis
c) Salvage pathway requires aminopterin and thymidine kinase enzyme to operate
d) Salvage pathway requires HGPRT enzyme to operate

10. Why are the monoclonal antibodies generated in mice not suitable for therapeutic purposes?
(a) Isotypic determinants of mouse antibodies are recognized as foreign by the patients' bodies
(b) Patients generate anti-antibodies against the isotypic determinants on the foreign mouse antibody
(c) Circulating complexes of mouse and human antibodies can cause allergic reactions and accumulate in organs
(d) All of the above

11. What are chimeric monoclonal antibodies?

(a) Contain mouse antibody's variable region and the human antibody's constant region

(b) Contain variable region from one mouse antibody and the constant region from another mouse antibody

(c) Contain human antibody's variable region and the mouse antibody's constant region

(d) Contain mouse antibody's variable region but with human CDRs and the human antibody's constant region

12. What are humanized antibodies?

(a) Mouse antibody's variable region grafted onto the human constant region

(b) Mouse antibody's CDRs grafted onto the corresponding region of human antibody

(c) Mouse antibody's FR grafted onto the corresponding region of human antibody

(d) Antibodies isolated directly from the recovered patients

13. How are transgenic mice created to generate fully human monoclonal antibodies?

(a) Entire mouse antibody genes are replaced with human antibody genes

(b) Genes encoding mouse antibody's variable region are only replaced with genes encoding human antibody's variable region

(c) Genes encoding mouse antibody's constant region are only replaced with genes encoding human antibody's constant region

(d) Genes encoding mouse antibody's CDRs are only replaced with genes encoding human antibody's CDRs

14. Fully human monoclonal antibodies can be generated by which of these methods?

(a) Transgenic mice

(b) Phage display library

(c) Both of the above

(d) None of the above

15. Which approach is followed to isolate monoclonal antibodies directly from humans?
(a) Bacterial two-hybrid system
(b) Biopanning
(c) Yeast two-hybrid system
(d) Bacterial cell surface display method

16. Which of these antibodies, when injected into patients, have more chances of generating Anti-drug antibodies or ADAs?
(a) Chimeric monoclonal antibodies
(b) Humanized monoclonal antibodies
(c) Fully human monoclonal antibodies

17. What is the role of the linker that links the cytotoxic drug to the mAB in ADC?
(a) Targets a specific antigen found or overexpressed on target cells
(b) Releases the cytotoxic drug once the ADC binds to the target cell and is internalized
(c) Acts as enzyme
(d) None of the above

18. β-glucuronide linker belongs to which category of linkers?
(a) pH-sensitive linker
(b) Lysosomal-protease sensitive linker
(c) Disulfide linker
(d) Non-cleavable linker

19. How do microtubule destabilizers act?
(a) Bind to β-tubulin and block the polymerization of tubulin dimers
(b) Bind to α-tubulin and block the polymerization of tubulin dimers
(c) Bind to microtubules and enhance tubulin polymerization
(d) Bind to β-tubulin and enhance tubulin polymerization

20. How is an immunotoxin prepared?
(a) By replacing the inhibitory polypeptide of toxin with a monoclonal antibody that is specific for a target cell

(b) By replacing the binding polypeptide of toxin with a monoclonal antibody that is specific for a target cell

(c) By conjugating Fv region of the antibody to the binding polypeptide of the toxin

(d) By conjugating mAb to the DNA damaging agents

21. How do toxins used in immunotoxin kill the target cells?

(a) By disrupting the cell membrane of the target cell

(b) By interfering with the microtubule formation in the target cell

(c) By inhibiting protein synthesis in the target cell

(d) By cross-linking DNA of the target cell

22. How is a recombinant immunotoxin prepared?

(a) By conjugating V_H and V_L region of the antibody to the inhibitory polypeptide of the toxin

(b) By conjugating Fab region of the antibody to the inhibitory polypeptide of the toxin

(c) By conjugating V_H region of the antibody to the inhibitory polypeptide of the toxin

(d) By conjugating V_L region of the antibody to the inhibitory polypeptide of the toxin

23. What is a humanized immunotoxin?

(a) Inhibitory component of toxin is fused with Fab region of monoclonal antibody

(b) Endogenous cytotoxic protein of human origin like proapoptotic protein or RNase is fused with monoclonal antibody

(c) Endogenous cytotoxic protein of human origin like proapoptotic protein or RNase is fused with human ligand like cytokine or growth receptor instead of the monoclonal antibody

(d) None of these

24. What is a fully human immunotoxin?

(a) mAb is fused with the RNase

(b) Fv region is fused with the RNase

(c) Cytokine or growth receptor is fused with RNase

(d) Cytokine or growth receptor is fused with a bacterial toxin

25. Which of the following statements is incorrect about ADEPT?
(a) It is an antibody-enzyme conjugate.
(b) When Ab-enzyme complex binds to the target cell, the enzyme converts the prodrug into a potent cell-killing agent and causes target cell death.
(c) Shows bystander effect; cytotoxic agents generated at the target cancer cell enable killing of neighboring cancer cells
(d) None of the above

26. Which monoclonal antibodies are of great interest for researchers to treat SARS-CoV-2 infection?
(a) That target the receptor-binding domain of the S1 unit of spike protein SARS-CoV-2
(b) That recognize the epitopes in the S2 unit of the spike protein of SARS-CoV-2
(c) Both A and B
(d) None of the above

27. Most common route by which mAbs are administered to patients?
(a) Intravenous
(b) Subcutaneous
(c) Intramuscular
(d) Oral

28. Which of the following roles is played by immune system checkpoints?
(a) Maintaining self-tolerance
(b) Prevents the T-cells from attacking cells indiscriminately
(c) Both of the above
(d) None of the above

29. Which of the following cytotoxic T cell immune checkpoint receptors are able to deliver inhibitory signals when bound to their respective ligands?

(a) CTLA-4

(b) PD-1

(c) B7

(d) a and b are correct

30. What are bispecific antibodies?

(a) Hybrids of two different antibody molecules that bind to one specific type of antigen

(b) Hybrids of two different antibody molecules that can simultaneously bind to two different types of antigens

(c) Hybrid of mouse and human monoclonal antibody

(d) Mouse antibody's CDRs from mouse antibody grafted onto the corresponding region of human antibody

31. In which scFv-based bispecific antibodies, two scFv fragments have their V$_H$ and V$_L$ domains exchanged?

(a) BiTE

(b) DARTs

(c) TandAds

(d) All of the above

32. Which of these scFv-based antibodies are tetravalent bispecific antibodies?

(a) BiTE

(b) DARTs

(c) TandAds

(d) All of the above

33. Which of the following statements is incorrect about quadroma technology?

(a) Hybridomas are formed by somatic fusion of two different hybridoma cells

(b) Hybridomas are formed by somatic fusion of four different hybridoma cells

(c) Used for generation of bispecific antibodies

(d) None of the above

34. Why is Knobs-into-holes (KIH) technology important in generating desired bispecific Abs?

(a) Promotes the correct pairing of the light chain and heavy chain

(b) Promotes the heterodimerization of heavy chains

35. In which domains of heavy chains, knob and holes are produced to generate bispecific antibodies?

(a) C_H1 domain

(b) C_H2 domain

(c) C_H3 domain

(d) All of the above

36. Why is CrossMab technology important?

(a) Enables the correct pairing of the light chain and heavy chain to form functional bispecific Ab

(b) Enables the correct pairing of heavy chains to form functional bispecific Ab

(c) Enables antibody to behave as enzyme

(d) Enables antibody to conjugate to cytotoxic drug

37. Abzymes are:

(a) RNA acting as enzymes

(b) Ribose sugar acting as enzyme

(c) Antibodies acting as enzymes

(d) Proteins acting as enzymes

354

38. How do abzymes hydrolyze ester?

(a) Synthesis of hapten-carrier complex in which hapten structurally resembles the transition state of an ester undergoing hydrolysis > Injected in mice > Production of anti-hapten monoclonal antibodies > Incubated with an ester substrate, causing its hydrolysis

(b) Synthesis of hapten-carrier complex in which carrier resembles the transition state of an ester undergoing hydrolysis > Injected in mice > Production of anti-hapten monoclonal antibodies > Incubated with an ester substrate, causing its hydrolysis

(c) Injection of ester substrate in mice > Production of anti-ester monoclonal antibodies > Incubated with an ester substrate, causing its hydrolysis

(d) None of the above

39. How do abzymes prevent the cells from getting infected with HIV?

(a) Bind to the protein gp102 of HIV virus, which is the CD4 binding site of the HIV virus and activates the complement system

(b) Hydrolyze the antigenic region of protein gp102 of HIV virus, which is the CD4 binding site of the HIV virus

(c) Bind to the protein gp102 of HIV virus, which is the CD4 binding site of the HIV virus and mediates destruction of virus by Natural Killer cells

(d) Attaches to the CD4 receptor and prevents attachment of HIV virus

40. How are the abzymes used for cancer treatment function?

(a) Activates T cells and NK cells to kill cancer cells

(b) Site-specific delivery of the prodrug and then activates the prodrug into the active anti-cancer drug

(c) One site of the abzyme binds to the cancer cell, and the other site binds to T cells

(d) Cause the hydrolysis of specific antigen present on cancer cells, eventually killing them

41. Importance of fusing biologically active protein to the Fc domain of IgG:
(a) Extends serum half-life of biologically active protein
(b) Decreases renal clearance of biologically active protein
(c) Both of the above
(d) None of the above

42. Which class of antibody is preferred for producing Fc fusion proteins?
(a) IgM
(b) IgG
(c) IgE
(d) All of the above

43. How does the Fc domain prolong the circulation time of Fc fusion proteins?
(a) By interacting with FcRn receptor
(b) By interacting with FcγR receptor
(c) By interacting with FcεR receptor
(d) By interacting with FcαR1 receptor

44. What are single-domain antibodies?
(a) Antibodies derived from single variable domain V_HH of the heavy chain
(b) Antibodies derived from V_H and V_L variable domains
(c) Antibodies derived from the single variable domain V_L of the light chain
(d) Antibodies derived from the single C_H1 domain of the heavy chain

45. In addition to tetrameric antibodies, camelids have antibodies that contain:

(a) homodimeric light chains only

(b) homodimeric heavy chains only

(c) only one light chain and one heavy chain

(d) no C_H domains

46. How many antigen-binding sites are present in camelids' heavy chain antibodies?

(a) 1

(b) 2

(c) 3

(d) 4

47. How many CDRs constitute antigen-binding site in V_HH domain of heavy chain only antibodies?

(a) 3

(b) 6

(c) 9

(d) 12

48. Which monoclonal antibodies cause reactivation of tuberculosis?

(a) mAbs directed against bacterial toxins

(b) mAbs directed against TNFα

(c) mAbs directed against immune checkpoints

(d) mAbs directed against growth factor receptors

49. Which monoclonal antibodies cause reactivation of viral infections?

(a) mAbs directed against immune cells

(b) mAbs directed against TNFα

(c) Both a and b

(d) None of the above

50. Which type of infusion-related reactions may occur on first exposure of infused mAbs?

(a) Non-IgE mediated anaphylactoid reaction

(b) Cytokine release syndrome

(c) Both a and b

(d) IgE mediated hypersensitivity reactions

Answer Key

1. (a) 2. (a) 3. (d) 4. (b) 5. (a) 6. (b) 7. (a) 8. (b) 9. (c) 10. (d) 11. (a) 12. (b) 13. (a) 14. (c) 15. (b) 16. (a) 17. (b) 18. (b) 19. (a) 20. (b) 21. (c) 22. (a) 23. (b) 24. (c) 25. (d) 26. (c) 27. (a) 28. (c) 29. (d) 30. (b) 31. (b) 32. (c) 33. (b) 34. (b) 35. (c) 36. (a) 37. (c) 38. (a) 39. (b) 40. (b) 41. (c) 42. (b) 43. (a) 44. (a) 45. (b) 46. (b) 47. (a) 48. (b) 49. (c) 50. (c)

References

Ahmad, Z. A., Yeap, S. K., Ali, A. M., Ho, W. Y., Alitheen, N. B. M., & Hamid, M. (2012). scFv antibody: principles and clinical application. *Clinical and developmental immunology, 2012*.

Akbari, B., Farajnia, S., Ahdi Khosroshahi, S., Safari, F., Yousefi, M., Dariushnejad, H., & Rahbarnia, L. (2017). Immunotoxins in cancer therapy: Review and update. *International reviews of immunology, 36*(4), 207-219.

Amly, W., & Karaman, R. (2014). Antibody Directed Enzyme Prodrug Therapy (ADEPT): a promising cancer therapy approach. *PRODRUGS DESIGN*, 233.

Antignani, A., & FitzGerald, D. (2013). Immunotoxins: the role of the toxin. *Toxins, 5*(8), 1486-1502.

Asai, A., Nagamura, S., & Saito, H. (1994). A novel property of duocarmycin and its analogs for covalent reaction with DNA. *Journal of the American Chemical Society, 116*(10), 4171-4177.

Asselin, B. (2016). Immunology of infusion reactions in the treatment of patients with acute lymphoblastic leukemia. *Future Oncology, 12*(13), 1609-1621.

Azhar, A., Ahmad, E., Zia, Q., Rauf, M. A., Owais, M., & Ashraf, G. M. (2017). Recent advances in the development of novel protein scaffolds based therapeutics. *International journal of biological macromolecules, 102*, 630-641.

Bagshawe, K. D., Sharma, S. K., & Begent, R. H. (2004). Antibody-directed enzyme prodrug therapy (ADEPT) for cancer. *Expert opinion on biological therapy, 4*(11), 1777-1789.

Bardia, A., Mayer, I. A., Vahdat, L. T., Tolaney, S. M., Isakoff, S. J., Diamond, J. R., ... & Kalinsky, K. (2019). Sacituzumab govitecan-hziy in refractory metastatic triple-negative breast cancer. *New England Journal of Medicine, 380*(8), 741-751.

Bargh, J. D., Isidro-Llobet, A., Parker, J. S., & Spring, D. R. (2019). Cleavable linkers in antibody–drug conjugates. *Chemical Society Reviews, 48*(16), 4361-4374.

Bazan, J., Całkosiński, I., & Gamian, A. (2012). Phage display—A powerful technique for immunotherapy: 1. Introduction and potential of therapeutic applications. *Human vaccines & immunotherapeutics*, *8*(12), 1817-1828.

Bellone, S., Black, J., English, D. P., Schwab, C. L., Lopez, S., Cocco, E., ... & Santin, A. D. (2016). Solitomab, an EpCAM/CD3 bispecific antibody construct (BiTE), is highly active against primary uterine serous papillary carcinoma cell lines in vitro. *American journal of obstetrics and gynecology*, *214*(1), 99-e1.

Bergamaschi, G., Perfetti, V., Tonon, L., Novella, A., Lucotti, C., Danova, M., ... & Cazzola, M. (1996). Saporin, a ribosome-inactivating protein used to prepare immunotoxins, induces cell death via apoptosis. *British journal of haematology*, *93*(4), 789-794.

Billetta, R., & Lobuglio, A. F. (1993). Chimeric antibodies. *International reviews of immunology*, *10*(2-3), 165-176.

Blick, S. K., & Scott, L. J. (2007). Cetuximab. *Drugs*, *67*(17), 2585-2607.

Bohra, C., Sokol, L., & Dalia, S. (2017). Progressive multifocal leukoencephalopathy and monoclonal antibodies: a review. *Cancer Control*, *24*(4), 1073274817729901.

Bradley, A. M., Devine, M., & DeRemer, D. (2013). Brentuximab vedotin: An anti-CD30 antibody–drug conjugate. *American Journal of Health-System Pharmacy*, *70*(7), 589-597.

Bugelski, P. J., Achuthanandam, R., Capocasale, R. J., Treacy, G., & Bouman-Thio, E. (2009). Monoclonal antibody-induced cytokine-release syndrome. *Expert review of clinical immunology*, *5*(5), 499-521.

Cai, H., Yip, V., Lee, M. V., Wong, S., Saad, O., Ma, S., ... & Shen, B. Q. (2020). Characterization of Tissue Distribution, Catabolism, and Elimination of an Anti–Staphylococcus aureus THIOMAB Antibody-Antibiotic Conjugate in Rats. *Drug Metabolism and Disposition*, *48*(11), 1161-1168.

Capdevila, J., Elez, E., Macarulla, T., Ramos, F. J., Ruiz-Echarri, M., & Tabernero, J. (2009). Anti-epidermal growth factor receptor monoclonal antibodies in cancer treatment. *Cancer treatment reviews*, *35*(4), 354-363.

Cerny, T., Borisch, B., Introna, M., Johnson, P., & Rose, A. L. (2002). Mechanism of action of rituximab. *Anti-cancer drugs*, *13*, S3-10.

Chari, R. V., Miller, M. L., & Widdison, W. C. (2014). Antibody–drug conjugates: an emerging concept in cancer therapy. *Angewandte Chemie International Edition*, *53*(15), 3796-3827.

Chen, H., Lin, Z., Arnst, K. E., Miller, D. D., & Li, W. (2017). Tubulin inhibitor-based antibody-drug conjugates for cancer therapy. *Molecules*, *22*(8), 1281.

Chen, X., Zhao, B., Qu, Y., Chen, Y., Xiong, J., Feng, Y., ... & Li, F. (2020). Detectable serum SARS-CoV-2 viral load (RNAaemia) is closely correlated with drastically elevated interleukin 6 (IL-6) level in critically ill COVID-19 patients. *Clinical infectious diseases*.

Cheong, W. S., Leow, C. Y., Majeed, A. B. A., & Leow, C. H. (2020). Diagnostic and therapeutic potential of shark variable new antigen receptor (VNAR) single domain antibody. *International journal of biological macromolecules*, *147*, 369-375.

Chowdary, P., Fosbury, E., Riddell, A., & Mathias, M. (2016). Therapeutic and routine prophylactic properties of rFactor VIII Fc (efraloctocog alfa, Eloctate®) in hemophilia A. *Journal of blood medicine*, *7*, 187.

Cooper, N., Hagan, D. R., Tiberghien, A., Ademefun, T., Matthews, C. S., Howard, P. W., & Thurston, D. E. (2002). Synthesis of novel C2-aryl pyrrolobenzodiazepines (PBDs) as potential antitumour agents. *Chemical communications*, (16), 1764-1765.

Courtenay-Luck, N. S., Epenetos, A. A., Moore, R., Larche, M., Pectasides, D., Dhokia, B., & Ritter, M. A. (1986). Development of primary and secondary immune responses to mouse monoclonal antibodies used in the diagnosis and therapy of malignant neoplasms. *Cancer research*, *46*(12 Part 1), 6489-6493.

Czajkowsky, D. M., Hu, J., Shao, Z., & Pleass, R. J. (2012). Fc-fusion proteins: new developments and future perspectives. *EMBO molecular medicine*, *4*(10), 1015-1028.

Dan, N., Setua, S., Kashyap, V. K., Khan, S., Jaggi, M., Yallapu, M. M., & Chauhan, S. C. (2018). Antibody-drug conjugates for cancer therapy: chemistry to clinical implications. *Pharmaceuticals*, *11*(2), 32.

Davies, A. J. (2007). Radioimmunotherapy for B-cell lymphoma: Y 90 ibritumomab tiuxetan and I 131 tositumomab. *Oncogene*, *26*(25), 3614-3628.

de Oliveira Dias, J. R., de Andrade, G. C., Novais, E. A., Farah, M. E., & Rodrigues, E. B. (2016). Fusion proteins for treatment of retinal diseases: aflibercept, ziv-aflibercept, and conbercept. *International journal of retina and vitreous*, *2*(1), 1-9.

Deissler, H. L., Lang, G. K., & Lang, G. E. (2017). Neonatal Fc receptor FcRn is involved in intracellular transport of the Fc fusion protein aflibercept and its transition through retinal endothelial cells. *Experimental eye research*, *154*, 39-46.

Doessegger, L., & Banholzer, M. L. (2015). Clinical development methodology for infusion-related reactions with monoclonal antibodies. *Clinical & translational immunology*, *4*(7), e39.

Duggan, S. (2018). Caplacizumab: first global approval. *Drugs*, *78*(15), 1639-1642.

Dumoulin, M., Conrath, K., Van Meirhaeghe, A., Meersman, F., Heremans, K., Frenken, L. G., ... & Matagne, A. (2002). Single-domain antibody fragments with high conformational stability. *Protein Science*, *11*(3), 500-515.

Elliott, W., & Chan, J. (2019). Caplacizumab-yhdp for Injection (Cablivi). *Internal Medicine Alert*, *41*(5).

Elliott, W., & Chan, J. (2020). Casirivimab+ Imdevimab Injection. *Internal Medicine Alert*, *42*(24).

Fan, G., Wang, Z., Hao, M., & Li, J. (2015). Bispecific antibodies and their applications. *Journal of hematology & oncology*, *8*(1), 1-14.

Frampton, J. E. (2016). Efmoroctocog alfa: A review in haemophilia A. *Drugs*, *76*(13), 1281-1291.

François, B., Garcia Sanchez, M., Eggimann, P., Dequin, P. F., Laterre, P. F., Huberlant, V., ... & SAATELLITE Study Group. (2019). Suvratoxumab reduces Staphylococcus aureus pneumonia in high-risk ICU patients: results of the SAATELLITE study. In *B14. LATE BREAKING CLINICAL TRIALS* (pp. A7358-A7358). American Thoracic Society.

Fu, Y., & Ho, M. (2018). DNA damaging agent-based antibody-drug conjugates for cancer therapy. *Antibody therapeutics, 1*(2), 43-53.

Garnock-Jones, K. P., Keating, G. M., & Scott, L. J. (2010). Trastuzumab. *Drugs, 70*(2), 215-239.

Gentile, G., & Foa, R. (2011). Viral infections associated with the clinical use of monoclonal antibodies. *Clinical microbiology and infection, 17*(12), 1769-1775.

Gerding, D. N., Kelly, C. P., Rahav, G., Lee, C., Dubberke, E. R., Kumar, P. N., ... & Dorr, M. B. (2018). Bezlotoxumab for prevention of recurrent Clostridium difficile infection in patients at increased risk for recurrence. *Clinical Infectious Diseases, 67*(5), 649-656.

Giles, F., Estey, E., & O'Brien, S. (2003). Gemtuzumab ozogamicin in the treatment of acute myeloid leukemia. *Cancer: Interdisciplinary International Journal of the American Cancer Society, 98*(10), 2095-2104.

Goebeler, M. E., Knop, S., Viardot, A., Kufer, P., Topp, M. S., Einsele, H., ... & Bargou, R. C. (2016). Bispecific T-cell engager (BiTE) antibody construct blinatumomab for the treatment of patients with relapsed/refractory non-Hodgkin lymphoma: final results from a phase I study. *Journal of Clinical Oncology, 34*(10), 1104-1111.

Gottlieb, A. B. (2004). Etanercept for the treatment of psoriasis and psoriatic arthritis. *Dermatologic Therapy, 17*(5), 401-408.

Govindan, S. V., Cardillo, T. M., Sharkey, R. M., Tat, F., Gold, D. V., & Goldenberg, D. M. (2013). Milatuzumab–SN-38 conjugates for the treatment of CD74+ cancers. *Molecular cancer therapeutics, 12*(6), 968-978.

Gravbrot, N., Gilbert-Gard, K., Mehta, P., Ghotmi, Y., Banerjee, M., Mazis, C., & Sundararajan, S. (2019). Therapeutic monoclonal antibodies targeting immune checkpoints for the treatment of solid tumors. *Antibodies, 8*(4), 51.

Grote, M., Haas, A. K., Klein, C., Schaefer, W., & Brinkmann, U. (2012). Bispecific antibody derivatives based on full-length IgG formats. In *Antibody Methods and Protocols* (pp. 247-263). Humana Press, Totowa, NJ.

Gu, X., Jia, X., Feng, J., Shen, B., Huang, Y., Geng, S., ... & Long, M. (2010). Molecular modeling and affinity determination of scFv antibody:

proper linker peptide enhances its activity. *Annals of biomedical engineering, 38*(2), 537-549.

Gunturi, A., & McDermott, D. F. (2015). Nivolumab for the treatment of cancer. *Expert opinion on investigational drugs, 24*(2), 253-260.

Hafeez, U., Parakh, S., Gan, H. K., & Scott, A. M. (2020). Antibody–Drug Conjugates for Cancer Therapy. *Molecules, 25*(20), 4764.

Hamers-Casterman, C. T. S. G., Atarhouch, T., Muyldermans, S. A., Robinson, G., Hammers, C., Songa, E. B., ... & Hammers, R. (1993). Naturally occurring antibodies devoid of light chains. *Nature, 363*(6428), 446-448.

Hansel, T. T., Kropshofer, H., Singer, T., Mitchell, J. A., & George, A. J. (2010). The safety and side effects of monoclonal antibodies. *Nature reviews Drug discovery, 9*(4), 325-338.

Hansen, J., Baum, A., Pascal, K. E., Russo, V., Giordano, S., Wloga, E., ... & Kyratsous, C. A. (2020). Studies in humanized mice and convalescent humans yield a SARS-CoV-2 antibody cocktail. *Science, 369*(6506), 1010-1014.

Harris, J., & Keane, J. (2010). How tumour necrosis factor blockers interfere with tuberculosis immunity. *Clinical & Experimental Immunology, 161*(1), 1-9.

Hartley, J. A. (2011). The development of pyrrolobenzodiazepines as antitumour agents. *Expert opinion on investigational drugs, 20*(6), 733-744.

Heil, F., Babitzki, G., Julien-Laferriere, A., Ooi, C. H., Hidalgo, M., Massard, C., ... & Lechner, K. (2021). Vanucizumab mode of action: Serial biomarkers in plasma, tumor, and skin-wound-healing biopsies. *Translational Oncology, 14*(2), 100984.

Heiss, M. M., Murawa, P., Koralewski, P., Kutarska, E., Kolesnik, O. O., Ivanchenko, V. V., ... & Parsons, S. L. (2010). The trifunctional antibody catumaxomab for the treatment of malignant ascites due to epithelial cancer: Results of a prospective randomized phase II/III trial. *International journal of cancer, 127*(9), 2209-2221.

Henderson, L. A., Canna, S. W., Schulert, G. S., Volpi, S., Lee, P. Y., Kernan, K. F., ... & Nigrovic, P. A. (2020). On the alert for cytokine storm: immunopathology in COVID-19. *Arthritis & Rheumatology, 72*(7), 1059-1063.

Hidalgo, M., Martinez-Garcia, M., Le Tourneau, C., Massard, C., Garralda, E., Boni, V., ... & Krieter, O. (2018). First-in-human phase I study of single-agent vanucizumab, a first-in-class bispecific anti-angiopoietin-2/anti-VEGF-A antibody, in adult patients with advanced solid tumors. *Clinical Cancer Research, 24*(7), 1536-1545.

Hoey, R. J., Eom, H., & Horn, J. R. (2019). Structure and development of single domain antibodies as modules for therapeutics and diagnostics. *Experimental Biology and Medicine, 244*(17), 1568-1576.

Hoffmann, R. M., Coumbe, B. G., Josephs, D. H., Mele, S., Ilieva, K. M., Cheung, A., ... & Karagiannis, S. N. (2018). Antibody structure and engineering considerations for the design and function of Antibody Drug Conjugates (ADCs). *Oncoimmunology, 7*(3), e1395127.

Hudis, C. A. (2007). Trastuzumab—mechanism of action and use in clinical practice. *New England journal of medicine, 357*(1), 39-51.

Iezzi, M. E., Policastro, L., Werbajh, S., Podhajcer, O., & Canziani, G. A. (2018). Single-domain antibodies and the promise of modular targeting in cancer imaging and treatment. *Frontiers in immunology, 9*, 273.

Isabwe, G. A. C., Neuer, M. G., de las Vecillas Sanchez, L., Lynch, D. M., Marquis, K., & Castells, M. (2018). Hypersensitivity reactions to therapeutic monoclonal antibodies: phenotypes and endotypes. *Journal of Allergy and Clinical Immunology, 142*(1), 159-170.

Jahanshahlu, L., & Rezaei, N. (2020). Monoclonal antibody as a potential anti-COVID-19. *Biomedicine & Pharmacotherapy*, 110337.

Jain, N., Stock, W., Zeidan, A., Atallah, E., McCloskey, J., Heffner, L., ... & Wieduwilt, M. J. (2020). Loncastuximab tesirine, an anti-CD19 antibody-drug conjugate, in relapsed/refractory B-cell acute lymphoblastic leukemia. *Blood advances, 4*(3), 449-457.

Jamali, F., Lemery, S., Ayalew, K., Robottom, S., Robie-Suh, K., Rieves, D., & Pazdur, R. (2009). Romiplostim for the treatment of chronic immune (idiopathic) thrombocytopenic purpura. *Oncology, 23*(8), 704.

Jolliffe, L. K. (1993). Humanized antibodies: enhancing therapeutic utility through antibody engineering. *International reviews of immunology, 10*(2-3), 241-250.

Jonker, D. J., O'Callaghan, C. J., Karapetis, C. S., Zalcberg, J. R., Tu, D., Au, H. J., ... & Moore, M. J. (2007). Cetuximab for the treatment of colorectal cancer. *New England Journal of Medicine, 357*(20), 2040-2048.

Jordan, M. A. (2002). Mechanism of action of antitumor drugs that interact with microtubules and tubulin. *Current Medicinal Chemistry-Anti-Cancer Agents, 2*(1), 1-17.

Ju, M. S., Min, S. W., Lee, S. M., Kwon, H. S., Park, J. C., Lee, J. C., & Jung, S. T. (2017). A synthetic library for rapid isolation of humanized single-domain antibodies. *Biotechnology and Bioprocess Engineering, 22*(3), 239-247.

Kahl, B. S., Hamadani, M., Radford, J., Carlo-Stella, C., Caimi, P., Reid, E., ... & O'connor, O. A. (2019). A phase I study of ADCT-402 (loncastuximab tesirine), a novel pyrrolobenzodiazepine-based antibody–drug conjugate, in relapsed/refractory B-cell non-Hodgkin lymphoma. *Clinical Cancer Research, 25*(23), 6986-6994.

Kalinchenko, N. Y., Golounina, O. O., Grebennikova, T. A., Melnichenko, G. A., Tiulpakov, A. N., & Belaya, Z. E. (2019). Clinical application experience of asfotase alfa for a young patient with childhood hypophosphatasia. *Osteoporosis and bone diseases, 22*(1), 24-29.

Kaplon, H., & Reichert, J. M. (2021, January). Antibodies to watch in 2021. In *Mabs* (Vol. 13, No. 1, p. 1860476). Taylor & Francis.

Keane, J., & Bresnihan, B. (2008). Tuberculosis reactivation during immunosuppressive therapy in rheumatic diseases: diagnostic and therapeutic strategies. *Current opinion in rheumatology, 20*(4), 443-449.

Kebenko, M., Goebeler, M. E., Wolf, M., Hasenburg, A., Seggewiss-Bernhardt, R., Ritter, B., ... & Fiedler, W. (2018). A multicenter phase 1 study of solitomab (MT110, AMG 110), a bispecific EpCAM/CD3 T-cell engager (BiTE®) antibody construct, in patients with refractory solid tumors. *Oncoimmunology, 7*(8), e1450710.

Kelsey, A., Chirch, L. M., & Payette, M. J. (2018). Tuberculosis and interleukin blocking monoclonal antibodies: Is there risk?. *Dermatology online journal, 24*(9).

Keske, Ş., Tekin, S., Sait, B., İrkören, P., Kapmaz, M., Çimen, C., ... & Ergönül, Ö. (2020). Appropriate use of tocilizumab in COVID-19 infection. *International Journal of Infectious Diseases, 99*, 338-343.

Khodabakhsh, F., Behdani, M., Rami, A., & Kazemi-Lomedasht, F. (2018). Single-domain antibodies or nanobodies: a class of next-generation antibodies. *International reviews of immunology*, *37*(6), 316-322.

Khongorzul, P., Ling, C. J., Khan, F. U., Ihsan, A. U., & Zhang, J. (2020). Antibody–drug conjugates: a comprehensive review. *Molecular Cancer Research*, *18*(1), 3-19.

Kim, Y. J., Bae, S. C., Sung, Y. K., Kim, T. H., Jun, J. B., Yoo, D. H., ... & Lee, H. S. (2010). Possible reactivation of potential hepatitis B virus occult infection by tumor necrosis factor-α blocker in the treatment of rheumatic diseases. *The Journal of rheumatology*, *37*(2), 346-350.

Kipriyanov, S. M. (2009). Generation of bispecific and tandem diabodies. In *Antibody Phage Display* (pp. 177-193). Humana Press.

Klein, C., Schaefer, W., Regula, J. T., Dumontet, C., Brinkmann, U., Bacac, M., & Umaña, P. (2019). Engineering therapeutic bispecific antibodies using CrossMab technology. *Methods*, *154*, 21-31.

Klute, K., Nackos, E., Tasaki, S., Nguyen, D. P., Bander, N. H., & Tagawa, S. T. (2014). Microtubule inhibitor-based antibody–drug conjugates for cancer therapy. *OncoTargets and therapy*, *7*, 2227.

Kontermann, R. E., & Brinkmann, U. (2015). Bispecific antibodies. *Drug discovery today*, *20*(7), 838-847.

Krah, S., Kolmar, H., Becker, S., & Zielonka, S. (2018). Engineering IgG-like bispecific antibodies—an overview. *Antibodies*, *7*(3), 28.

Krah, S., Schröter, C., Zielonka, S., Empting, M., Valldorf, B., & Kolmar, H. (2016). Single-domain antibodies for biomedical applications. *Immunopharmacology and immunotoxicology*, *38*(1), 21-28.

Kreitman, R. J. (1999). Immunotoxins in cancer therapy. *Current opinion in immunology*, *11*(5), 570-578.

Kreitman, R. J., & Pastan, I. (2011). Antibody fusion proteins: anti-CD22 recombinant immunotoxin moxetumomab pasudotox. *Clinical Cancer Research*, *17*(20), 6398-6405.

Kreitman, R. J., Tallman, M. S., Robak, T., Coutre, S., Wilson, W. H., Stetler-Stevenson, M., ... & Pastan, I. (2012). Phase I trial of anti-CD22 recombinant immunotoxin moxetumomab pasudotox (CAT-8015 or HA22) in patients with hairy cell leukemia. *Journal of Clinical Oncology*, *30*(15), 1822.

Kummerfeldt, C. E. (2014). Raxibacumab: potential role in the treatment of inhalational anthrax. *Infection and drug resistance*, *7*, 101.

Laffleur, B., Pascal, V., Sirac, C., & Cogné, M. (2012). Production of human or humanized antibodies in mice. In *Antibody Methods and Protocols* (pp. 149-159). Humana Press, Totowa, NJ.

Lambert, J. M. (2013). Drug-conjugated antibodies for the treatment of cancer. *British journal of clinical pharmacology*, *76*(2), 248-262.

Ledsgaard, L., Kilstrup, M., Karatt-Vellatt, A., McCafferty, J., & Laustsen, A. H. (2018). Basics of antibody phage display technology. *Toxins*, *10*(6), 236.

Lee, J. Y., Lee, H. T., Shin, W., Chae, J., Choi, J., Kim, S. H., ... & Heo, Y. S. (2016). Structural basis of checkpoint blockade by monoclonal antibodies in cancer immunotherapy. *Nature communications*, *7*(1), 1-10.

Lehar, S. M., Pillow, T., Xu, M., Staben, L., Kajihara, K. K., Vandlen, R., ... & Mariathasan, S. (2015). Novel antibody–antibiotic conjugate eliminates intracellular S. aureus. *Nature*, *527*(7578), 323-328.

Leonard, D. S., Hill, A. D. K., Kelly, L., Dijkstra, B., McDermott, E., & O'Higgins, N. J. (2002). Anti-human epidermal growth factor receptor 2 monoclonal antibody therapy for breast cancer. *Journal of British Surgery*, *89*(3), 262-271.

Li, Q., & Sham, H. L. (2002). Discovery and development of antimitotic agents that inhibit tubulin polymerisation for the treatment of cancer. *Expert Opinion on Therapeutic Patents*, *12*(11), 1663-1702.

Lin, T. S. (2010). Ofatumumab: a novel monoclonal anti-CD20 antibody. *Pharmacogenomics and personalized medicine*, *3*, 51.

Liu, H., Saxena, A., Sidhu, S. S., & Wu, D. (2017). Fc engineering for developing therapeutic bispecific antibodies and novel scaffolds. *Frontiers in immunology*, *8*, 38.

Lonberg, N. (2005). Human antibodies from transgenic animals. *Nature Biotechnology*, *23*(9), 1117-1125.

Lord, J. M., Roberts, L. M., & Robertus, J. D. (1994). Ricin: structure, mode of action, and some current applications. *The FASEB journal*, *8*(2), 201-208.

Lu, R. M., Hwang, Y. C., Liu, I. J., Lee, C. C., Tsai, H. Z., Li, H. J., & Wu, H. C. (2020). Development of therapeutic antibodies for the treatment of diseases. *Journal of biomedical science*, *27*(1), 1-30.

Lubran, M. M. (1988). Bacterial toxins. *Annals of Clinical & Laboratory Science*, *18*(1), 58-71.

Lundgren, J. D., Grund, B., Barkauskas, C. E., Holland, T. L., Gottlieb, R. L., Sandkovsky, U., ... & Neaton, J. D. (2020). A Neutralizing Monoclonal Antibody for Hospitalized Patients with Covid-19. *The New England journal of medicine*.

Madhumathi, J., & Verma, R. S. (2012). Therapeutic targets and recent advances in protein immunotoxins. *Current opinion in microbiology*, *15*(3), 300-309.

Magdaleno, A. L., Singh, S., Venkataraman, S., Perilli, G. A., & Lee, Y. Y. (2019). Adult-onset hypophosphatasia: Before and after treatment with asfotase alfa. *AACE clinical case reports*, *5*(6), e344-e348.

Mariathasan, S., & Tan, M. W. (2017). Antibody–antibiotic conjugates: a novel therapeutic platform against bacterial infections. *Trends in molecular medicine*, *23*(2), 135-149.

Marovich, M., Mascola, J. R., & Cohen, M. S. (2020). Monoclonal antibodies for prevention and treatment of COVID-19. *Jama*, *324*(2), 131-132.

Martinelli, E., De Palma, R., Orditura, M., De Vita, F., & Ciardiello, F. (2009). Anti-epidermal growth factor receptor monoclonal antibodies in cancer therapy. *Clinical & Experimental Immunology*, *158*(1), 1-9.

Mastroianni, C. M., Lichtner, M., Citton, R., Del Borgo, C., Rago, A., Martini, H., ... & Vullo, V. (2011). Current trends in management of hepatitis B virus reactivation in the biologic therapy era. *World journal of gastroenterology: WJG*, *17*(34), 3881.

Mathew, M., & Verma, R. S. (2009). Humanized immunotoxins: a new generation of immunotoxins for targeted cancer therapy. *Cancer science*, *100*(8), 1359-1365.

Mathew, M., Zaineb, K. C., & Verma, R. S. (2013). GM-CSF-DFF40: a novel humanized immunotoxin induces apoptosis in acute myeloid leukemia cells. *Apoptosis*, *18*(7), 882-895.

McCafferty, J., Griffiths, A. D., Winter, G., & Chiswell, D. J. (1990). Phage antibodies: filamentous phage displaying antibody variable domains. *nature*, *348*(6301), 552-554.

McCormack, P. L., & Keam, S. J. (2008). Bevacizumab. *Drugs*, *68*(4), 487-506.

McDermott, J., & Jimeno, A. (2015). Pembrolizumab: PD-1 inhibition as a therapeutic strategy in cancer. *Drugs of today (Barcelona, Spain: 1998)*, *51*(1), 7-20.

Middlebrook, J. L., & Dorland, R. B. (1984). Bacterial toxins: cellular mechanisms of action. *Microbiological reviews*, *48*(3), 199-221.

Monnier, P. P., Vigouroux, R. J., & Tassew, N. G. (2013). In vivo applications of single chain Fv (variable domain)(scFv) fragments. *Antibodies*, *2*(2), 193-208.

Moore, P. A., Zhang, W., Rainey, G. J., Burke, S., Li, H., Huang, L., ... & Johnson, S. (2011). Application of dual affinity retargeting molecules to achieve optimal redirected T-cell killing of B-cell lymphoma. *Blood, The Journal of the American Society of Hematology*, *117*(17), 4542-4551.

Motley, M. P., Banerjee, K., & Fries, B. C. (2019). Monoclonal antibody-based therapies for bacterial infections. *Current opinion in infectious diseases*, *32*(3), 210.

Mukherji, S. K. (2010). Bevacizumab (avastin). *American journal of neuroradiology*, *31*(2), 235-236.

Muyldermans, S. (2013). Nanobodies: natural single-domain antibodies. *Annual review of biochemistry*, *82*, 775-797.

Naito, K., Takeshita, A., Shigeno, K., Nakamura, S., Fujisawa, S., Shinjo, K., ... & Ohno, R. (2000). Calicheamicin-conjugated humanized anti-CD33 monoclonal antibody (gemtuzumab zogamicin, CMA-676) shows cytocidal effect on CD33-positive leukemia cell lines, but is inactive on P-glycoprotein-expressing sublines. *Leukemia*, *14*(8), 1436-1443.

Nanda, S., & Bathon, J. M. (2004). Etanercept: a clinical review of current and emerging indications. *Expert opinion on pharmacotherapy*, *5*(5), 1175-1186.

Nolting, B. (2013). Linker technologies for antibody–drug conjugates. *Antibody-drug conjugates*, 71-100.

O'Mahony, D., & Bishop, M. R. (2006). Monoclonal antibody therapy. *Frontiers in bioscience: a journal and virtual library*, *11*, 1620-1635.

O'Mahony, D., & Bishop, M. R. (2006). Monoclonal antibody therapy. *Frontiers in bioscience: a journal and virtual library*, *11*, 1620-1635.

Pandey, S. (2010). Hybridoma technology for production of monoclonal antibodies. *Hybridoma*, *1*(2), 017.

Pandey, S. (2010). Hybridoma technology for production of monoclonal antibodies. *Hybridoma*, *1*(2), 017.

Pechtner, V., Karanikas, C. A., García-Pérez, L. E., & Glaesner, W. (2017). A new approach to drug therapy: Fc-fusion technology. *Prim Health Care*, *7*(255), 2167-1079.

Peck, M., Rothenberg, M. E., Deng, R., Lewin-Koh, N., She, G., Kamath, A. V., ... & Tavel, J. A. (2019). A phase 1, randomized, single-ascending-dose study to investigate the safety, tolerability, and pharmacokinetics of DSTA4637S, an anti-Staphylococcus aureus thiomab antibody-antibiotic conjugate, in healthy volunteers. *Antimicrobial agents and chemotherapy*, *63*(6), e02588-18.

Peng, M. (2020). Outbreak of COVID-19: An emerging global pandemic threat. *Biomedicine & Pharmacotherapy*, 110499.

Pintea, I., Petricau, C., Dumitrascu, D., Muntean, A., Branisteanu, D. C., Branisteanu, D. E., & Deleanu, D. (2021). Hypersensitivity reactions to monoclonal antibodies: Classification and treatment approach. *Experimental and Therapeutic Medicine*, *22*(3), 1-8.

Ponziani, S., Di Vittorio, G., Pitari, G., Cimini, A. M., Ardini, M., Gentile, R., ... & Giansanti, F. (2020). Antibody-drug conjugates: The new frontier of chemotherapy. *International Journal of Molecular Sciences*, *21*(15), 5510.

Psarras, K., Ueda, M., Tanabe, M., Kitajima, M., Aiso, S., Komatsu, S., & Seno, M. (2000). Targeting activated lymphocytes with an entirely human immunotoxin analogue: human pancreatic RNase1-human IL-2 fusion. *Cytokine*, *12*(6), 786-790.

Rath, T., Baker, K., Dumont, J. A., Peters, R. T., Jiang, H., Qiao, S. W., ... & Blumberg, R. S. (2015). Fc-fusion proteins and FcRn: structural insights for longer-lasting and more effective therapeutics. *Critical reviews in biotechnology*, *35*(2), 235-254.

Rossotti, M. A., Bélanger, K., Henry, K. A., & Tanha, J. (2021). Immunogenicity and humanization of single-domain antibodies. *The FEBS Journal*.

Rouet, R., & Christ, D. (2014). Bispecific antibodies with native chain structure. *Nature biotechnology*, *32*(2), 136-137.

Ruck, T., Bittner, S., Wiendl, H., & Meuth, S. G. (2015). Alemtuzumab in multiple sclerosis: mechanism of action and beyond. *International journal of molecular sciences*, *16*(7), 16414-16439.

Saerens, D., Ghassabeh, G. H., & Muyldermans, S. (2008). Single-domain antibodies as building blocks for novel therapeutics. *Current opinion in pharmacology*, *8*(5), 600-608.

Schaefer, W., Regula, J. T., Bähner, M., Schanzer, J., Croasdale, R., Dürr, H., ... & Klein, C. (2011). Immunoglobulin domain crossover as a generic approach for the production of bispecific IgG antibodies. *Proceedings of the National academy of Sciences*, *108*(27), 11187-11192.

Schifferli, A., Nimmerjahn, F., & Kühne, T. (2019). Immunomodulation in primary immune thrombocytopenia: a possible role of the Fc fragment of romiplostim?. *Frontiers in immunology*, *10*, 1196.

Seimetz, D., Lindhofer, H., & Bokemeyer, C. (2010). Development and approval of the trifunctional antibody catumaxomab (anti-EpCAM× anti-CD3) as a targeted cancer immunotherapy. *Cancer treatment reviews*, *36*(6), 458-467.

Seligson, J. M., Patron, A. M., Berger, M. J., Harvey, R. D., & Seligson, N. D. (2021). Sacituzumab Govitecan-hziy: An antibody-drug conjugate for the treatment of refractory, metastatic, triple-negative breast cancer. *Annals of Pharmacotherapy*, *55*(7), 921-931.

Shimabukuro-Vornhagen, A., Gödel, P., Subklewe, M., Stemmler, H. J., Schlößer, H. A., Schlaak, M., ... & von Bergwelt-Baildon, M. S. (2018). Cytokine release syndrome. *Journal for immunotherapy of cancer*, *6*(1), 1-14.

Slaney, C. Y., Wang, P., Darcy, P. K., & Kershaw, M. H. (2018). CARs versus BiTEs: a comparison between T cell–redirection strategies for cancer treatment. *Cancer discovery*, *8*(8), 924-934.

Smith, L. L., Mosley, J. F., II, C. P., Brown, J., Barris, L. S., & Phan, L. D. (2016). Dulaglutide (Trulicity): the third once-weekly GLP-1 agonist. *Pharmacy and Therapeutics*, *41*(6), 357.

Soetens, E., Ballegeer, M., & Saelens, X. (2020). An Inside Job: Applications of Intracellular Single Domain Antibodies. *Biomolecules*, *10*(12), 1663.

Sondak, V. K., Smalley, K. S., Kudchadkar, R., Grippon, S., & Kirkpatrick, P. (2011). Ipilimumab. *Nature reviews Drug discovery*, *10*(6), 411-413.

Stamova, S., Koristka, S., Keil, J., Arndt, C., Feldmann, A., Michalk, I., ... & Bachmann, M. (2012). Cancer immunotherapy by retargeting of immune effector cells via recombinant bispecific antibody constructs. *Antibodies*, *1*(2), 172-198.

Stern, M., & Herrmann, R. (2005). Overview of monoclonal antibodies in cancer therapy: present and promise. *Critical reviews in oncology/hematology*, *54*(1), 11-29.

Suvvari, T. K. (2020). Therapeutic Uses of Monoclonal Antibodies for COVID-19. *Biomedical Research Journal*, *7*(2), 60.

Tabor, D. E., Oganesyan, V., Keller, A. E., Yu, L., McLaughlin, R. E., Song, E., ... & DiGiandomenico, A. (2018). Pseudomonas aeruginosa PcrV and Psl, the molecular targets of bispecific antibody MEDI3902, are conserved among diverse global clinical isolates. *The Journal of infectious diseases*, *218*(12), 1983-1994.

Thompson, A. M., & Trujillo, J. M. (2015). Dulaglutide: the newest GLP-1 receptor agonist for the management of type 2 diabetes. *Annals of Pharmacotherapy*, *49*(3), 351-359.

Tian, Z., Liu, M., Zhang, Y., & Wang, X. (2021). Bispecific T cell engagers: an emerging therapy for management of hematologic malignancies. *Journal of Hematology & Oncology, 14*(1), 1-18.

Tietze, L. F., & Krewer, B. (2009). Antibody-directed enzyme prodrug therapy: A promising approach for a selective treatment of cancer based on prodrugs and monoclonal antibodies. *Chemical biology & drug design, 74*(3), 205-211.

Tomita, M., & Tsumoto, K. (2011). Hybridoma technologies for antibody production. *Immunotherapy, 3*(3), 371-380.

Tomita, M., & Tsumoto, K. (2011). Hybridoma technologies for antibody production. *Immunotherapy, 3*(3), 371-380.

Trichonas, G., & Kaiser, P. K. (2013). Aflibercept for the treatment of age-related macular degeneration. *Ophthalmology and therapy, 2*(2), 89-98.

van Schouwenburg, P. A., van de Stadt, L. A., de Jong, R. N., van Buren, E. E., Kruithof, S., de Groot, E., ... & Wouters, D. (2013). Adalimumab elicits a restricted anti-idiotypic antibody response in autoimmune patients resulting in functional neutralisation. *Annals of the rheumatic diseases, 72*(1), 104-109.

Vaswani, S. K., & Hamilton, R. G. (1998). Humanized antibodies as potential therapeutic drugs. *Annals of Allergy, Asthma & Immunology, 81*(2), 105-119.

Waldmann, H. (2019). Human monoclonal antibodies: the benefits of humanization. *Human Monoclonal Antibodies*, 1-10.

Walter, R. B., Raden, B. W., Hong, T. C., Flowers, D. A., Bernstein, I. D., & Linenberger, M. L. (2003). Multidrug resistance protein attenuates gemtuzumab ozogamicin–induced cytotoxicity in acute myeloid leukemia cells. *Blood, 102*(4), 1466-1473.

Wang, Q., Chen, Y., Park, J., Liu, X., Hu, Y., Wang, T., ... & Betenbaugh, M. J. (2019). Design and production of bispecific antibodies. *Antibodies, 8*(3), 43.

Warnke, C., Hermanrud, C., Lundkvist, M., & Fogdell-Hahn, A. (2012). Anti-drug antibodies. *Drugs and Therapy Studies, 2*(1), e11-e11.

Weidle, U. H., Maisel, D., Klostermann, S., Schiller, C., & Weiss, E. H. (2011). Intracellular proteins displayed on the surface of tumor cells as targets for therapeutic intervention with antibody-related agents. *Cancer genomics & proteomics*, *8*(2), 49-63.

Weiner, L. M., Dhodapkar, M. V., & Ferrone, S. (2009). Monoclonal antibodies for cancer immunotherapy. *The Lancet*, *373*(9668), 1033-1040.

Wilcox, M. H., Gerding, D. N., Poxton, I. R., Kelly, C., Nathan, R., Birch, T., ... & Dorr, M. B. (2017). Bezlotoxumab for prevention of recurrent Clostridium difficile infection. *New England Journal of Medicine*, *376*(4), 305-317.

Wing, M. (2008). Monoclonal antibody first dose cytokine release syndromes–mechanisms and prediction. *Journal of immunotoxicology*, *5*(1), 11-15.

Wu, J., Fu, J., Zhang, M., & Liu, D. (2015). Blinatumomab: a bispecific T cell engager (BiTE) antibody against CD19/CD3 for refractory acute lymphoid leukemia. *Journal of hematology & oncology*, *8*(1), 1-7.

Xu, Y., Lee, J., Tran, C., Heibeck, T. H., Wang, W. D., Yang, J., ... & Yin, G. (2015, January). Production of bispecific antibodies in "knobs-into-holes" using a cell-free expression system. In *MAbs* (Vol. 7, No. 1, pp. 231-242). Taylor & Francis.

Yamamoto, B. J., Shadiack, A. M., Carpenter, S., Sanford, D., Henning, L. N., Gonzales, N., ... & Serbina, N. V. (2016). Obiltoxaximab prevents disseminated Bacillus anthracis infection and improves survival during pre- and postexposure prophylaxis in animal models of inhalational anthrax. *Antimicrobial agents and chemotherapy*, *60*(10), 5796-5805.

Yusakul, G., Sakamoto, S., Pongkitwitoon, B., Tanaka, H., & Morimoto, S. (2016). Effect of linker length between variable domains of single chain variable fragment antibody against daidzin on its reactivity. *Bioscience, biotechnology, and biochemistry*, *80*(7), 1306-1312.

Zhang, B., Wu, T., Chen, M., Zhou, Y., Yi, D., & Guo, R. (2013). The CD40/CD40L system: a new therapeutic target for disease. *Immunology letters*, *153*(1-2), 58-61.

Zhou, C., Cai, H., Baruch, A., Lewin-Koh, N., Yang, M., Guo, F., ... & Kamath, A. V. (2019). Sustained activity of novel THIOMAB antibody-antibiotic conjugate against Staphylococcus aureus in a mouse model:

Longitudinal pharmacodynamic assessment by bioluminescence imaging. *Plos one*, *14*(10), e0224096.

Zurawski, D. V., & McLendon, M. K. (2020). Monoclonal antibodies as an antibacterial approach against bacterial pathogens. *Antibiotics*, *9*(4), 155.

Antibodies and their role in therapeutics

Made in the USA
Monee, IL
18 October 2023

44820876R00213